A WARTIME TRILOGY

James Sinclair

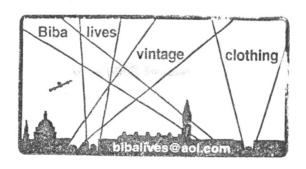

Biba lives vintage clothing

bibalives@aol.com

Once again James Sinclair relives his childhood as he relates the continuing story of his return from evacuation, for yet another life in another town, Nelson in Lancashire. From what he had seen earlier on the train he wasn't impressed, the ugly mill town, with towering mill chimneys spewing out grimy black smoke. He was missing north Wales already, with the clean sea air, and surrounding hills and mountains.

For all who enjoyed reading A WAY OUT, and WELSH SCOUSE, you are surely in for a treat as Sinclair completes his trilogy with THE COBBLED SLOPE.

As before, all the experiences are true as remembered by James Sinclair. So make a cup of tea, get a box of tissues, and put your feet up for a jolly good read.

A WARTIME TRILOGY
BY
James Sinclair

*Jimmie with his mother when he was
just 6 months old in 1929.*
CREMER PRESS

This Trilogy First Published in Great Britain in 2006 By
James Sinclair
c/o Cremer Press, Blackburn.

ISBN 1 898722 69 2

ISBN 978 1 898722 69 4

Printed and Bound By
Edmund Mercer, Cremer Press,
45 Harrison Street, Blackburn.
Lancs. BB2 2JE

CREMER PRESS

A WARTIME TRILOGY

PART ONE   -   A Way Out

PART TWO   -   Welsh Scouse

PART THREE   -   The Cobbled Slope

By James Sinclair

ACKNOWLEDGEMENTS

This is to acknowledge that this book was first published as a sequel only, under the titles of *'A Way Out'* and *'Welsh Scouse'* by The Bluecoat Press Publishers in 1999

The author wishes to give his grateful thanks to the late author, Catherine Cookson, for reading the above sequel, and her **personal comments** stating that this book is in her personal opinion, "Very authentic… a really enjoyable read."

At the time that Miss Cookson read the book, the third part had not been written at all, and the whole thing had not been updated. The book now appears for the very first time as this newly revised trilogy.

Sadly by this time, Miss Catherine Cookson, had passed away, and is still so greatly missed by all her readers.

I also express my thanks to The Liverpool Echo and The Nelson Leader.

Lastly I wish to thank Madeleine Fish, my editor, (Cremer Press), for her expert advice and help - a big 'Thank you'.

DEDICATION

I wish to dedicate this book to
My best girl, Joyce,
For understanding me,
And for all her hard work
And assistance.

I further wish
To dedicate this book
To my sister Mary,
Never did say goodbye!

Also my dad, Robert (1895-1950)
My mam, Kate   (1898-1989)
'Together again'.

Part One
A WAY OUT

CHAPTER ONE
The Glorious Twelfth

A warm, gentle breeze wafted across the rooftops from the River Mersey. The dirty, grey, net curtains flapped nonchalantly against the grimy windows, half-open on their sashes. Inside the room, a strip of stained wallpaper dangled loosely from the ceiling, as if screaming out to be ripped off because of its age and inferior quality. The original rose pattern was badly faded, and the once-white background had deteriorated into a series of ugly brown stains.

Dotted around the walls, brown bugs could be seen making their way in and out of the cracked surfaces. They had had a busy night, biting the tender skin of the child sleeping on the bed. The child stirred in his sleep and scratched his little bottom, arms and chest, in an attempt to ease the itching torment.

Jimmie, for that was the boy's name, was hot and sweaty, and as he slumbered, he kicked the army greatcoat to the floor. This gave some temporary relief from the irritation, and he tucked his ragged vest under himself and dozed off again. However his sleep was soon interrupted, for in the distance could be heard the sound of drums beating out a noisy tattoo, accompanied by the ringing of concertinas and accordions becoming louder and louder, disturbing the stillness of this poor room.

Jimmie turned onto his right side, facing the open window. Vaguely he could see daylight through his half-open lashes. He was becoming aware of his surroundings; as he realised that he was alive at least for another day. His ears were soon vibrating to another loud banging of drums; this time accompanied by the wailing of bagpipes.

'I'll bet that's the Liverpool Scottish,' he murmured to himself, as he rolled out of the deep hollow in the ancient flock mattress and off the bed. As he wobbled to his feet, he rubbed his eyes which were sticky and sore, 'Oh no! Not that flippin' old junkvitis again!' he moaned.

Jimmie was susceptible to conjunctivitis, so suffered regular recurrences of that very unpleasant condition. Again he rubbed his sore eyes with the back of his hand, trying to free them from the dry, matted, mucus on his long eyelashes.

Unable to do so, he fumbled his way to the foot of the brass bedstead, clutching at the cold metal with his hot little hands. He felt around blindly on the corner of the bedpost for his clothes, his navy-blue trousers, with the red and yellow snake belt, which he always kept close by, for he never knew when he would next encounter this problem with his eyes.

He pulled on his trousers and fastened the belt, then fumbled for his jersey, which was very much the worse for wear, and handed down, as usual, from an older brother. He dragged it over his auburn hair, which framed a cheeky round freckled face.

'Have to be quick,' he said aloud, 'I'm goin' ter miss it. Nobody woke me.' Again he groped around the bed, finally locating one of his socks, then felt on the floor for the other.

Instead he found his pumps, so decided to dispense with the socks. He forced his feet into his footwear, his big toes peeping out of each one as he did so.

'Mary! Willie! Bobby!' he shouted, his cry echoing through the two up, two down, terraced house. 'Oh well,' he complained, 'have ter try an' get meself downstairs.'

This was no easy task, for although there was a handrail, the stairs were narrow and slightly twisted, making his descent both difficult and slow. During all this time, the sound of marching bands was getting louder, and people could be heard cheering and shouting.

'Going ter miss it if I don't hurry,' he scolded himself.

He stumbled his way to the small kitchen-cum-living-room, with its shallow sandstone sink. The cold water felt good to his swollen sticky eyes, with a piece of old towel as a face-cloth, he patted, wetted and coaxed his eyes into more open positions. As the bright daylight penetrated his lashes, the familiar surroundings came into focus.

There was the usual large iron fire-grate, with its oven on one side and the water boiler on the other, dominating the whole length of one wall. The grate was choked with ash and cinders, and the heavy oven door gaped open like a huge mouth, wanting to say something.

A big square table stood in the centre of the room; it had great bulbous legs, each standing in a heavy glass holder. Jimmie always thought that they looked like his nin's (grandma) salt cellars. On the table were two crusts of dry bread and a tin of condensed milk, next to which was a cracked mug, half-full of cold tea.

Jimmie cupped his little hands under the cold running water. They were lucky, he reflected, to have their very own tap, lots of other people had to share one in the back square. He drank deeply, feeling more refreshed and alert afterwards.

The bright sun filtered through his eyelashes, making him blink until his eyes adjusted to the light, then he headed for the parlour; a small room with a horsehair sofa, which always prickled his legs when he sat on it. A large, iron-framed piano took pride of place across the window-wall, which was two steps down, below the level of the front street. Again, grubby net curtains hung listlessly from a string, threaded through an untidy hem, and held in position by two rusty nails.

Jimmie held onto the sides of the walls as he ascended the two steps into the street, blinking and shielding his eyes with his other hand. Instinctively he made his way towards the rhythmic sound of the bands.

There was a distance of thirty yards or so to Netherfield Road. People of all ages were lining the top of India Street, two and three deep, waving and cheering, and laughing and shouting. They didn't notice the little lad crawling along the cobblestones, in and out between the jungle of feet and legs.

Jimmie had found himself a suitable spot, where he had a good view of all the proceedings by the time the Orange Lodge were passing by. He was glad that he hadn't missed them. The accordion band were dressed in sailor suits, with orange marigold flowers displayed in the marchers' caps. The bellows of their accordions were fully extended. Was this to make them sound better, or was it just to show off?

Immediately behind the bass drummer, came a flat-topped lorry, decorated around its edges and wheel rims with orange ribbon, and red, white and blue flowers. On top of the lorry stood pretty little girls, all dressed in white satin, with white headbands. They held onto a rope which was secured around the edges of the lorry.

Sitting on a makeshift throne, a girl of about twelve or thirteen years of age, was dressed in the garb of King Billy himself, with a long black curly wig on her head. In her right hand she held aloft a silver-painted wooden sword, and as she waved it, the crowd screamed and cheered all the more. She had it off to a fine art, and she knew it!

'The clever little bitch,' thought the small onlooker.

The drummers rattled away, hardly seeming to touch the tightly-stretched skins of the drums. They were followed by the families of the Orange Lodge members, marching along in two lines, one on either side of the road.

Then again came girls in white dresses, some satin, some cotton, according to their means, but all of them feeling like princesses for that one glorious day; their special day; the

Twelfth of July. Each one feeling so very proud of the orange sash that she wore.

There were all shapes and sizes of girls, each accompanied by mothers, aunts or older sisters, who also came in all shapes and sizes, clutching onto the youngsters' hands to help them keep up with the marching. Some of them were shy, their eyes following the tramlines, and at the same time shuffling to keep in step with the girl in front.

Marching between the two columns, were the men, both young and old, dressed in their best suits, (some of them brought out of the pawnshop for this special event). They carried huge banners, which almost touched the overhead tram wires, and were guided and supported by polished wooden poles, and gaily-coloured ropes with tassels blowing in the light breeze. The whole was a wonderful sight indeed, that stirred up the crowds to a frenzy of excitement.

They were proud people, proud to be seen in their regalia, and proud to be carrying the banner with the picture of their King Billy seated on his white horse, with the shining sword in his hand, looking defiant and aggressive, as if in pursuit of some enemy force.

Jimmie's eyes were still smarting and watering; he turned his head away from the glare of the sun, and as he did so, he caught sight of his mother in the procession, holding the hand of his younger sister, Lily. It was a very special day for her, for it was her birthday, and she was named after the orange lilies which were such an important feature of the Twelfth of July. Her red hair underlined the fact, as it gleamed and shone like gold in the bright sunlight, competing with the orange sash worn over her shoulder. They were all off to Southport for the celebrations.

The fifes and drums of the Stanley Blues struck up their lively march, setting everyone's feet a-tapping, but Jimmie turned away, resentment welling up in his heart, after all, he was only nine years' old. The brightness of the day was spoilt for him. He didn't notice the other bands that followed, and hardly even heard them; all he was aware of was his mother skipping merrily along, laughing and enjoying the day with his sister and their friends.

He elbowed his way through the crowds of people and walked slowly down India Street to his home. On reaching his destination, he gave way to sobs and tears.

He wasn't the kind of lad who cried for long though, in reality, he was a tough little guy who had learned how to look after himself. He had had to! He wiped his eyes with the sleeve of his rough jersey, then slid the same sleeve across his runny nose.

The cold stone step on which he had been sitting, made him more aware of how alone he was. They'd all gone out and left him as usual, they hadn't even bothered to wake him up to watch the Orange Day Parade, as the rest of the family were doing, no doubt. His two older brothers, Bobby and Willie and his big sister, Mary, were nowhere to be seen.

His father, Rob MacLean, a merchant seaman for many years, was home from sea, but of course he was out with the rest of the revellers. Though Rob earned good pay from his long voyages, he never had anything to show for it, either in cash or home comforts. He would return with a full wallet, then fritter his money away on drink, treating all and sundry, friends and strangers. In fact anyone at all with a hard luck story to tell. No wonder he was so popular!

As Jimmie's thoughts returned to the present, the sounds of the bands were fading away in the distance, and crowds of happy people tagged along behind one another down Netherfield Road, jostling good-naturedly as they headed towards Prince Edwin Street, Everton Brow, into Shaw Street, past Brunswick Road, and down through the large shopping area to Exchange Station, where they would board the train for Southport, which was set to be the highlight and culmination of their day.

'Hey, Jimmie,' came a soft call.

The lad looked up with red, swollen eyes. He grinned happily on seeing his older sister Mary, hurrying down the street accompanied by her pal, Nellie Mather.

'Sorry lad,' she apologised breathlessly, 'I had to wait for the shop to open to get a loaf of bread, Mrs Carmichael had shut up to watch the bands. Sorry lad!'

Turning to Nellie, she said, 'Come on in Nellie,' then again to Jimmie, 'Come on lar, let's do yer eyes fer yer.'

In no time at all, she did what she could with cold water and bicarbonate of soda, cleaning his eyes, then gently smearing them with yellow ointment from a round wooden box.

After washing her hands with carbolic soap, Mary cut a thick slice of bread from the loaf which she had just bought. 'Here y'are Jimmie.'

Jimmie, who had just been upstairs to find his socks, jumped the last two stairs down into the kitchen. 'Ooh ta!' he grinned.

'What d'yer want on it, sugar or connie-onnie?'

'Connie-onnie,' Jimmie replied, as he put his socks on.

Mary spread the condensed milk on the fresh bread and handed it to him. By now the kettle was boiling on the gas ring and Mary said to Nellie, 'Would you like a drink girl?'

'Go on then, I wouldn't mind.'

Mary poured the scalding water into the old brown teapot, hardly waiting for it to brew, they were so eager. She poured it into three mugs, two of which were badly chipped. 'You can 'ave the good one,' she said, generously handing Nellie the one good mug they owned.

It felt like heaven to Jimmie as he tucked into his butty, the sticky milk glued to each side of his mouth as he took big bites. 'Mmm, that's good,' he murmured, as he watched the floating tea leaves, swirling around inside his mug, 'China tea, this is,' he added.

'How d'yer know?' asked Nellie, intrigued by the little lad's knowledge.

'Cos there's junks on top,' he chuckled, exposing the contents of his mouth at the same time.

'Yer'll be a comic when yer grow up,' laughed Nellie.

Mary joined in the laughter. 'You're always laughing Nellie Mather, there's always summat tickling yer fancy.'

'Where do you gerrall yer jokes from?' asked Jimmie, licking his fingers, 'yer rhymes 'em off one after another, is it summat yer ma puts in yer tea?'

'No lar,' laughed Nellie, looking at the lad affectionately, 'it comes natural like. If yer don't smile an' laugh, or 'ave a good chuckle among yerselves, yer might as well pack it in lad, life is miserable enough, so don't make it any worse. If yer in a tight spot, talk yer way out of it, or crack a joke or two, that's my remedy ferra happier life.'

Nellie took a gulp of the hot tea then continued. 'Look at all them toffee-nosed sods down in the city. They might 'ave lots of money an' all that, but they 'aven't got a smile fer the cat. All they're interested in is makin' money, they've no feelin's fer anybody. We don't want ter be like that do we?'

The wee lad, older than his years, commented thoughtfully, 'No, we don't, yer right there Nellie. Though I wouldn't mind a bit o' their money, why if they fell down the shit-house, they'd come up smellin' o' roses!'

He and Nellie fell about laughing.

'There y'are lad, yer made me laugh again that time,' she tittered.

Mary interrupted, 'We'll 'ave less of that talk, Jimmie Mac. An' don't you encourage 'im, Nell.'

'Aw! It's only a bit o' fun, there's not a lot we can laugh about is there? I don't mean any 'arm.'

Nellie knew that Mary had high principles, even though she was only a girl from a poor family like herself, and wouldn't do anything to upset her, as they had been close friends since starting school together.

'Anyway, it's time I was goin,' announced Nellie, draining her mug, 'the tea was good, thanks.'

'Yer welcome. What time will I see yer ternight?'

'I'll come round about seven,' answered Nell, as she stepped into the street.

'Okay, ta-ra girl,' called Mary, waving her pal off.

By now the whole area was deserted, even the number thirty tram that passed the top of the street, was empty. In the distance, the familiar sound of a ship's horn could be heard as it made its way up the Mersey.

Mary returned indoors, and as she swilled the mugs under the cold tap, she asked Jimmie, 'What are yer plans for this afternoon?'

'Dunno. Don't know where the lads are.'

'Give Arthur a whistle, he'll be in.'

Mary saw that Jimmie was hesitating, so she gave him a playful shove, 'Go on, lad, don't need so much coaxin'.'

Jimmie leapt up the two steps to the door, and placing his two little fingers between his teeth, blew a piercing whistle in the direction of Arthur's house, just across the street.

He immediately received a similar whistle in acknowledgement from the boy in question.

Arthur was Nellie's brother, and was a year older than Jimmie. Jimmie's face lit up on hearing Arthur's whistle, 'At least they hadn't **all** gone to Southport.'

Arthur emerged from the house; a lanky lad with mousy hair and a sallow complexion, with ears that looked too big for his head, sticking out like the handles of a jug. His sad-looking eyes were reminiscent of a cocker spaniel's, but he grinned from ear to ear when he saw his pal. 'Look at this I've made,' he said

'Gosh it's a whip, a real whip, plaited an' wi' a lash at the end. Go on, Art, crack it fer us.'

Art could see his friend was impressed, 'Okay, look out!' He twirled the plaited whip over his head and brought it down with a sharp crack.

'Giz a go, giz a go!' pestered the smaller boy, jumping up and down with excitement.

Arthur handed the coveted whip over to his best pal, who tried to twirl it as he had seen Arthur doing. He ended up cracking his leg instead, causing an angry stinging red weal to appear.

Jimmie's interest in the wonderful whip quickly evaporated, and he was glad to return it to its proud owner. Arthur rolled it up, twisting the plaited rope round its wooden handle, then flung it through the open door of his house. 'Put that away, will yer Nell?'

'I'll burn the soddin' thing,' she retorted sharply, 'Yer'll end up wrappin' it round yer bloody neck an' throttlin' yersel!'

Arthur resented the idea of his beloved whip being sacrificed to the flames, especially as he'd spent days creating it.

Jimmie secretly agreed with Nellie, as now he didn't care if he never saw the damn thing again either.

The two lads were in appearance, almost as different as they possibly could be. Arthur, as already mentioned, was lanky, without an ounce of flesh on his skinny body, whereas Jimmie was nicely-rounded and in proportion, except for his pot belly, which Arthur teased him about from time to time, today being no exception.

'Me mam's gorra belly like yours.'

'So what!' Jimmie was touchy about his belly. 'It's all mine, so what?'

'You're not 'avin' a kid are yer?'

'That's not where kids are. Me mam said I came from under a strawberry bush, and that's why I've got red hair. So how did yer mam get one in her belly?'

Arthur laughed, 'Hell, you're thick. What do yer think 'appens when yer old man comes 'ome from sea an' gets a skinful? An' yer mam too?'

'They're sick 'alf the night in the bucket.'

'Yes, an' what do yer think's 'appenin' the rest o' the night?'

'Ow do I know?' came the innocent reply. 'What's that got to do wi' kids anyway?'

'Can't yer see, yer silly little bleeder; yer mam an' dad, they make kids.'

Arthur's explanations didn't seem to make any sense to the younger lad.

'An' yer old feller misses 'is ship, pissed out of 'is mind, lyin' in 'is fleapit. One an' one makes three! Oh never mind!' said Arthur, seeing the look of bewildered innocence on his friend's face, and realising that he was getting nowhere. 'Never mind, it'll sink in sometime, yer dumb sod!' and he smirked to himself. 'Come on, I'll race yer!'

The two boys ran and jumped, their bellies landing on the unspiked railings separating India Street from Bala Terrace. Giving a half twist of their little bodies, they whirled themselves over, landing on the uneven ground, where they clapped the dust from their hands and the seats of their pants.

'Bloody mongrels!' snorted Arthur, as he scraped the substance from the side of his shoe on the edge of the kerb.

'Yer wants ter keep yer eyes open when yer land,' laughed Jimmie, 'ow many times 'ave yer landed in it?'

'Not as many as you. At least I don't sit in it, like you did last time!'

Arthur shoved his pal's shoulder good-naturedly, and they both collapsed in a fit of the giggles.

At last they reached the home of one of their pals, Billy Thomas. Arthur put his mouth to the open letter-box and yelled out the boy's name.

There was no reply, so they moved on to the house next door, where another of their mates lived. This time Arthur let out one of his piercing whistles.

Mary Ellen Gilbert, known as Meg, from her initials, was startled from her nap by the shrill blast, 'Wadder-yer-want? 'she grumbled, wearily scratching her head.

'Is Bobby in?' asked Art.

'Just a minute,' Meg said, as she adjusted her rounded plaits over her ears. 'Come in.'

The lads entered the small room, then gasped on seeing their pal, sprawled out on the horsehair sofa, his left leg completely encased in plaster of Paris.

'Gosh!' exclaimed Jimmie. 'What 'appened ter you?'

'I'll tell yer what 'appened,' butted in Meg, 'been at Alder Hey Hospital all night, worn out I am.'

The lads tried to console her, knowing full well that she was more annoyed at missing the Orange Day celebrations, than by what had happened to her unfortunate son.

'Want any messages? Want us ter stay wi' Bobby while yer gets yer 'ead down fer a bit?' offered Jimmie, trying to be helpful.

'Daft little sod!' Meg grumbled, ignoring Jimmie's offer, 'fell off the backyard wall, didn' 'e? Second time this is, and the same leg too!' She turned to the poor victim, 'I'll 'ave yer shot, like they do 'orses at Aintree if yer does it again. I'm warnin' yer lad!'

Bobby's face was tear-stained; his nose and chin also bore evidence of his fall from the wall, and he was in considerable pain.

'Ere, 'ave this,' his mother handed him an aspirin and half a cup of water, 'I'll go an' get me 'ead down fer an hour. Yer'll be alright won't yer? I mean the lot of yer, if I leave yer tergether?' As she spoke, she unwrapped her shawl from her shoulders and laid it over her son's chest. 'There, lar.' Her voice softened, she was really quite fond of the lad, but never showed her feelings in front of others. She yawned as she headed for the stairs, 'G'night, I mean g'mornin.'

The boys smirked, 'Ta-ra, Mrs Gilbert.'

It wasn't long before Bobby fell into a deep sleep, and the other two were at a loss as to how to spend their time, regretting slightly that they had offered to stay indoors on such a beautiful day.

Arthur wandered over to the door and opened it wide, allowing a shaft of bright sunlight to fall into the room, illuminating the large plaster cast on Bobby's leg. 'Gorra pencil on yer, Jimmie?' he asked.

'No, I 'aven't.'

'Never mind, there's one 'ere on the sports page. Mrs G must 'ave been usin' it.'

Arthur put the indelible pencil to his lips and wet it, then drew a large cross on Bobby's cast. Jimmie then took the pencil and proceeded to put a nought below the cross. So it went on, until none of the beautiful whiteness of the plaster remained visible.

'Gotcher!' shouted Arthur. 'Oxo!' he yelled triumphantly, drawing a line through the winning letter combination.

They were so engrossed in their mischievous game, that they were unaware of Meg's approaching footsteps, until the last minute, when Arthur quickly grabbed the shawl and flung it across Bobby's injured leg.

'Phew! That was a close shave!' he whispered to Jimmie.

Bobby's mother entered the room, and asked the lads if they would like a bite to eat? 'What about a jam butty?' she suggested, but as much as Jimmie and Arthur relished the idea, they hurriedly declined her offer.

'No thanks, Mrs G,' said Art politely, ''ave ter be goin' now. See yer later. Er -Bobby's okay, 'asn't woke up at all.'

The two boys then beat a hasty retreat. Meg thought it was rather strange that the boys hadn't stopped for something to eat. 'Ah! Well, never mind,' she mused aloud, as she made herself a pot of tea.

She reached for the racing page to study the form and Bobby moaned in his sleep.

'Poor lad,' she murmured, as she covered him once again with the shawl that had somehow slipped down his leg.

'What the...? What the ... ? Those two little sods! No wonder they didn't stop!' she cried aloud, uncovering the offending pot leg, and revealing the game that Bobby's two pals had been playing. 'Just let them wait till I gets me 'ands on 'em, the little devils, me poor Bobby's leg, just look at it!' She consoled herself with a sip of hot tea and inhaled deeply on her Woodbine.

'Never mind, lar, we'll see what yer da' can do when 'e gets 'ome. Might be able to scrub it off with carbolic or Aunt Sally.' She glanced across the racing page to the 3.30 at Ripon. 'Well, nuttin' to rant about 'ere,' but then her grey blue eyes sparkled as she scratched behind her ear with the blue pencil. 'That's it! That's it!' Her voice rose two octaves higher, betraying her mounting excitement. 'That's it, Bobby me lad!'

Bobby groaned in his sleep completely oblivious to all the goings on.

'A bit of paper, some paper!' Meg was in a panic to get her bet on for the 3.30, 'Sixpence to win, no a shillin', no two shillin's to win, that's what I'll do,' she muttered, hurriedly tearing a piece of paper in half to write down her bet. Then she had an afterthought and stopped abruptly. 'What if it goes down, or comes in second or third? I know, I'll back it each way, three shillin' stake.'

She hesitated once more, it was a lot of money to lose. At last she succumbed to temptation and quickly jotted down the horse of her choice to win, and also to have it placed first, second, or third. She reached for her purse, which contained all the money she had to last the rest of the week, which was just seven shillings and ninepence ha'penny. She drew out a florin and two silver sixpences, then wrapped them in the betting slip, then grabbing her shawl from Bobby, she scurried off to the corner of Roscommon Street and Netherfield Road, where Teddy Latham, the local bookie's runner, made his collections.

'There y'are, Ted,' Meg blurted out, 'an see that it gets in on time!'

Meg slowly made her way back to Bala Terrace, agonising over whether she had done the right thing? 'What if the bloody 'orse falls an' breaks its leg like our Bobby?' Then she chuckled, seeing the funny side of it, 'Probably finish up as stew in a pan of scouse!' she laughed out loud.

She knew she would be able to get the results from the Liverpool Echo when her husband Mick, brought home the paper that evening. That's if he came home sober. He might be too drunk to stand up, never mind, remember to get a paper. Mick would be like all the rest of them when they all returned from Southport.

At the thought of Southport and missing the procession and all the bands, Meg felt miserable and depressed, and plodded wearily along until she reached the door of her small terraced house. Through the half-open door, the room looked dull and cheerless, the rays of sunshine had disappeared, and the gloom reflected her own feelings. Once again she laid her shawl over Bobby, who by this time was fully awake and glad to see his mam.

She sat down near the window and lit a Woody, drawing heavily upon it. Then the realization of what she had done dawned on her, 'Good God! what have I done?' she muttered to herself, 'Mick'll kill me when 'e finds out I've been bettin', an all that money too!'

CHAPTER TWO
Denny

The smell of dog muck lingered on Arthur's pumps, 'Yer don't arf stink!' Jimmie complained.

'Shut yer gob!' snapped Arthur, 'or I'll shut it fer yer!'

'Come on then, shut me up. Come on, I dare yer!'

They both jumped to their feet.

'Fer real?'

'Yeah fer real!'

Grubby little fists were clenched, and both boys moved cautiously around, each anticipating the other's blow, wondering who would strike first? Glaring angrily at each other, in an instant they had lunged fiercely, Jimmie striking his opponent across the left ear, at the same time receiving a forceful blow to the side of his chin.

'Hey! Hey!'

Suddenly the two boys were grabbed from behind by the scruff of their necks by two large hands. 'What the 'ell d'yer think youse two are doin'? Yer little bleeders!'

Arthur glanced round awkwardly and immediately recognised the huge frame of Tim Cranley, a local heavyweight boxer.

'Keep yer conk out o' this,' snorted Arthur cheekily, his dander up.

'If yer wants ter scrap, I'll fix one up fer yer, at Clive's Gym!'

Jimmie responded immediately to this suggestion, 'Right yer are then,' simultaneously thinking that the intruder was an angel in disguise.

'Frig off!' snapped Arthur, angrier than ever. The next thing he knew was that the flat of Cranley's hand had cuffed him painfully over the ear.

'Knock it off, I said!'

By now, Art could hardly hear, due to the ringing in his head from the knocks to both his ears from his two opponents.

Cranley persisted, 'Fix a time between yersels, an' I'll sort it out fer yer at the gym. By the way,' he added, 'I'm just going down ter see young Denny Rodgers in Bala Terrace. I'll be back in ten minutes.' Then he swaggered off, his broad shoulders swaying menacingly as he did so.

The name Denny Rodgers suddenly hit home to the boys. They knew him well, and also knew that he was seriously ill with consumption. They felt ashamed that they hadn't visited him earlier that day when they had been in Bala Terrace; after all they had a lot of time to spare. Cranley was a rotter they agreed, to make them feel so guilty.

Arthur looked away, avoiding Jimmie's eyes. Both were stubbornly unwilling to compromise or make peace, even if it was only temporarily.

'What's up wi' youse two?' Jimmie's sister Mary called out as she was sandstoning the steps of the house. 'You look as if you've lost a shillin' and found a farthin'.'

'Nowt,' mumbled Jimmie, with his head down.

The rough sandstone grated on the steps, and prompted Arthur to start grinding his teeth.

Unable to bear the sound Jimmie snapped, 'I'll knock them out for you one of these days.'

Of course this didn't help the present situation between them, and Arthur's response was predictable, 'Just you try it.'

'Alright now, I've heard enough,' Mary snapped. 'You can both behave yersels, or you'll come in, and stop in our Jimmie!'

Jimmie was relieved at his sister's intervention, as he didn't really want to fight his pal. Besides that, they were both upset at having neglected to visit Denny.

Mary finished mopping the steps and went back inside the house, and Jimmie finally held out his hand to Arthur. The two chum's hands joined together, and they grinned at each other, happy to be friends again.

Mary returned to the door and handed them half an apple each. 'Ere y'are, these'll put yer on fer a bit. Yer can 'ave some chips ternight from Polly's. She'll be open I think.'

'Yeah, she will be, fer all them lot comin' back from Southport,' Arthur mumbled resentfully, his mouth full of apple.

He suddenly remembered the gym, and the fight that Cranley was arranging, and his stomach churned.

As they sat there on the step, chewing their last bits of apple, Tim's huge figure seemed to pick up from nowhere. 'Nice ter see yer lads. Sorted it out 'ave yer?'

'Wadder yer mean?' they asked feigning ignorance.

Tim chuckled to himself, egging them on. 'Have yer fergot already? The fight at the gym!'

'Oh, we don't need ter fight now, we're pals again,' Jimmie assured him.

'An' apart from that, I'm not goin' ter get me 'ead knocked off wi' me best mate,' added Arthur.

Jimmie nodded in agreement. 'Might as well do it 'ere in the back street. It costs nowt either. Probably 'ave ter pay at Clive's gym.'

Tim strolled away smiling, feeling smugly that at least for the moment, he had achieved his purpose.

Arthur was picking bits of apple out of his teeth, and Jimmie was thinking how glad he was that the explosive situation had died down once again. Agitation and boredom had stalked them all that day.

'Come on, Art, let's go and see Denny. I think we should, don't you?'

Art agreed, they both knew Denny when he was in their class at Netherfield Road Junior School and had missed him. They didn't vault over the railings into Bala Terrace this time, but scuttled down the well-worn steps.

At Denny's house, the second on the street, the door was open. People often left their doors open in Everton. After all, there was nothing to steal, and besides everyone knew everyone else; their business and their problems. They were poor, but respected one another's paltry possessions. When the rent man was coming around, or the moneylender, the neighbours would signal to each other like ships in distress, so they could pretend to be out. They were indeed a close-knit community.

Arthur tapped at the door of Denny's house. 'Hello Mrs Rodgers, we've come to see Denny.'

'Come in lads,' she whispered.

The frail little woman led them into the parlour. Everyone had a sofa in their parlour in those days, and they came into their own on occasions like this, when they suffered their all-too-frequent cases of sickness.

Denny lay on a white, cotton sheet, well-patched but spotlessly clean, and was covered with a cream-coloured blanket. His blond head sank deeply into a flock pillow, and his face was pale and expressionless, his light blue eyes looked bluer than ever.

He smiled when Art and Jimmie entered, obviously glad to see his school friends, 'Hello, Jimmie, hello Arthur,' he whispered feebly.

'How are yer, mate? It's good ter see yer.'

'I'm alright, I suppose. I'll be glad ter get up an' go out wi' the lads again, down to the Cast Iron Shore (a particular part

of the beach that was a favourite with the lads), I like it there.'
Denny gave a cough, and it was plain to see that it caused him
a lot of pain. A second bout of coughing resulted in him
bringing phlegm up into his mouth.

'Spit it out lad, spit it out.' Mrs Rodgers held a white
enamel bucket to her son's face, the strong, antiseptic smell of
Aunt Sally emanated from the receptacle.

Denny flopped back down, exhausted after his ordeal.

'There now, you'll feel better,' his mother said softly, as
she gently wiped his brow and straightened the blanket over
him.

The two boys just stood and stared helplessly, they hadn't
realised how ill their pal really was, and they felt
uncomfortable, because they were both so fit and active. They
were familiar with the progress of the dreaded disease, and
upset by their pal's obvious deterioration. Denny was fighting
hard, but losing his battle, as so many others had done before
him.

Jimmie cuffed his jersey sleeve into his hand and
awkwardly wiped away a tear from the corner of his eye.

'Are yer alright, lad?' asked Denny's mother, knowing full
well that, although the two boys had come to cheer up her
sick son, they were overcome with grief, and were trying in
their childish way, to hide the fact. After all they were only
kids themselves.

'It's me bad eyes, Mrs R,' replied Jimmie.

Arthur knew otherwise, and he didn't have that excuse, so
he just turned aside and wiped his own tears away with his
grubby hand. Mrs Rodgers gave a wry smile, she knew what
they must be feeling, and appreciated the cost of their visit.

'Just goin' ter say,' blurted out Jimmie, desperate to make
conversation, 'the Stanley Blues have a new mace bearer.'

Arthur quickly supported him by adding, 'Yeah, an' did
yer see that piper out of step?'

'Ow did you see im? Where were you watchin'?' asked Jimmie, feeling a bit put out; Art hadn't mentioned that he'd seen the parade.

'I was watchin' on the landin'. Yer gets a better view from up there.'

'Yer didn't tell me yer was goin' up there,' snapped Jimmie.

'Yer was in bed when I called fer yer. I couldn't make yer 'ear!'

The two boys glared at one another. If they weren't careful, there would be a repetition of their earlier squabbling, which would be unforgivable in their pal's sick room.

Denny smiled, he could see the rising tempers, 'As long as yer didn't miss the procession, that's the main thing,' then a look of sadness clouded his face. 'I heard them passing along the top of the street. It sounded good. Perhaps I'll be well enough ter see it next year.'

Art's voice butted in loudly, 'Aye, an' did yer see that drunken old cow? Er sorry, Mrs Rodgers, er that old woman, she lifted a Scottie's kilt up. 'e 'ad 'is missus's white bloomers on underneath.'

'Cor! Didn't know that. I thought they er wore er nuttin' underneath!' exclaimed Jimmie.

The four of them just roared with laughter at that, and Arthur and Jimmie were happy that they had been able to cheer up Denny and his mother, if only for a little while.

'Good ter see yer smilin' again Ma,' said Denny, looking up at his mother. 'Yer've been lookin' a bit down'earted lately.'

'Gerraway, I'm smilin' all the time, aren't I lads?'

'Yeah, course yer are,' they chorused.

Suddenly there was another prolonged bout of coughing, and the small boy's body rattled and shook, until he sobbed, while Mrs Rodgers supported his fair head. Beads of sweat glistened on his brow.

When the coughing fit was over and Denny was resting on his pillow, Arthur said, 'We're goin' ter leave yer now, so's yer can rest, but we'll pop in again real soon, if that's alright wi' youse.'

'Sure, call anytime, lads.' Mrs Rodgers smiled at them both, opened her purse and held out two shiny pennies. Before the lads could refuse them, she pushed the coppers into their small hands. 'No, no, take them,' she insisted.

'Ta very much,' said Jimmie, 'but yer don't need ter do that.' Then, turning to Denny, he patted his shoulder, 'See yer, Den, yer'll soon be out wi' us again.'

The boys left, and as they walked away from the house, Arthur said, 'I'm glad we went.'

'Me too.'

The visit to their sick friend had made them feel good; a pleasant, almost reverent feeling, that of doing a good deed, especially on the Twelfth of July.

CHAPTER THREE
White Horse

The heat of the day had cooled considerably, except inside Polly's chip-shop, where the brown fat bubbled and spluttered noisily in the large pans. The jolly, round-faced woman, expertly jostled the golden chips back and forth in her long-handled chip basket. She and her husband Frank, had laboriously peeled mountains of potatoes in anticipation of plenty of custom when the revellers returned from Southport later that evening. Polly shook and banged the chip basket on the side of the pan, then tested one of the chips between her finger and thumb.

'Won't be long, lads,' she smiled at Jimmie and Arthur, 'what's it to be?'

'Three penn'orths o' mix please, with salt an' vinegar,' said Jimmie, his mouth watering at the sight and smell of those beautiful slivers of fried potato.

Polly shovelled the chips in her usual professional way, placing the three portions onto the pages of the Liverpool Echo. Then taking a huge pan of mushy peas from the gas stove, she scooped a ladleful on top of each heap of chips, shaking the salt pot with one hand. After replacing the peas on the stove, she shook the vinegar bottle vigorously onto the parcels. Jimmie almost fainted to think that soon he would be eating them.

After wrapping them in a larger sheet of newspaper, Polly smiled again at the boys, 'There we are,' she said, 'three pence please. Ta-ra lads.'

The two friends raced off together to Jimmie's house dying to get started on the appetising parcels.

'Gosh, yer've been quick!' said Mary, taking the steaming parcels from them.

Jimmie and Arthur stood at the large square table, on which were three thick slices of bread. They each opened the greasy papers and drooled over the sight, so eager were they to begin their banquet.

'Right! Get yer mouths round that!' said Mary, 'sorry there's no marge fer the bread.'

'That's alright,' said Arthur, 'don't matter, they'll be good anyway.'

Jimmie said nothing, as both his cheeks were already bulging with food.

'Hey! Take it easy! Yer'll get indigestion, yer greedy little pig. Eat slowly!'

Jimmie felt a smack on the side of his head from his sister's hand. Point taken, the boy ate more slowly, savouring every mouthful like a connoisseur, then washed it all down with a mug of hot tea.

'Sorry, Mary,' he grinned, wiping his mouth on the back of his hand. 'Boy! I could eat that again, it was good!'

'Greedy guts,' laughed Mary, wanting to scold him, but unable to do so, because of the look of satisfaction on her brother's face.

Arthur just watched and ate, enjoying himself immensely.

After their appetising feast, they screwed up the greasy papers and handed them to Mary to use for lighting the fire; nothing was ever wasted in the MacLean household.

As Mary raked out the ashes in the fire-grate with a heavy, brass-handled poker, she wondered when Willie would be coming home? She decided that she wouldn't light the fire just yet, as there wasn't much coal left. Anyway the day had been quite warm, so they'd do without. The noise of a tram could be heard plainly from the open door.

'Go an' see if our Willie got off that tram, will yer, Jimmie?'

Willie was two years younger than Mary; a wiry lad, tall for his age, sharp-featured with light brown hair.

'Yeah, 'e's comin' now. I can see 'im.'

Half a dozen lads had jumped from the green and cream tram before it had stopped.

'Yer'll be jumpin' under the soddin' wheels one o' these days,' shouted the conductor, waving his fist at them.

The gang laughed as they ran off down India Street, making rude signs and gestures at the conductor as they went.

'See yer later, Johnny.'

'So long, Mick.'

'Ta-ra, Willie.'

'S'long, Hambone.'

They all bade each other ta-ra in their broad Evertonian accents, and made their various ways home.

As Willie entered the house, he was met with a barrage of questions from his younger brother.

'Where've yer bin?'

'Aigburth.'

'Why didn't yer wake me up this mornin' ter go wit' yer?'

'I keep tellin' yer, yer too small, yer can't keep up wi' us,' Willie snorted.

'Well, what about Arthur? He's not small, or slow. He's only skinny-legged, so if 'e's goin' ter get in yer gang, why can't I?'

'I keep tellin' yer, when yer big enough an' old enough.' This kid brother of his would try the patience of a saint, he thought to himself, as he sprawled across the sofa. He was three years older than Jimmie, and constantly tried to assert his authority; but Jimmie was very shrewd for his age, a quality born of necessity, so Willie didn't always come off best.

Jimmie was very persistent, and he continued to pester Willie. 'Go on Willie, let's join yer gang,' the little rascal pleaded.

'Shut it!' snapped Willie, who by now was beginning to lose his cool.

'Aw! Come on, Willie, don't be a spoilsport, let's join.'

'It's not up ter me, an' it's not my gang.'

Jimmie thought he detected a softening in his brother's attitude.

Willie continued, 'It's up ter Hambone, 'e's the leader.'

'Well yer can put a word in fer us can't yer?'

'Ave ter wait an' see. Now stop yer natterin' an' let me read, yer pest!' Willie turned back to the pages of the Hotspur, his favourite boys' magazine.

'Can I 'ave that when yer've finished?' asked Jimmie, hopefully.

'Gerrout!' shouted Willie angrily, determined to settle down to a quiet read.

Jimmie ran out, not wanting to push his luck for he knew just how far to go.

Arthur was waiting outside, 'Don't tell me, I heard it all. We'll just 'ave ter 'ang around an' wait fer 'em, you'll get in the gang don't worry,' he sounded more confident than he felt.

While they were waiting outside, another tram stopped and Gerry Magee, a neighbour, alighted with two of his daughters, Tess and Moira. His other daughter Jean, had stayed at home to look after their mother, who was ill.

'Where've yer bin, Tess? 'ow's yer mam? Where's your Jean?' Jimmie's questions followed one after the other, for he liked to be well informed about the happenings in India Street.

'Go on,' said Gerry to his girls, 'play out with Jimmie and Arthur fer a bit, while I get the tea on.'

Gerry entered his house, not a basement like Jimmie's, but above street level, and up a flight of stone steps. The front room had no window and was used as a bedroom. The other room was a kitchen-cum-living-room, the same as everyone else's in that area. It also doubled as a bathroom on bath night, when the tin bath was hauled in from the backyard. This room was blessed with a small window, which was kept open day and night, as was the door which divided the two rooms, allowing a breath of fresh air to drift in.

Mr Magee had left Ireland with his then young bride, seeking work, as so many of his countrymen had done before him, only to find that there wasn't enough work for the people who already lived there, so he had been trapped in one of the poorest parts of the city, with no way out. He would never be able to raise enough money to take all his family back home, so he had learned to make the best of the situation.

He and his wife Mary, were good Catholics, accepting their three lovely daughters as blessings from God, but because they had been born in quick succession, the family was thrown into even deeper poverty. They were a close and loving family; not for Gerry the drinking in the ale-houses, or wasting money on gambling. He had resorted to rag-tatting to earn a few shillings to help his family to survive.

He entered the bedroom, putting on a brave face, 'Hello me darlin,' he greeted his wife cheerfully, 'an' how are yer terday?'

Then, addressing Jean, his eldest daughter, 'How's Mammy been, dear?'

'Just the same,' Jean replied quietly, 'she's had her medicine.'

Gerry bent over his wife and gently kissed her pale cheek then sighing sadly, he turned and went into the other room, thinking remorsefully, 'Perhaps his darlin' Mary wouldn't have been so ill if she'd had her way and they had stayed in Ireland?'

The air at least, was fresh and clean over there, not like this dirty city with its foul-smelling streets. Mary had agreed to move because she loved Gerry, and they were convinced that a fine future could be found in another country.

'Shall I help with the tea, Daddy? You can sit with Mam, she'd like that.'

So Jean left Mary and Gerry together, while she went to sort out something for a meal. Meanwhile, the little group of children sat outside on the edge of the pavement, listening to Tess relating the day's events, and how she had been to visit her grandma at the Salvation Army Hostel.

Arthur looked puzzled, 'Yer grandma?' he asked curiously.

'Yes, me grandma, is in the Sally Army Hostel, she lives there.'

'Thought she'd be in Ireland wi' King Billy's lot!' chipped in Jimmie.

'No, she's been here a long time, before me mam and daddy came here.'

'So, is she not well?'

'No, not really, she's getting old,' Tess looked sad, 'then there's me poor mammy of course. She's very sick.'

'What's up wi' 'er, Tess?' asked Arthur.

'Don't know,' said Tess sadly, 'I only know that me daddy cries at night. I can hear him when everything's quiet, an' he thinks we're asleep. He whispers, 'Don't leave me Mary. Please get well. I don't want yer to leave me.' Then he pretends to cough so that no one will think he's crying, just in case we're awake.'

A look of fear spread across the boys' faces, and they glanced at each other, as if they could read each other's minds. Thoughts of Denny Rodgers were uppermost in their thoughts. 'She'll be alright, Tess,' comforted the boys.

'I hope so,' replied the blue-eyed, dark, curly-headed girl.

'She's a real Irish beauty, that one,' thought Jimmie, as he looked at her with tenderness.

'We'd better go in now, Jimmie, see yer tomorrow. Won't be out again tonight, there's bound to be trouble along Neddy Road later.' With that, the two girls disappeared into the house, closing the heavy door behind them.

'Gosh!' said Jimmie to Art, 'I hope Tess's mam's gonna be alright.'

'Yeah, me too!' Art answered, 'Do yer like 'er?' he asked, 'is she yer girl?'

'Gerraway, yer daft bleeder,' Jimmie scoffed, only too aware that his face was giving him away, for he was turning bright red, 'besides, she's a Catholic.'

'Ow do yer know that?'

'Well they wear them blue frocks an' blue capes, an' they don't go to our school. I heard our Mary say that they went up St Domingo Road, or summat like that.'

'Is that in Everton?'

'Don't know. Do yer like their Jean?' asked Jimmie, changing the subject, and trying to get one back on his pal at the same time.

'No, do I 'eck!' smirked Arthur.

'Bet yer do, yer liar.'

Arthur's face coloured slightly. It was his turn to be teased.

'See, yer giving yersel' away!'

He was making the most of his friend's embarrassment and ran away as fast as he could, with Arthur in hot pursuit. They reached Jimmie's house, and as usual Jimmie leapt down the two steps, almost knocking Willie backwards into the room.

'Yer daft little pig!' shouted Willie, staggering to keep his balance.

'Are yer goin' out?' Jimmie asked, ignoring the remark.

'Yeah I am,' grunted Willie.

'Can we come, me an' Art?'

Mary's voice called through the house, 'Our Willie, if yer takin' the kids, look after 'em, d'yer 'ear?'

'They'll 'ave ter look after themsels if they're comin' wi' me.'

The two young lads couldn't believe their ears. Willie hadn't actually said they could go with him, but he hadn't refused either! He was going to meet the gang! So they both set off at a gallop down India Street, behind Willie. This was the moment they had been waiting for, and they scurried along as fast as their legs could carry them.

David Ambrose (Hambone), Billy (Snotty-nose) Thompson, whom the lads had tried to contact earlier that day, and Meg's older son Johnny Gilbert, were already mustered.

Johnny greeted the minors with, 'You wait till me mam gets 'er 'ands on youse two. You're goin' ter get it in the neck fer scribblin' all over our Bobby's pot leg.'

Jimmie and Art shrugged their shoulders, to convey a couldn't care less attitude.

'Cleggie an' Greenie shouldn't be long,' Hambone was saying, when suddenly they arrived.

On seeing the younger lads they turned to Willie. 'What's these two little squirts doin' 'ere?'

'Aw! They wanna join us,' Willie told the leader, and ignoring the remark from the other lad, added, 'give em a chance Hambone, they can run an' jump well, an' I'm sure they'll be useful fer summat.'

Hambone gave a sly grin. Then without further comment, he wiped his twisted nose with the back of his hand and suddenly yelled, 'Right, let's go!'

He sprinted off like a fox with a pack of hounds at his heels. Jimmie glanced at Art in amazement.

'Come on!' shouted Willie. 'What yer waitin' for? Yer wanted yer chance didn't yer? So get to it, show 'im what yer can do!'

The two young ones followed the rest of the pack behind their leader, up the steps of Hambone's house in Lower India

Street, through two downstairs rooms, and on reaching one of the open windows, the leader jumped out of it across the entry and onto a kitchen shed. One by one they all followed, like frogs, hopping across the narrow space after their leader.

Jimmie reached the window and shouted to Art, 'Hell! I can't jump that!'

'Belly flop!' screamed Art, 'belly flop, go on, yer can do it!'

Instead of his feet landing on the opposite wall like the older boys, Jimmie wildly flung his little body across the gap, his hands slapping the walls, and his pot belly landing between them. Then he clambered down, and set off in pursuit of the others, wondering how Art had fared?

Arthur had made it, and joined them in their follow-my-leader frog leaps over lavatory roofs, whose occupants reacted angrily at being interrupted, and objected in the strongest possible terms, shouting abuse, their trousers flapping around their ankles.

Then, over the backyard walls separating Cornwall and India Streets, went the gang, running along Netherfield Road, regardless of who stood in their path, past Spot's sweet shop, Polly's chippy, and back to their original starting position.

The two newcomers lagged behind, but eventually they came tearing along, neck and neck, to join the older lads, who were all shouting encouragement, 'Come on, lads, come on. Well done!'

This was praise indeed for Jimmie and Art!

Jimmie stopped and rested both hands on his knees, gasping for breath, 'Phew! Phew!'

Arthur did likewise, panting like a dog puffing for air, and groaning with relief at satisfactorily finishing their test.

'Yer did alright, youse two,' commended one big lad.

'Not bad fer beginners, an' kids at that,' said another.

Before the lads could feel any elation at their achievement, the leader, Hambone, was selecting two teams of four, tapping them on their shoulders and saying, 'You, you, you and you,' the last being Arthur.

Hambone had placed the two younger lads into different teams, so that the contest would be fair. Then having made his choice, he stated, 'Right, White Horse, we'll jump!'

'Come on,' called Willie to his brother, 'you can be the post!'

Jimmie stood with his back to the wall, whilst Willie and the two other team members bent over, one behind the other, their heads between the legs of their companion in front, and hanging onto the waistband of each other's trousers.

Willie, who was the leading horse, hung onto Jimmie's snake belt. 'Brace yerselves!' he yelled, 'get ready!'

The opposing team took ten paces backwards, and Hambone gave a shriek of, 'White Horse!' With that, he careered along and dived forward at the boys' arched backs, almost knocking Jimmie into the wall's stonework as he did so, then hanging onto the collar of his opponent, as he landed on his back, like a jockey hanging onto the reins of his racehorse.

The next boy in the team let out the same cry, and copied Hambone's example, running, then jumping, onto the next bent back and so on. Arthur was last, and he hung precariously onto his team mate's belt in front of him. Finally, the whole team were seated upon their white horses, and then the real fun began. The horses started to rock from side to side in their efforts to unseat their riders, amidst howls of laughter and screams of excitement.

'Ride 'em, gee-up,' they called, as each one slapped the backside of his imaginary horse.

Snotty-nose Thompson's knees were buckling.

'Hang on!' shouted Willie, 'hang on, shake 'em off!'

Cleggie smacked his opponent, Greenie's backside, taking advantage of the long tear in his trousers revealing bare flesh.

'Ouch!' yelled Greenie, 'I'll get yer fer that, Cleggie, yer sod!'

The hysterical laughter continued. The team of horses were still swaying from side to side, raising their behinds and shaking their shoulders. Again Greenie's bare bum proved too much of a temptation to Cleggie, who pinched it hard!

Greenie's voice hollered from underneath.

Suddenly a foul smell drifted upwards; someone had broken wind! The stink drifted right along the line of boys.

Voices came from beneath the huddle, 'Who's farted?'

With that, the rollicking, rolling and swaying came to an abrupt end, with the lads tumbling to the ground amid jubilant laughter. They piled on top of each other, roaring and screaming with exultation, Jimmie landing on top of them all, with his pants half-way down, and tears rolling down his grubby face.

'Hurrah for White Horse!' he shouted.

'Three cheers fer King Billy!' echoed Arthur.

Then another shout was heard from the middle of the youthful heap, 'Bet King Billy's horse didn't fart like that!'

The gang were all hysterical.

'Come on, clear off the lot of you!' cried Miss Fields, the little old lady who owned the nearby sweetshop, 'I'll get the bobbies on ter yer!'

Several minutes passed before the noise subsided, and each boy got to his feet, inspecting his arms and legs for scratches and bruises; all proud evidence of a glorious battle.

No one ever identified the culprit, but Jimmie and Art suspected that it was someone who'd had mushy peas for tea!

CHAPTER FOUR
The Revellers Return

'They're comin'! They're comin'!' someone shouted.

The cry echoed around the almost empty streets, and a few women emerged from their houses, hoping that their sleeping young ones wouldn't be disturbed. The residents of Netherfield Road, and those who lived on the landings, were already perched at their open windows, in anticipation of later events.

The ale-house at the corner of Roscommon Street was packed with a noisy, mixed crowd. Tobacco smoke thickened the air, and outside the wide-open door, a busker strummed his guitar, and played his mouth-organ, which was fixed to a frame supported on his shoulders. Above the noise of the merrymakers, outside in the street, there seemed to be a lull and a mixture of suspense, as euphoria gripped the onlookers who waited expectantly.

In the distance, from as far away as Shaw Street and Brunswick Road, came the sounds they had been waiting for; wailing pipes and beating drums. One could just make out the tune they played, *Blue Bonnets over the Border.*

Huge banners swayed in the distant haze and the noise intensified. Then, as abruptly as it had started, the music stopped, except for the regular beat of a side drum. Then the fifes joined in, whistling one of their merry tunes.

Men with their bowler hats perched on the backs of their heads, and brollies waving in the air, swaggered along haphazardly. Most had bright red faces from spending all day either in the sun, or in the ale-houses, on this hot Twelfth of July.

Some of the marchers pressed bloodstained hankies to their faces or heads. Two men chair-carried one of their comrades, his arms slumped around their shoulders. The skin of one side of the bass drum had been ripped apart, where a missile, most likely a bottle, had found its target. It seemed like a miniature repetition of the Battle of the Boyne all over again. There had been a lot of fighting on the return journey from Exchange Station, mainly around Islington. There had always been rivalry at these celebrations, and today had been no exception.

The leading band was passing Everton Brow and Prince Edwin Street. Crowds upon crowds of people swelled their ranks, jostling and dancing and patting each other on the back as if they had been away for years.

The return procession seemed endless. The jaunty sailor bands were by now, a little less jaunty, yet those who were able, played their concertinas with gusto, to make up for the rest. Women and girls alike, linked their arms and kicked their legs up high in time to the merry music.

The little girls who'd had such a fine time in their white dresses, were now fast asleep on their parent's shoulders, their drooping orange lilies clutched in their grubby little hands, they were all fully worn out after their seaside adventures.

The sea of faces seemed to go on forever, but finally the noisy human tide ebbed away, dispersing into countless terraced homes. Once inside, shoes and boots were kicked off swollen and blistered feet. The satin dresses, now not so white, were pulled over sleepy heads, and those hot, sweaty, little faces were wiped with a cold flannel, removing stains of ice-cream and sticky Southport rock. So for many an eventful day was ended, but for others the round of pleasures continued.

The ale-houses closed precisely on time, but those who hadn't had enough to drink, smuggled out bottles of beer under their jackets or shawls; some were even loaded into prams. The city police force usually turned a blind eye to all this, their busy spell of duty was only half over. They'd spent the first half marshalling everyone away from the danger zones, where mobs waited to disrupt the procession, which could spark off the infamous skirmishes associated with the Twelfth of July celebrations. On these occasions, the police patrolled in groups of four, or sometimes six. However this year, everything had passed off without any major incident, but the night was still young.

'The fleet's in port again.
Back home, in port again,
Yo-ho, yo-ho,
And we'll have a jolly good time.'

Jimmie and Arthur had left the gang doing a job down in Roscommon Street. Hambone didn't say what or where, only that it was too dangerous for the young ones to be there. Just to be part of the gang was honour enough for our young heroes, and they felt a sense of achievement at being accepted by Hambone and the rest, so they didn't mind being left behind in this instance.

They raced past Meg Gilbert's house, still afraid of recriminations about their game of Oxo.

'Gosh!' whispered Jimmie, hearing the singing, 'me mam and dad!'

'I know, my two as well,' Art sighed.

They crouched near the top of the steps in Bala Terrace, watching the two couples staggering down the street.

'Ladies turn out in yer thousands,
Put on yer red, white an' blue.
All the nice girls love a sailor.

There'll be a sailor fer you,
Because the fleet's in port again.'

'Will yer shut yer bleedin' mouths, yer lot o' sods!' came a shout from behind some entry wall, which was totally ignored by the singing drunks, as they continued in full voice.

'Back home in port again,
Yo-ho, yo-ho,
And we'll have a jolly good time'

As they finished their singing, they unlinked their arms, and practically fell down the steps into the MacLean house. Six bottles of beer, like flat-sided medicine bottles, were placed on the table.

'Any glasses, Mary?' demanded Rob MacLean.

Mary, experiencing a sickening disgust at the drunken display, replied sharply, 'No! They were all smashed last night!'

'Give us some cups or summat, then,' he snapped.

The only three cups that they possessed came into use once more. Corks were dragged from two of the bottles with stained teeth, and Threlfall's ale was frothed into the waiting cups.

'Here y'are, Bill. Here y'are, Bessie.'

Arthur's parents took the cups of ale.

'Ta Rob!'

'Here y'are Kate,' Rob said, handing his wife the other cup.

Then Rob put the bottle to his own mouth, and gulped the rest down without even pausing for breath.

Mary left the house unnoticed and ran across the street to Nellie's. 'They're all at it,' she reported to her friend, scornfully.

'Aye, I know, I've 'eard 'em.'

'An' people poorly across the street!'

'Who's playin' your piana?' asked Nellie.

'Sounds like our Bobby, must 'ave just come in,' Mary replied, 'glad I'm not in!'

'Is 'e still goin' wi' that tart from Wallasey?'

'Think so, won't be gettin' up in the morning, like the rest of 'em. Been wi' 'er all day I bet, in some sand-dune, or on Stanny Park lake.'

Bobby, two years Mary's senior, worked at Edmonson's lemonade factory in the loading bay. Ellen, the girl in question, was an office worker at the same factory. Bobby was an older version of Jimmie, with his auburn hair, he was growing to be quite good-looking. But he was a bit stupid when it came to drink and he was easily led.

'Good-bye-ee, good-bye-ee,
Wipe the tear, baby dear, from your eye-ee.'

Kate MacLean was standing beside the piano, eyes half-closed, wailing out the song in what she imagined to be true, music-hall, style. The zip on her navy-blue, pleated skirt had slid down, because of the six month bulge at the front; the fastener being secured by a large safety-pin. She tapped her foot energetically, trying to keep time with Bobby's vamping left hand. An awful noise being emitted from the instrument, which was being played as no other piano had been played before.

Kate sang on:-

'Though it's hard to part I know,
I'll be tickled to death to go ...'

'Go on, Bobby, yer doin' alright,' shouted Bessie, puffing on her fag. The so-called pianist was encouraged all the more, and banged and thumped on the keys with renewed gusto. His left hand hit the same four black keys continually, whilst he stretched the thumb and little finger of his right hand to find the melody, which somehow always seemed to elude him! Nevertheless he was enjoying himself immensely, and surprisingly, so was his audience.

'There's a silver lining in the sky-ee.
Bon soir old thing,
Cheerio, chin-chin,
Na-poo, toodle-oo, good-bye-ee.'

Kate was strutting up and down as she sang. Bessie Mather sat on the sofa between her husband, Bill, and Rob MacLean. They were all singing along with Kate, and were well and truly tanked.

'Sounds as though they're all pissed to the eyeballs,' whispered Art to Jimmie.

'Aye, an' our Lily asleep upstairs. I wonder who brought her home, an' Mrs Magee sick, an' Denny as well, then there's old Mrs Grimes next door. Still I suppose they're used to it by now, like we are!'

Kate had finished her song, amid noisy applause, then she made her way to the backyard to relieve herself, toppling awkwardly over the oustretched legs of Bill Mather, cursing him and laughing at the same time. The other three continued their drinking, lighting up fresh Woodbines with a match that had been split in half with a razor blade, to make it go further.

'Do yer know this one, Bobby?' asked Mr Mather, jumping to his feet and tottering over to the piano.

'Go on, sing it an' I'll foller yer,' bragged the accompanist.

Bill cleared his throat, then sang out in a loud voice. No one seemed to notice that the musical accompaniment, if it could be called that, was the same as that for *Good bye-e.*

'Please don't knock our lavat'ry down,
Mother is willin' ter pay,
Father's afloat on a big sailin' boat,

'Sister's in the fam'ly way.'

'What the 'ell are they singin' now?' yawned Jimmie, as he rubbed his bottom, as it was cold and numb now from sitting on the stone steps.

'Oh! It's one o' me dad's Navy songs, 'e always sings that when 'e's drunk.'

'Brother Bill's got diarrhoea,
Life is so terribly 'ard,
So please don't knock our lavat'ry down,
Or we'll all 'ave ter shit in the yard.'

'All tergether now!' piped Bill,
'Or we'll all 'ave ter shit in the yard.'

Loud, coarse, laughter pervaded the house, and Kate emerged from the yard, giggling and pulling her skirt down behind her. 'I 'eard yer,' she sniggered. 'Giz a Woody, Mac,' beckoning to her husband.

'Ere 'ave this. I've just lit it,' he said, handing her the Woodbine as he headed for the lavatory himself, then debating if the yard would be more convenient?

The bedroom window of the MacLean house was still open, and Jimmie could hear his young sister, Lily, crying.

'Gosh!' he gasped, 'ow long 'as she been at it? Thought she'd be fagged out after terday at Southport.'

Arthur was yawning, it was almost midnight, and now and again a couple could be seen and heard singing their drunken songs and swaying from side to side, as they made their way along Netherfield Road. The trams had stopped running long ago. The bobbies on their beat were trying the handles of shop doors, in case anyone had forgotten to lock up, in their eagerness to get away.

'Better go now Art,' said Jimmie sleepily, 'see yer termorrer.'

'Right yer are Jim; see yer.'

The two boys parted, Arthur ran across India Street, fifteen yards away, whilst Jimmie nipped past the side entry to his house, a distance of seven yards or so, and on reaching the front door, made his way into the smoke-filled room.

'Hello lad,' said Bessie, 'as our Arthur gone 'ome?'

'Yeah, just left 'im.'

Rob MacLean reeled in from the yard, 'Where've yer bin?'

'Out Dad.'

'Thought yer were in bed.'

'No, been wi' our Willie.'

'Where is 'e?'

'Don't know, Dad.'

'Gerrup them stairs then. An' be quick about it.' Jimmie knew better than to argue, and though there was no light on the stairs, he'd negotiated them many times when his eyelids were stuck together, so the darkness was no obstacle to him. Lily was still crying.

'Stop whingeing, will yer?'

'I wanna go down!' sobbed his little sister.

'Well yer can't, they're all drunk, an' there'll be hell later if anyone bangs on the door tellin' 'em to shurrup. Come on now, go back ter sleep, an' I'll get yer an Arrer Bar termorrer.'

The loud crying died down to a whimper, and Jimmie covered her with a rough blanket.

'Not too much over me. I'm 'ot.'

'Okay then, just a bit. Leave yer arms out. Mary'll be comin' up soon,' Jimmie comforted her. 'If yer quiet, yer can 'ear the big ships in the Mersey, lettin' off.'

Lily giggled.

'An' if yer look through the winder,' he continued, 'yer can see shootin' stars, goin' ter the moon an' Mars.'

'Where's the moon ternight, Jimmie?'

'Aw! It's gone ter sleep,' e yawned, 'Move over a bit now, an' let me get in. I'm sleepy too.'

Jimmie climbed into bed, and thought of Willie, wondering if he'd been copped? Then he started giggling as he remembered their game of White Horse and King Billy's charger, rearing up and blowing off, and with these thoughts uppermost in his mind, he finally fell asleep.

All was quiet downstairs except for the occasional laugh. The singing had stopped, and Bobby came upstairs to his single bed on the other side of the room. Mary had decided to stay at Nellie Mather's, not wanting to become involved in the coarse fun.

Cats wailed mournfully as they scratched around in the back entries, sounding just like babies crying, then spitting and fighting with each other. An empty beer bottle crashed against a wall somewhere, as it was flung at the retreating felines, interrupting their mating. Then suddenly, above the din, came the piercing screams of a woman, abruptly awakening the two children.

'It's alright girl,' Jimmie whispered to Lily, 'it's only somebody gettin' chased, yer see what yer get fer stayin' out late. Yer get put in a sack, an' thrown into the Mersey, go ter sleep now.'

It was past two o'clock and the party had broken up. The Mathers and the MacLeans were bidding one another goodnight.

'G'night, Bessie, g'night, Bill,' the MacLeans whispered, putting on a show of respectability for the benefit of the neighbours, especially the sick ones in the street.

'Ta-ra!' bellowed Bessie, not caring who heard her, and shouting as though it were two in the afternoon.

'Ssh, ssh, quiet will yer? Yer gorra mouth like the Mersey Tunnel,' scolded her husband in a low voice.

'Ha ha!' snorted his wife, as she wiped a drip from off the end of her nose, 'an you'll 'ave an 'ead like Birken'ead when yer wakes up in the mornin.'

They strolled across the street to their home, grumbling at each other. Rob and Kate went back indoors. Rob pulled down the chain that hung from the gaslight in the middle of the ceiling, and the

spluttered and flickered as the room was plunged into darkness. The couple stumbled and fumbled their way up to their bedroom, which was sparsely furnished with a double bed and a flock mattress, two striped pillows and an army blanket for covering. They both noisily kicked off their shoes, puffing and blowing as they struggled to undress in the darkness, then eventually fell into bed and all was quiet at last.

Willie had waited across the street until his parents had gone to bed, then he jumped from the wall across Bala Terrace, across the entry and caught the bottom of the open window of the room where his brothers and sister lay asleep. As he landed, his hands made a loud slap on the window-sill and Jimmie awoke, startled by the noise.

Willie put his finger to his mouth, 'Ssh!' he warned, 'I'll get a batterin' if they hear me,' pointing to his parents' room. 'That's why I waited until they went to bed.'

He hauled himself through the window and onto the bed.

Jimmie greeted him with his usual question, 'Where've yer bin?'

'Tell yer termorrer,' whispered Willie, taking off his jersey and trousers, then climbing into the bottom half of the bed that he shared with Jimmie and Lily.

'G'night, kid.'

'G'night, Willie. Oh! an' thanks fer lettin' me join yer gang.'

With that, the house fell silent once more, except for Bobby's snores and Rob's grunts in the other room.

CHAPTER FIVE
Meg's Generosity

'I'll be over in a minute!' Jimmie called through the open window, in response to Arthur's familiar whistle.

Jimmie knew that Arthur would wait for him until he could get himself organised. His eyes were bad again, so he was faced with the same struggle to get dressed, as on the previous day. He could hear loud snores coming from his parents' room, and young as he was, he felt disgusted and ashamed.

'Huh! Out to the bloody woods as usual.'

Mary was in the kitchen, and greeted him in her usual happy, cheerful way. 'Hello lar! Be with yer soon. Our Bobby was late this mornin'. I knew 'e would be. Couldn't see his arse fer dust.' She laughed at the recollection of Bobby earlier that morning, dashing through the door.

'Taken all the bleedin' bread too by the looks of it,' Jimmie complained, 'thinks 'e's carryin' a pair o' dockers boots in 'is parcel when 'e takes 'is grub.' Then turning to Mary, 'Just a drop o' tea, Art's waitin' fer me.'

Mary noticed Jimmie scratching his belly and thighs. 'Let's wash yer wi' carbolic. There's some 'ot water left in the kettle. Come on don't be shy, yer 'aven't got anythin' different to anyone else. Yer'll feel better. Art'll still wait fer yer, an' I'll do yer eyes as well.' She began to wash him down. 'Now then, there y'are.'

The young girl's eyes roamed sadly over her brother's skinny, undernourished frame, and she felt a warm sisterly affection for him, but at the same time, a sick disgust at his neglect. The red sores and blisters covering his body were nothing new. She then washed his eyes in clean warm water, and smoothed the yellow ointment on them as before.

'I feel better now Mary. Thanks a lot.' He gulped down the tea she had made for him, and ran out to meet his mate.

Mary called after him, 'Take care now!'

The boys were wondering what they should do that day, when suddenly Art cried, 'Bloody 'ell, it's Mrs Gilbert.'

They both cringed, they hadn't seen her to speak to since the Oxo game, and didn't want to either! So they scuttled off like a couple of frightened rabbits, and round to Pearson's sweet shop, which was nicknamed Spots.

'Before yer ask, no yer can't 'ave any Woodbines, yer'll get me 'ung. So what will it be?' asked Mr Pearson, as he screwed on the lid of a jar of sarsaparilla tablets, and replaced them on the shelf.

'Two ha'penny punches,' they chorused.

Art punched a hole in a board with a nail-like peg, and a small piece of rolled up paper fell out of the board.

'Arrer bar,' the shopkeeper read out.

Jimmie punched the board, hoping for something better.

Mr Pearson unrolled his paper, watching Jimmie's face slyly as he did so. 'Arrer bar,' he announced smugly, enjoying the boy's disappointment.

The boys took their 'prizes' then added, 'Giz two sherbets as well.' They placed their money on the counter; the pennies that Mrs Rodgers had given them the day before.

'Got any tacks, Mr Pearson?' Art asked as they were leaving the shop.

'Why yes, somewhere.'

'Well sit on the bloody things!' the lads called out, noisily sucking up the sherbet through their liquorice tubes.

'Won't serve the little sods again,' muttered Pearson, all the time knowing that he would have to, as he needed all the money he could get. Times were hard and pennies added up. He busied himself by scooping out the dead flies from the open boxes of goodies in the window.

'Gerraway wi' yer!' he shouted, as a group of scruffy-looking lads banged on the chewing-gum machine outside the shop door, in the hope of getting a free packet of PK. The troupe ran off, empty-handed.

By this time, Art and Jimmie had finished their sherbets, their fingers sticky from dipping in, their mouths black with liquorice. Jimmie gave his Arrow Bar to Lily, as he had promised the night before.

'Just run down to Field's fer a tape of Aspros, Jimmie,' called his mother, 'an' a bottle of sarsaparilla fer yer dad, an' mind yer don't drop it!' and she gave him a sixpence.

'Probably got a mouth like the bottom of a baby's pram,' commented Arthur, out of Mrs Mac's earshot.

'Hurry up, now!' nagged Kate, 'yer da's gaspin'.'

Off down the street trotted the two boys, not daring to glance in the direction of Mrs Gilbert's house. They reached Field's grocery shop and Jimmie made his purchases, while Art stayed outside and peered down a large cast-iron grate in front of the shop window.

'Hey! Jimmie!' Art whispered to his mate, 'look down there!'

'Where? What can yer see?'

'There,' Art pointed, 'look, next to that bit of silver paper!'

'What is it?'

'Some ha'pennies.'

The two lads ran home as fast as they could with the Aspros and pop, then returned to the grate with two long brush handles, and a piece of soft carbolic soap, which they stuck onto the ends of the handles. They lowered them down the grate, peering through the bars on bended knees, their bottoms swaying to and fro as they manoeuvred their sticks towards the coins.

'Gotcher!' Art cried, exhilarated by his success.

Better still, Jimmie had spotted a silver threepenny bit, so he retrieved his pole, spit on the soap, then gingerly lowered it again amongst the dirt and rubbish and prodded the coin.

'Gotcher, me little beauty!' he yelled triumphantly.

The pole had scarcely been pulled out of the grate with the treasure on the end of it, when Miss Field came out, brandishing her long brush at them. 'What the 'ell d'yer think yer doin'?' she shouted angrily.

Jimmie jumped up, rubbing his knees, an excuse already springing to his lips, 'I've dropped me mam's change down yer grate. I'm tryin' ter get it back.'

He sounded bolder than he actually felt, for he was really quite scared to be caught in the act.

'Well why didn't yer come an' tell me?' said Miss Field. 'Ow much was it?'

'A penny.'

'Here!' she grumbled, taking a penny from her pinny pocket, 'an' clear off now, yer lyin' young frigger!'

'Yer'll gerrus both in bother one of these days,' Arthur said to Jimmie, as they ran off, giggling, the penny clutched tightly in Jimmie's hand, together with the threepenny bit. Jimmie laughed with his mouth wide open, displaying his tongue, still bright red from the sherbet.

'What did you get out of the grate?' he asked Art.

'A ha'penny, look! What about you, what 'ave you got?'

'A threepenny bit,' Jimmie swanked, as he opened his hand, revealing the small silver coin, 'and a penny off Miss Field,' he added, laughing again.

'Jammy sod, an' yer supposed to 'ave bad eyes as well!'

The boys felt like millionaires, but their joy was short-lived because, as they approached Jimmie's house, a loud voice hailed them.

'Hey! You two come 'ere!'

'Now we're fer it, Art,' said Jimmie as they went into the house, 'it's Mrs Gilbert. Looks like trouble!'

Mary Ellen Gilbert was indeed in their front room. 'Come 'ere yer pair of little sods, I want you!'

Kate Mac was pressing her husband's navy-blue serge suit with a flat iron, ready for it to go back into pawn. Jimmie wondered exactly what Mrs Gilbert had been telling his mother, and anticipated getting the strap from his father. Kate didn't raise her eyes from the iron, as steam arose from a wet cloth covering the trousers.

'Yer know what yer did, don't yer?' Meg scolded. 'Purple pencil all over our Bobby's pot leg.'

The lads studied their feet and shuffled uncomfortably.

'It was only a game of Oxo, Mrs G. I'll get some white Blanco to cover it over,' offered Jimmie, apologetically.

'Blanco! Blanco!' she spluttered, then she burst out laughing, unable to keep up the pretence of being angry any longer. She continued to laugh hysterically until the lads were afraid that she was about to have a fit.

'She's flipped 'er lid,' whispered Art out of the side of his mouth.

'Don't think so. I think she's been on the piss! What's up wi' Mrs G, Mam?' he asked, feeling a bit bolder.

'Well, it's like this, she told me what 'appened wi' youse two scribblin' Oxo on Bobby's pot leg. So when she saw what was runnin' in the 3.30 at Ripon, she backed it,' explained Kate.

During all this time, Mrs Gilbert was still convulsed with laughter.

'So what was it that yer backed, Mrs G?' asked Jimmie, confident now that he wasn't in any trouble.

'Oxo, lads, Oxo! A lovely bay horse called Oxo!' She slapped her thighs in delight, 'It won! It WON! At 6-1!' Meg shrieked. She then slid a ten shilling note from her purse and waved it triumphantly in the air.

The lads stared, goggle-eyed in amazement. 'Ere y'are lads, a penny each fer yer,' she said, as she stuffed the ten bob note back into her purse.

'Skinny old bag!' Jimmie complained to Art behind his hand, as he heard the purse clasp snap shut.

'Wouldn't be screamin' an' laughin' if the bloody 'orse 'ad stopped fer a shit!' Art commented, as he and Jimmie left the house, joyfully jingling the money they had accumulated in their pockets. They'd had quite a good day, money-wise.

'Don't go far!' Kate called after them, 'I want yer ter take yer dad's suit ter the pawn fer me.'

The boys sat on the front doorstep, gloating over their wealth, smugly contemplating how to spend their fortunes?

The pawnshop was near the old wash-house, up the hill along Netherfield Road, and the lads took their place in the long queue.

Behind the enormous counter, a bespectacled, thin-faced, man, in a brown overall, shouted, 'Next!'

It was Jimmie's turn. 'Me da's suit,' he announced, handing over the parcel.

'Two shillins an' sixpence.'

'Is that all?'

'Yep! An' 'ere's yer ticket, and don't lose it!'

'Me mam said yer've ter wrap it up fer me,' said Jimmie.

The money and the ticket were wrapped up in a piece of brown paper and handed over to the freckled lad.

'Go straight 'ome now, an' mind yer don't lose ...'

'Can't go straight 'ome Mister, can't,' interrupted Jimmie

'Why not, lad?'

'Got ter turn the corners!' The boys skipped off singing:

'Mary Ellen at the pawn-shop door,
A bundle in 'er 'and, an' a bundle on the floor,

She asked fer seven an' six, an' only got four,
So she knocked the rusty 'andle off the pawm-shop door.'

At last they reached home and Jimmie said, 'Ere y'are Mam, arf a crown.'

'That all?' asked Kate. 'It was worth five bob.'

'Yep!' said Jimmie, imitating the pawn-broker.

There was a sudden rumble of thunder.

'Lucky to get back before it rained,' remarked Kate, putting the money in her pinny pocket. 'It's been threatening all day.'

'Blinkin' well would do,' grumbled Jimmie, fingering his coins in his trouser pocket and heading for the door with Arthur.

They ran across the street, heavy drops of rain bouncing off the cobbles, as the two scurried through Art's front door.

The faithful, one o'clock gun could hardly be heard above the claps of thunder, as if there was a contest between the two.

'I don't like thunder,' said Arthur,

'Me neither. It's like elephants in the sky, and they're kickin' bricks around. Go an kick 'em somewhere else,' he yelled up at the darkened sky.

There was a terrific flash of lightning that lit up the whole street. People stood and watched from their doorways, as the water cascaded down drainpipes and into the gutters, then rushed along the street in a torrent, threatening to flood the nearby houses.

Jimmie and Art stood at the door along with all the other onlookers, finding the sight quite exhilarating. It suddenly occurred to them, that here was an opportunity for earning themselves a bit more cash.

Further down the street, the drains had become blocked, and were unable to cope with the volume of water. No one had come up with any bright ideas as to how to avert the floodwaters.

'Come on,' said Jimmie, grabbing Art's arm, 'get yer pole, 'an' let's go an stick 'em down the blocked grids.'

Having retrieved their brush handles, the boys stripped to the waist and were soon furiously digging them into the blockages.

'That's it, lads,' came an old woman's encouraging shout from a doorway, 'give it a good shove!'

The rain was warm and felt good on the boys' bodies, and they were quite enjoying the job they had undertaken, but before they had realised it, they were surrounded by the rising flood, which by now had reached the thresholds of the first two houses in Bala Terrace.

'There'll be another ha'penny apiece if yer get it away,' Meg hollered, as the water crept up to her front door.

The enterprising pair industriously thrust and rammed their poles into the bunged-up sewers.

'Any luck?' Jimmie had hardly got the words out of his mouth, when up rose a splurge of filthy, swirling water. Then, with a sudden gulp and a squelch, a whirlpool almost swept Arthur off his feet. He waded his way unsteadily to his pal's side.

'Come on, altogether now!' As they lunged once more, they were almost overcome with the sickening stench from the sewer.

'No wonder people get soddin' sick around 'ere,' Art groaned, trying to avert his nose.

'Aye,' agreed Jimmie, 'hope we don't get the fever.'

Silt began to appear around their legs, and as before, there was a sudden gurgling gyration. The poles quivered as the lads pulled them out from the muddy, stinking waters. Slowly but surely, the waters subsided.

They paddled back up the gutter, their legs clear of all the mud, amid cheers and claps from the onlooking women.

Collecting their ha'pennies from Meg as they went; for a workman is surely worthy of his wages! They then dripped their way into Arthur's house, totally drenched.

'Are yer alright?' Mrs Mather asked them, 'I saw it all, a couple o' little 'eroes yer are!'

The lads were dried off with a rough old towel.

'Giz yer trousers, an I'll dry 'em fer yer. You too, Jimmie Mac. 'Ere put this around yer,' and she handed him another old towel, which he promptly tied around his waist.

Jimmie emptied the contents of his sodden pockets onto the table next to Art's. Then, after sliding their trousers down underneath the towels, they sat in front of the fire to dry off.

'Blackcurrant jam or raspberry?'

They both turned to find that Mrs Mather had cut two thick slices of bread, her knife poised, waiting for their reply.

'Blackcurrant please, Mrs Mather,' said Jimmie.

'Me too!' echoed Art.

The lads felt a warm glow, as they sat in front of the fire, having eaten their butties and drunk their watery cocoa, they felt as contented as two cats with a saucer of cream.

'Ooh! I feel better now,' sighed Art.

Then suddenly, 'Aah! Ooh! Jimmie Mac! I can see yer periwinkle.'

'An' yours too, our Arthur!' teased Nellie.

'No yer can't! Take no notice of 'er lads, she's just kiddin' yer,' assured Bessie.

Jimmie blushed and grabbed the towel tightly, to make sure it was secure around his little pot belly. He wasn't taking any chances.

'Is me kecks dry now, Mrs Mather?'

'Yeah, 'ere yer are,' Bessie laughed, handing them both their trousers.

Both boys struggled into them underneath the towels, and retrieved their belongings from the table. There was quite an assortment; wet bubble-gum wrappers, tram tickets, cigarette cards, bits of string and other paraphernalia, and most important of all, their money.

'By the way,' said Nellie, 'did yer 'ear all the commotion last night?'

'I 'eard someone scream,' said her mother; 'seemed to be coming from down our back entry.'

'Yeah, there's been two bobbies lookin' down there this mornin,' Nellie informed her.

'I 'eard a woman scream last night,' young Jimmie added, 'we were in bed, an' I said to our Lily, that's what yer get if yer out late, someone'll grab yer.'

'The poor woman, whoever she was!' said Bessie.

'Yeah, she was graped,' Nellie added, continuing with her story.

'Graped?' asked her mother. 'Don't yer mean raped?'

'No, graped,' the serious look on Nellie's face turned into an impish grin, then a burst of sudden laughter issued forth, 'Graped,' she went on, 'yer see there was a bunch of 'em!'

Bessie's eyes filled up with tears through trying to suppress the laughter. Then, giggling and screaming, she ran into the other room, gripping her skirt between her legs.

'She's done it again,' screamed Nellie.

'Done what?' asked Jimmie unable to see the joke.

'Wet 'er bloomers!' laughed Nellie.

'What's graped mean?' Jimmie persisted.

Nellie and Arthur burst out laughing again, a crescendo of rollicking laughter so loud, that Blackie the cat scurried off in fear for his life, while Bessie sat trickling into a bucket in the other room, unable to restrain herself any longer.

Jimmie shrugged his little shoulders innocently, neither receiving an answer to his question, nor understanding what all the fuss was about?

CHAPTER SIX
A Day At Aigburth

The gang filed one after the other, up the winding stairs of the number twenty-five tram to the Pier Head. Each paid for his own ticket, 'Penny one, please.'

Each ticket was clicked in the metal machine which was strapped to the conductor's waist.

'Two penny ones, please,' Jimmie said, then turned to his mate and whispered, 'don't tell the others we've got any money will yer?'

'Bloomin' 'eck - no!'

The windows on both sides of the upper deck were pulled back, and whistles and cat-calls were hurled at the passers-by, as the tram trundled down past Bunny's in Church Street, then down Lord Street, past the Compton Hotel, and towards the Pier Head.

On reaching their destination, they clambered off and jumped onto the awaiting connection tram. 'Aigburth please.' They proffered their tickets and another hole was punched into them.

As the tram gathered speed, it started to sway, and the overhead cable flashed on the connecting rod. A burst of song rang out from the happy band of travellers:

'And when we travel on a tram-car,
We open the windows wide,
We can dance, we can sing,
We can do most anything,

We are the Liverpool boys.'

'Quiet up there, youse lot!' barked the conductor, 'or I'll put the lot of yer off!'

Oblivious to this warning, they struck up another song:

'Auntie Mary, 'ad a canary,
Up the leg of 'er drawers,
If yer don't believe me - come an see it,
Up the leg of 'er drawers.'

The conductor was no doubt relieved when the tram reached its destination, although he could see that the lads were harmless enough.

As the gang was leaving, Hambone asked, 'What time is the last tram, Mister?'

'This'll be **yer** last,' the conductor joked, grinning at the cheeky crew.

'Make 'im laugh on the other side of 'is face if I see 'im again,' threatened Hambone, half-heartedly, shaking his fist at the retreating tram.

Finally they all made their way down to the seashore, and were soon jumping down a large concrete barrier and onto the sand, kicking and shouting, pushing and shoving, laughing and joking, like a playful pack of mongrels. Those who had brought some tuck, shared it with those who hadn't.

Mouthfuls of bread and dripping and connie-onnie butties, were washed down with a large, shared bottle of water, and so when it came to the younger boys' turn to have a drink, crumbs of bread floated around in the bottle, but they didn't care, it was all jolly good fun; as the comradeship of being in the gang made up for everything.

Besides, their mothers had frequently said, 'They would eat worse before they died.'

The older boys ran off, larking about along the seashore, kicking sand and throwing pebbles at each other, until they were quickly out of sight.

It was quiet and peaceful, as the two young ones sat on the sand watching the waves gently lapping the shore. They gazed out across the Mersey, digging their toes into the sand. The weather was clear and sunny after the previous day's thunderstorm.

Jimmie leaned over and patted the sand with his hands, 'We did okay with the grates yesterday. Stank a lot though,' he stated, as he enjoyed the sensation of the dry sand trickling through his fingers.

'Yeah,' agreed Art, dreamily, then added as an afterthout; 'as yer dad gone back ter sea yet?'

'No, missed 'is ship again, silly frigger.'

'My dad's gone.'

'Yeah! All them fellers along Neddy Road beggin' fer a ship, an' can't get one, an' that lazy bleeder of ours is stuck in the ale'ouse till all 'is money's done.'

It vexed him, to think of all the money that was being squandered, for though he was young in years, he was old in his head, and could see that there must be a better way of living than that of his family and most of the folk around their area of Liverpool.

'Are you going ter sea when yer grows up, Art?'

'Guess so. Are you?'

'Don't know.' Jimmie shrugged his shoulders. 'Like to go around the world to different places like Australia. Me old feller missed 'is ship there, yer, in 'Obart, 'ad ter get another one, trimmin' (barrowing coal for the stokers) 'is way back 'ome.'

'Missed 'is ship in Aussie, did 'e?'

'Yep! Pissed! Should 'ave kept 'im there wi' the cannibals, ferget what they call 'em, Abbos or summat.'

Jimmie started to daydream aloud, his pal listening intently, 'Yeah, they would 'ave put us in a 'ome or summat, an' looked after us, an' fed us good grub, gi' us clean clothes ter wear, an' a nice bed ter sleep in, all of our own, not sharin' with yer brother an' sister. Just think of it, a bed all to yerself!' For a time, his attention was taken by the white, woolly, clouds drifting by, and he tried to fit figures and faces to them. 'Think we'll ever leave Liverpool, Art?'

Art shrugged his shoulders, 'Dunno,' he said, 'maybe when we grow up.'

'If I do, I'll write about all this.' He was off on his daydreaming again. 'I'll write about the gang, an people'll remember me. An' I'll write about you Art, yeah I'll write about you, an' you'll think about me, that's if I ever get me book printed.'

'That'll be the gear. Remember to put me name in it then,' piped up Arthur, approvingly.

'I'll write about all the poor people, like them that come over from Ireland, like Tess's nin.' Jimmie was getting carried away on the wings of his imagination.

'Then there's the ice-cream fellers that came from Italy, I think, like lots of others that came, me dad says, to go to America. Only they couldn't go, 'cos they'd no money left, so they 'ad ter stay in Liverpool. Yeah, people like them I'll write about.' Jimmie's thoughts raced on, his young mind trying hard to understand why all these things happened, wondering, searching, and as he sat there deep in reverie, he unwittingly kicked a large shell from the sand.

'Cor! That's a belter!' gasped Art.

Jimmie came back to the present, 'What did yer say, Art?'

'Look what yer found in the sand.'

Jimmie looked down, scrutinizing the object of Arthur's admiration. 'Yeah it's nice isn't it?' he said, shaking the sand from the large shell.

Time had slipped by almost unnoticed by the two pals, so engrossed were they in their thoughts of yesterday and the future, and their happiness at being somewhere that they both enjoyed.

The gang, now well out of sight, had been jumping and chasing around and jostling one another good-naturedly, play-fighting and falling over in the sand. They were having such a good time that they had failed to notice that the tide had silently crept in, trapping them in an inlet. They were completely ignorant of their serious situation, until they heard Art's and Jimmie's voices calling for them.

The sky had clouded over and the weather seemed to change, suddenly a strong breeze had started to blow. Art and Jimmie, on getting no answer to their calls, decided they had better go and search for the others.

Jimmie picked up his shell, and they both sprang quickly to their feet, grabbing their socks and pumps and heading for the steps up the side of the concrete barrier.

The water was already lapping against the sea-wall and the boys became frightened, though they would never have admitted it even to one another. They waded towards the slimy green exit.

'Phew!' said Art, gasping for breath. 'Come on hurry, let's get to the top of the hill and see if we can spot the others.'

Jimmie shoved his socks into his pockets as he ran. They scrambled under some barbed wire fencing, and made their way along the top of the rugged knap, the sea lapping the base of the rocky shore-line. Their hearts thumped as they puffed and panted their way through the long twitch grass, stopping now and then to peer over the edge of the cliff.

They continued to run along in this manner until Art suddenly gasped, 'Gosh! Look down there, Jimmie. There they are. Bleedin' 'eck! They're trapped!'

The boys were desperately running to and fro, wondering how they were going to help their pals, who were twenty-five feet below them.

The trapped gang spotted them and yelled frantically, 'Hurry up! Get a move on! Do something, get us some help!'

They were all howling desperately now, for the tide was coming in fast, 'Be quick! We 'aven't got all bleedin' day!'

The two young lads looked around worriedly; there was no one else in sight, and the houses were too far away to go for help, the sea would reach their mates well before they could get back. They couldn't climb down, but even if they could, what use was that? It was too steep and rugged for the gang to climb up, or they would have already done so. What were they going to do? They were their pals' only hope.

The situation seemed hopeless with every second vital, and could mean the difference between life and death. Some rickety wire fencing zig-zagged its way along the edge of the cliff, and both lads seemed to hit on the same idea simultaneously. With two large stones, they hammered at the rusty wire, which was stapled to the rotten wooden posts.

As they hit the posts, they continually banged their fingers until they bled, but, eventually they managed to free a good length of the wire, and lowered it down to the trapped boys. Jimmie and Art had twisted and secured their end of the wire around a nearby post, but this left the lifeline just above the gang's reach.

'Giz a bit more!' they each shouted fearfully, 'giz some more, it's not long enough!'

'I can't, yer'll 'ave ter try an' jump up to it!' replied Jimmie.

'Look at the stupid sods,' scoffed Art, sucking a blood-blistered finger, 'avin' a game o' White Horse, an' the sea arf-way up their legs!'

They both peered over the cliff to see what their pals were up to. They were indeed having a game of White Horse, but this time it wasn't just a game, for this time their lives really depended upon it!

Two of them bent over and arched their backs, and one by one, the others jumped on and managed to grab the wire, that swayed above their heads, each boy, in his turn, hauling himself onto a narrow ledge in the cliff side, six feet above the beach, until only two of them were left, one of them being Hambone, who cupped his hands to make a step for Billy.

'Go on, Billy, get yer foot in!'

Snotty-nose was heaved up to the safety of the ledge, to join his pals, Suddenly, an enormous wave appeared from nowhere, like Neptune himself emerging from the depths, and with one great surge, it lifted Hambone to within reach of the wire, and his pals' arms and safety.

'Phew! That was a close one!' he panted.

After that it was an easy matter to pull themselves, one at a time, with the aid of the wire, up the cliff to the top, where Jimmie and Art were waiting. They appeared over the edge of the cliff, gasping with relief, leaving the angry sea far below them. Hambone was the last to appear, like the captain of a sinking ship. Fortunately, thanks to the two youngsters, no one had lost his life.

'Youse two took yer bleedin' time, didn't yer?' Hambone joked, grinning broadly at the two heroes, as he squeezed the water out of his trousers.

Someone noticed that Greenie still had the tear in his trousers, and that his bottom was now bright purple. Teasing him, and trying to pinch his bare bum, provided a new source of amusement, and diffused the anxiety of their recent narrow escape. They headed back across the fields to the tram terminus in a light-hearted mood, and they impulsively burst into song:

'And when we travel on a tram-car,
We open the windows wide,

We can dance, we can sing,
We can do most anything,
We are the Liverpool boys. '

CHAPTER SEVEN
A Way Out

The hot summer days seemed endless. Jimmie and Art were inseparable, and would spend their evenings sitting on the doorstep reliving the day's adventures, good or bad. They stretched their days out as long as they possibly could, dreading the inevitable familiar cry from one of their parents.

'Come on, it's time fer bed!'

Suppers were non-existent in the MacLean household, a cup of water was Jimmie's usual bedtime drink. He hated bedtime; it wasn't so much the darkness of the bedroom that made him fearful, but the bugs biting. Their bites kept him awake half the night, itching and scratching, scratching and itching, it became a never-ending cycle of irritation and torment.

'Wet the blisters wi' yer finger,' Willie would advise him, 'an' stick yer fingernail in, that'll stop the itch.'

It did give temporary relief, but it didn't stop them from crawling all over him.

It wasn't long before Rob and Kate came up to bed that night. They'd spent up all their money, so they couldn't go to the pub, and the gas had run out. There was no money for the meter, so bed was their only option.

'Who's comin' wi' me in the mornin'?' Rob called out to the two boys. 'Can yer 'ear me? I know yer awake!'

Jimmie kept quiet.

Willie said, 'I can't come, I'm 'elpin' down at Leggie's stables termorrer.'

'Right then, Jimmie can come then,' said Rob, sliding his braces off his shoulders, and almost kicking over the half-filled bucket of urine near the bedroom door.

'Where's 'e goin' termorrer?' Jimmie whispered to Willie.

'Aven't yer seen what 'e's been doin' ternight?' asked his brother.

'No. What?'

'Been makin' vases, an' wax flowers ter put in 'em.'

'Vases?'

'Yeah, vases!'

'Ow the 'ell 'as 'e done that?'

'Been heatin' some old gramophone records, big uns an' little uns, an' fixin' 'em tergether wi' a screw. They bend yer know when they're 'ot. Then 'e shapes 'em into vases. 'E's dyed some sawdust, an' puts it in the top of the vase, then sticks the wax flowers in. He's takin' 'em out on an 'and cart termorrer.'

'Oh! 'eck! I'm not lookin' forward ter that!' Jimmie was more agitated than ever, what with the bugs biting, and now this to worry about.

'Keep still, will yer? An' stop shufflin' around!' grumbled Willie.

'Can't. I just can't,' he cried, getting out of bed and lying down on the floor at the side of the bed.

'Ere - 'ere's the coat ter put over yer.'

'Thanks, Willie.'

Jimmie wrapped the old coat around himself and tried to make himself comfortable on the hard floor. 'Night, kid.'

'G'night, Jimmie!'

The house fell silent.

The next morning Jimmie apprehensively offered his dad a feeble excuse to avoid the humiliating outing.

'Me nin said she was takin' me ter Greaty, shoppin', Dad!'

'Yer comin' wi me! Lily can go wi' yer nin instead.'

'Yer know I allus go wi' 'er on a Saturday,' countered Jimmie, against his better judgement. He had never before dared to argue with his father, for fear of a strapping, but on this occasion, his voice ran on ahead of him. He would risk anything to avoid this outing, he might only be a kid, but he had a measure of pride. 'Just suppose anyone saw him, he would feel so ashamed.'

Without warning, he felt the blow of a heavy hand on the side of his head, which sent him sprawling across the red and black tiled floor, banging his head on one of the thick table legs.

Tears welled up in his eyes. Though he had used his nin as an excuse, he really did go shopping with her as a rule on Saturdays, and always looked forward to the trip which started in her one-room apartment in China Street, and took in the many big shops in Great Homer Street. He would accompany her, holding onto the tassels of her heavy, grey, shawl. Saturday was a special day for them both, as they enjoyed each other's company immensely.

Mrs Carmichael was a neat little woman, Irish by descent. She always wore low-heeled, shiny, black shoes with wool and lisle stockings covering her slightly-bowed legs. She wore her meticulously-brushed, steel-grey hair in a large bun, which nestled in the nape of her neck. Her eyes were bright blue and had a twinkle in them, giving the impression that she was permanently laughing.

Kate MacLean came downstairs, 'What you whingeing for? Ave yer 'ad summat ter eat?'

'Yeah,' Jimmie lied, in answer to her second question. He really didn't want anything, except to go to see his nin. She rarely visited India Street, though Kate would visit her mother quite often. Jimmie was Mrs Carmichael's favourite grandson, she thought the world of him, for he resembled her own son, Kate's brother William, who had been lost at sea. However, Jimmie wouldn't be seeing her today, Lily would go instead.

So, as soon as Rob had gulped down his strong tea, he said to Jimmie, 'Right! We'll be off lad, come on!' which signalled the end of the matter.

One of Rob's drinking pals had already brought round a hand-cart, so the black, moulded vases were loaded onto it in neat rows. The red and yellow wax tulips swayed precariously, as Rob gripped the shafts and commenced pulling the unique load up India Street, with little Jimmie pushing behind at the tail-board.

'We're headin' for Sefton Park,' Rob informed him, 'you'll like it, there's lots of posh people, we should shift this lot without any bother.'

The lad just stared ahead, as if hypnotised by the turning wheels. Now and again, the cart skidded on the tramlines, jerking him back to reality.

They wended their way in and out of the rows of terraced houses. Dirty unkempt children, even worse off than Jimmie, jeered and mocked them as they passed by, and women laughed at their gaudy display of artificial flowers. Rob was oblivious to their jibes, but Jimmie felt them acutely, and his face reddened in shame.

'Ain't nuthin' ter be ashamed of lad,' his father said, on seeing Jimmie blush. 'It's honest work, we ain't beggin.' Then, as if to cheer the lad up, he added, 'Won't be long now, there's the park over there!'

Jimmie hadn't been to this part of Liverpool before, it was like another world to him. As large Victorian houses came into view, Rob halted and cheerfully announced, 'Right, we'll start 'ere. You watch the cart, okay?' He eagerly grabbed two of the flowerpots.

'Yeah okay,' Jimmie mumbled, unable to share his father's enthusiasm for the project. He sat on the shafts of the cart, feet dangling, hoping this awful day would soon pass, or better still, that his old man would quickly sell his wares and then they could go home.

Rob ran back to the cart, he had sold his first two vases to a lady who wanted two more for a friend. 'Been okay 'ave yer?' he asked his son, but before Jimmie had time to answer, the lean figure of his father had bounded down the street to deliver his order.

'Jump down now, lad, an we'll go a bit further on with the cart.'

The vehicle was trundled noisily along past the posh houses, some of whose occupants were sitting inside the bay windows, eating lunch. They peered out at the curious spectacle of Jimmie and his dad with their cart, and its bizarre load, and again Jimmie held down his head and blushed deeply, stung by the looks that those people were giving them.

Rob didn't care, and undaunted he moved swiftly from house to house selling his pots, and smiling broadly at everyone. He made sale after sale, and Jimmie began to think that perhaps his father's idea was a good one after all. Rob could be charming when it suited him, and also possessed an infectious smile, so perhaps that helped contribute to his success.

It wasn't long before all the items had gone, and Rob said to his son, 'Come on jump up! Let's get back!'

Jimmie felt a huge sense of relief as he climbed up onto the cart. He was delighted to be leaving, though he had loved looking at the big houses, and at least he didn't have to walk back. His dad was in a good humour, having sold all the vases, and of course his pockets were bulging with coins, which jingled as he trotted off with Jimmie hanging on for dear life.

It was early afternoon when they arrived home. A large, cast-iron pan of scouse simmered on the side of the grate. Kate had managed to buy a few things on tick, promising to pay for them on Rob's return.

The hot meal was most welcome to the breadwinners; the fresh air had given them both an appetite, for it was the first food Jimmie had had all day. They gulped it down voraciously, mopping up the gravy with huge chunks of dry bread, until their plates were clean.

Rob gave a sixpenny piece to his mate for the use of the cart, then stacked the other coins in piles on the table.

'Here,' he said to his wife, handing her a shilling, 'take this to Tom's fer what yer got on tick.' Then to Jimmie, 'see if he's got any fades left (old or bruised fruit),' and he gave him a penny.

'Generous bugger!' mumbled Jimmie, under his breath, but his father didn't hear him, he was busy saying to his wife, 'I'll be away next week, Kate. Got a coaster, last about six weeks.'

He lit a cigarette stub. He had been down to the Pool Shipping Offices and had signed on as a fireman, sailing to different ports around the British Isles.

'That'll be 'andy,' said Kate, 'yer'll be home then, when the baby's due.'

'Yeah should be, Kate,' he agreed.

He had finished his cigarette, and was now stripped to the waist and washing himself at the sink. Though lean, he had strong muscular arms, decorated with tattoos. Kate also had a tattoo, an anchor on her right forearm, and on her left arm she had a scroll with Rob's name on it.

'Has our Willie been home yet?' Rob asked, as he tucked his shirt into his trousers.

'No, not yet, I think 'e's at the stables,' answered Kate.

As she spoke, Willie came in, 'Had a good day, lar?' his mother asked. 'Cor! Yer don't arf stink!' she added, holding her nose.

'Yeah I've 'ad a good day, an' I can't smell it!' he laughed,

He had been with Cleggie, one of the gang, down to the stables in Roscommon Street, tending the horses, feeding them and brushing their coats till they shone like silk, then cleaning out and laying new straw. Willie loved the beautiful shire-horses; they were magnificent animals, and he saw to it that they were justly rewarded, after finishing their heavy work of hauling great loads to and fro at the docks. He was only paid a paltry sum for the job, but he loved the horses so much, that he would have done it for nothing anyway.

'Get the tin bath off the nail in the yard,' ordered Kate, 'you need a good scrubbing.'

Soon the strong smell of carbolic soap permeated the whole room, and the tepid water, combined with a scrubbing brush, soon removed the horsey smell of manure from Willie's body.

'Our Jimmie can get in after you, when 'e gets back,' snapped Kate. 'Go an' tell 'im when you're dressed, an' if yer see our Mary, tell 'er to get 'ome, there's some cleanin' up to do.'

CHAPTER EIGHT
Finger In The Door

Mary often visited Tom Travis's fruit shop, he was a close friend of the MacLeans. Tom rather fancied himself as a dancer, and had offered to teach Mary how to tap-dance. Nellie had agreed to accompany her, not to dance, but only for the laughs. When it came to the dance routine, only Mary's right foot would perform, while the left one just shuffled on the sawdust floor.

'She's my lady-love, tappety-tap,
She is my girl, my baby-dove, tappety-tap.'

Jimmie had just entered the shop to buy his pennyworth of fades, so Tom served him then turned back to the girls.

'Now where were we? Oh! Yeah!
She's no gal, fer sittin' down ter dream, tap, tap.
She's the only queen Laguna knows, shuffle here.'

Nellie giggled at Tom's instructions.

'Shuffle, tap,
I know she likes me, tappety-tap,
I know she likes me, tap, tap,
Because she said so, tappety-tap,
She is my Lily of Laguna, tap, tap,
She is my lily and my rose, tappety-tap.

Now curtsy,' finished Tom.

They were all deeply engrossed, and enjoying the dance routine, when Willie entered the shop.

'Hey youse two, yer gorra get 'ome, an' be quick about it, mam wants yer.'

On arriving home, Kate soon barked her orders at them, first to Mary, 'Get cleaned up, see that our Lily gets ter bed soon, see that he (meaning Jimmie), washes his hair.'

Then pointing to him, 'an' you get in that bath, an' be sharp, the water's nearly cold.' The grubby little lad didn't need to be told twice, and after shedding his few clothes, jumped into the water. He shivered. It was stone cold, and it wasn't very clean either after Willie had been in it.

Rob and Kate of course, now feeling flush with their new-found wealth, left the house arm in arm.

'Ere,' said Mary, after her parents had gone, 'mind yer legs, lar, let's freshen it up a bit,' and she poured a large panful of hot water into the bath. 'There that's better? A bit warmer is it?'

'Yeah that's a lot better Mary, but don't let Nellie Mather into the house will yer? She always makes me go red when she says things.' He hadn't forgotten what she had said about his periwinkle.

'What things?'

'Aw! It's nothin', ferget it,' he said, as Mary lathered his hair with the block of red soap. He was glad that his burning cheeks were covered with soap suds. She rinsed his hair in water, colder than he had anticipated, which fortunately cooled him down and made him gasp for breath. He felt clean and fresh, and after dressing, Mary combed his thick unruly, hair.

'There now, lar, how's that?'

'Great! I'm goin' ter see Tess before she goes ter bed.'

Willie was slouched over the table, reading his latest Hotspur and ignoring all that was being said around him.

'I've got a big shell that I found at Aigburth,' Jimmie told Mary, 'look!' He proudly displayed it for his sister. 'I found it in the sand. I'll give it ter Tess, she'll like it, yer can 'ear the tide comin' in. Listen!'

He held the shell to Mary's ear. Willie's ears had pricked up at the words 'Aigburth' and 'tide'. He hadn't forgotten the close shave he and the gang had had, or the horrible feeling of the waves lapping around his legs in the cove.

Jimmie noticed him sit up and looked him straight in the eye, 'Yeah, I'll give it ter Tess,' he beamed, fully aware that Willie hated any mention of the incident. 'Where's me mam gone?' he asked Mary.

'Her an' me dad 'ave gone ter the shops, ter get yer a new jersey fer school on Monday.'

Jimmie's smile immediately evaporated, 'It's not school already, is it?'

'Fraid so, lar.'

'It'll be a new teacher.'

Jimmie had imagined the summer holidays would go on for ever, so the thought of returning to school in two day's time was unwelcome news indeed.

Willie looked up, joining in conversation, 'Yeah, school, Jim lad,' he smirked, glad of the opportunity to get back at Jimmie, 'an yer'll be gettin' cropped as well!'

'So what?' Jimmie replied, trying not to think of the impending haircut, 'Yer'll be at St Augustine's with Corky Green. Yeah old Corky.'

Like all the other children in the neighbourhood, Willie was afraid of the man who would soon be his headmaster. Mr Green had been so-named because he had a cork foot, having had his real one shot off in the Great War.

'Don't take any notice of our Jimmie,' laughed Mary, 'e's not at all like some of the kids say, 'e gave me an' Nelly a lovely report when we left. Just do yer work an' behave yerself, that's all, an' yer'll be okay, 'e's a good 'eadmaster.'

Mary smiled as she scraped the tin bath across the tiled floor, the water swishing and slopping about over the sides. 'Willie,' she panted, 'go an' get our Lily. She's over at Nellie's.'

By now, Mary had managed to pull the bath outside, and had tipped its contents out into the backyard, swilling the soapy water into all the corners. Next using a bottle of diluted Aunt Sally, she sprinkled it all over the yard and around the ash-pit, 'Mmm, that smells a lot sweeter, and it's cleaner too!' she commented, brushing her golden sandy hair from her eyes.

She then hung the bath on the big nail in the wall, and went back into the house.

Mary had washed Lily and was just putting her to bed as the two lads were leaving the house. She called out after them, 'Don't be late youse two; be in before me mam an' dad get 'ome!'

Once outside, Jimmie turned to Willie, 'See yer in a bit, just goin' ter Tess Magee's, tell Arthur.'

So Willie ran off to meet the gang and when Jimmie reached the Magee house, three doors away, he called, 'Tess! Tess! Are yer comin' out?'

A sad face peered down the stairs at him, 'No I'm not,' she whispered.

'Come out, Tess, look what I've got fer yer.'

Tess ran down the stairs and said quietly, but emphatically, 'No, me mam's sick. I can't come out.'

'Here y'are then,' and he handed her the white, shiny, shell, 'it's fer you. Here, take it!'

She seemed upset and confused, her mother's illness had put a huge strain on the whole family. 'No! I don't want it! I don't want anything. I only want me mammy ter get better,' and with that, she slammed the door shut, unaware of Jimmie's hand resting in the door jamb. He screamed out in pain.

Mary heard him and ran over, hammering furiously on the door for Mr Magee.

'Fer pity's sake, can't yer keep quiet, lass,' was Mr Magee's initial reaction to the knocking and banging, 'yer know me poor wife's ill.'

Then he caught sight of Jimmie's hand, dripping blood all over the threshold, 'Good God! Oh, the poor wee lad.'

He grabbed Jimmie's hand, and taking the thin cotton scarf from around his own neck, he bound it tightly around the little lad's fingers. 'I'm afraid one of them might have to be stitched,' he said to Mary, 'better take him to the hospital.'

Mary and Nellie pushed Jimmie up to Mill Road Hospital in an old pram. The first joint of the little finger was only attached by a bit of skin and was stitched back on. The others were badly bruised, but not broken. They were heavily bandaged, and a sling was put around his arm for support.

'You're a lucky wee laddie indeed,' said the Scottish casualty nurse, kindly.

Jimmie, though feeling poorly, saw the funny side, and said to her, 'I don't think that I'm a bit lucky.'

'Come back in two weeks to have the stitches out,' she laughed.

Jimmie fell asleep in the pram on the way home, and the two girls sniggered at a smart Alec who had glanced into the pram.

On seeing Jimmie, he'd exclaimed, 'Gosh! 'e's a big baby, when did yer 'ave 'im?'

'Shut yer bleedin' gob!' Nellie retorted.

Then the two girls managed between them to manoeuvre the pram down the steps into the house, with Jimmie still fast asleep.

'Thank goodness our Lily's still asleep,' said Mary, for they'd had to leave her on her own when the accident occurred.

The gaslight was almost exhausted, and Mary inserted a penny into the meter. As the mantle flared up, so did Nellie's voice. She let out a piercing shriek, leaping onto the nearest chair. Cockroaches scuttled in every direction across the tiled floor; some were even half-way up the walls. Mary grabbed the long brush and swatted as many as she could, before they all disappeared into their hiding places.

Nellie's face had turned ashen, 'They make me toes curl up, an' me flesh goes all goosey,' she shuddered, horrified. 'Thought yer mam an' dad 'ad bought a new 'earth rug,' she joked. 'Ow can yer do that?' she asked, squirming, as Mary shovelled the dead cockies onto the fire.

'Get used to anything around 'ere Nell, just a way of life,' shrugged Mary resignedly.

'Me mam puts a dish of beer down at night, an' they drown themselves in it,' said Nellie.

'Pah! there's never any beer to spare in this 'ouse fer cockroaches. Well only the two-legged kind, an' they drown themselves in it by choice!'

'Yer know,' said Nellie, displaying her beautiful white teeth as she grinned, mischievously, 'them cockies are dirty devils, they don't even get out of the beer fer a pee!'

At this, they roared with laughter.

After all the jobs and the cleaning up were done, Mary suddenly realised that there would be a rumpus when her parents arrived home later that evening, because of what had happened to Jimmie's hand, and she panicked when she thought of the leather belt, with the ends cut into strips, hanging on a nail near the fireplace. She knew that her parents would most likely be the worse for drink and she didn't fancy a strapping.

'Nellie, do yer think? Well I don't like askin'.' Mary was at a loss for words.

'What is it, Mary?'

'Do yer think our Jimmie could sleep with your Arthur, just fer ternight?'

'Course 'e can,' replied Nellie without hesitation, 'don't worry, nobody knows what happened, only me, an' I won't say anythin'. Then termorrer we'll go out fer the day. He'll be feelin' a bit better by then, we'll get up early an' take our dinner, an' go to Stanley Park.'

'Thanks Nell, yer a good pal, don't know what I'd do without yer. Yes we'll do that. Who knows, me dad might be out when we get back.'

Mary gently shook Jimmie awake, 'Come on lad, Nellie's takin' yer to 'er 'ouse fer the night, ter sleep wi' Arthur. Yer'll like that, won't yer?'

So they all bade one another goodnight, Mary breathing a sigh of relief when her brother had left the house. She put the pan of scouse on to warm up, as it might put her mam and dad in a good mood when they got back.

It was late when they finally did arrive, swaying and staggering into the house, and flopping onto the sofa in a giggling heap.

'Do yer want somethin' ter eat?' asked Mary, 'there's some scouse ready.'

'No, I don't want no bloody scouse, I'll 'ave somethin' else,' said Kate awkwardly. 'Run down ter Maggie Hislop's, she's always open late, an' get me a bit of cheese. 'ere's threepence, an' take a cup wi' yer, an' get a bit o' piccalilli as well.'

Mary hated going out in the dark, but had no choice if she wanted to keep her mother in a good mood, so off she ran to Maggie Hislop's, with the money and cup in her hands. In the small, dimly-lit shop, the old lady cut four slices of Cheddar cheese, then spooned the yellow pickle from a large jar into Mary's cup.

'Ere y'are, dear,' Maggie said, as she picked up the silver coin. 'Run straight home won't you?'

'Yes I will Maggie,' Mary assured her. 'G'night.'

It was dark outside and Mary hurried home, scurrying along down the middle of the street, so that nobody could grab her from around a corner. 'Can't see why they couldn't 'ave the scouse anyway,' she grumbled. 'Won't be wasted though, our Willie an' Bobby'll eat it when they come in.'

After she had prepared the sandwiches for her parents, she made her way to the foot of the stairs, 'I'm goin' ter bed now, is that all?' Then she added, as casually as she could, 'Oh! By the way, Jimmie's sleepin' at Arthur's, me an Nellie are takin' 'em out in the mornin.'

'Yeah that's alright Mary,' said Rob, licking his fingers, 'you go to bed now girl.'

Mary crept into her small bed in the dark bedroom. She shared the same room as Lily and her three brothers, but at least she had her own bed, small though it was. She always contrived to retire before her brothers, so that she could undress in a little bit of privacy.

Her thoughts turned to her parents downstairs; 'They didn't even know which of their children was in or out, and seemed not to care. In Jimmie's case, it was as well that they didn't know.' She lay in bed thinking of him and the planned day out. Then she thought of the sweet factory on Monday; at least Nellie would be there with her. She drifted off to sleep humming her favourite hymn.

'Now the day is over,
Night is drawing nigh,
Shadows of the evening,
Steal across the sky.'

She was suddenly awakened by someone slapping her arms; it was Lily.

'Where's our Jimmie?' she asked.

'Oh! He's comin' up soon, come an' get into bed wi' me,' Mary said, and she pulled Lily into bed with her, putting her arm around her, and the two of them soon fell asleep.

Willie was talking in his sleep, and Bobby was snoring as usual, but except for those sounds, everything was peaceful again.

CHAPTER NINE
Face The Music

Mary left the house quietly, not even bothering to make herself a drink. She'd had a swill in cold water, rinsing her mouth at the same time, and though the day promised to be warm, she felt a chill of apprehension as she imagined her parent's reaction when they found out about Jimmie.

'Gosh Nellie, I'm sorry I'm a bit late,' Mary apologised, on arriving at Nellie's house.

'Don't worry, we're all ready, and I've put up some sandwiches,' said Nellie, showing Mary the brown paper carrier bag. 'We had porridge fer breakfast, the boys enjoyed it.'

Mary's stomach rumbled at the thought of food, 'What time is it, Nellie?'

'Oh about ten o'clock. I've been up since eight.'

Nellie always was an early bird.

'I thought I'd get up early fer your Jimmie. You know 'is eyes, an' now 'is 'and. E's 'ad a good night though, me mam gave 'im a Settlers powder, an' 'e slept like a baby.'

They left the house with the two boys walking on ahead, suddenly laughing at an unfortunate cyclist who had fallen off his bike, its wheels having become firmly trapped in the tramlines. Then, as if that wasn't enough, he had lost a shoe, revealing to his dismay, a ragged old sock, with holes in the heels and toes.

'Yer want ter send them 'oley socks ter the Pope!' Nellie shouted.

Mary, who always sympathised with the underdog, scolded her friend, 'Don't laugh at 'im, 'e might 'ave 'urt 'imself.'

'Not 'im,' laughed Nellie, 'e does it all the time. 'e'll buckle the tramline one of these days wi' 'is nut, an' 'e'll not feel a thing.' Nellie waved to the man in the road. 'He tries ter get ter the Pier Head ridin' in the tramline, an' always comes off before 'e gets ter Cornwall Street, the daft sod!'

The man returned Nellie's wave, grinning and trying to adjust the handlebars, not even realising at first that he had lost a shoe. His bike was his most important consideration, and it was only when he started to wheel the contraption away, that he noticed that the shoe wasn't on his foot. He gave an embarrassed snigger, as he eased his foot into the shoe, then set off with his bike to restart his marathon.

The four youngsters turned right up Everton Valley, to the park. Time passed quickly for them, enjoying the constant stream of Nellie's jokes.

'Yer must stay awake all night thinkin' of them,' laughed Mary. 'Better not stay awake ternight though, it's work in the morning, don't want ter be late.'

Nellie's expression changed abruptly, 'Oh aye it's work, isn't it?' she recalled. 'An' fer you, our Arthur, it's school!'

That put a stop to his laughter for a while.

'I'm goin' too,' piped up Jimmie. 'It'll be a new class, I'm goin' ter school, even if I 'ave got a sore 'and. I want ter see me new teacher, an' get me milk as well!' Jimmie's mind was already made up, he was looking forward to school.

'We'll 'ave ter wait an' see what yer dad says, when 'e sees yer 'and.'

Mary was still very worried about the outcome of what was becoming to her, a terrible nightmare. She knew full well that she would have to face the music when she returned home, and also that she would inevitably be blamed for Jimmie's accident.

Observing the anxiety etched on her friend's face, Nellie said cheerfully, 'Ere y'are, our kiddo, 'ave a jam butty.'

'Thanks a lot Nellie,' Mary said, her mind elsewhere. She chewed automatically, staring out across the lake, watching the rowing-boats as they skimmed over the water, their occupants laughing and enjoying themselves, as young people usually do. On this occasion though the day was marred for Mary, by thoughts of the impending return home.

'Glad someone's happy, anyway,' she commented, thinking out loud.

Nellie was busy watching the two lads, who were having the time of their lives, watching minnows in the lake, darting in and out of the rocks.

'Be careful youse two, we don't want any more accidents!'

Nellie's warning brought Mary abruptly back to the present and where she was. The warmth of the sun soon had its effect on the girls as small freckles appeared across Mary's nose and under her eyes, whilst Nellie's face was becoming gently tanned. With closed eyes they chatted and day-dreamed about school, their new jobs, the laughs they'd had teasing the boys who had been attracted to them, and their refusals of the many offers of dates. They giggled about the funny white caps they had to wear at the sweet factory, and big fat Bess, the female chargehand, who Nellie had joked was more like a feller.

'She's got an arse like one of the boilers on the Mauritania,' she remarked.

Mary laughed in agreement, 'Aye, an' a mouth like a fog'orn!'

'I'm not lookin' forward to goin' back slavin' away fer a few bob a week,' Nellie continued.

The factory had been forced medicine for both girls, having been pushed into the jobs in order to bring home money for their parents. They were offered no alternatives.

'Never mind,' said Mary, trying to cheer up her pal, 'one of these days something will turn up. Something we will like doin', then we'll be able ter use our talents.'

They were unsure of exactly what those talents were at that time, but they knew instinctively that there were other things in life, if they just watched out and waited for their opportunity. The important thing was to recognise that opportunity when it turned up.

'Come on gang, let's be goin'!' Nellie called to the two lads.

So the weary wanderers ambled their way home, the boys lagging behind and whistling, *Wish me luck as you wave me good-bye.*

'Aye, I'll need some luck when I get 'ome,' moaned Mary, becoming more fearful with each step.

'It'll be okay Mary,' said Nellie, trying to reassure her, 'maybe it won't be as bad as you think.'

'An' where the 'ell d'yer think you've been till now?' yelled Kate, grabbing her daughter by the arm and dragging her roughly into the kitchen.

This was all too much for the poor girl, who was already a bag of nerves, and she broke down and sobbed.

'Just stop yer whingeing. It's a good job yer dad's not 'ere, or yer wouldn't be able ter sit down fer a week. An' look at our Jimmie's 'and, yer sneaky little devil, goin' off this mornin' an' not lettin' on.'

Kate went on at her hammer and tongs and Mary was too terrified to defend herself. To be accused of neglecting her young brother, whom she cared for deeply, was too much for her, and in her grief, she appealed to her mother.

'But Mam, I thought I told you last night that I was takin' Jimmie to Stanley Park?'

Kate looked away puzzled. She had no recollection of the night before, as she had been too intoxicated.

'Where is me dad?' asked Jimmie, attempting to divert the attention away from his sister.

'Got a telegram, askin' 'im ter join 'is ship, 'e's sailin' ternight, an' won't be back fer six weeks.'

Mary's eyes lit up at the good news, she felt as if she had been pardoned from a heavy sentence, relieved of a burden that was too heavy for her to carry. She lifted the hem of her cotton dress and wiped her eyes.

Jimmie took her hand in his good one and squeezed it, as if to say, 'You're okay now.'

In contrast to this gentle gesture, Kate's voice grated in Mary's ears, 'Alright now I've 'eard enough, mardy arse, the more yer cry, the less yer'll piss.'

Mary tried to shut out the foul language from her mind, she hated that kind of talk.

Kate, oblivious to her daughter's sensibilities, now turned her attention to Jimmie.

'Good job Nellie's mother told me about you,' she snapped, displaying a total lack of sympathy for her injured son.

'Aw it's nowt,' Jimmie claimed bravely, 'don't know what all the fuss is about. It won't stop me goin' ter school.'

As he spoke, he slid his hand defiantly from the sling. He was determined to get there, no matter what, he wanted to see his new teacher.

Mary rubbed her arm where her mother had held her in a vice-like grip, 'Be bruised in the morning, no doubt,' she thought. She wiped her face with the wet flannel, she didn't dare look up, or say anything, for fear of rekindling Kate's anger. She decided that she had really got off lightly; if her father had been there, she would definitely have had the strap across her legs and buttocks.

Mary always showed respect for her parents, even though she knew that at times, their treatment of their children was severe and unfair, but she vowed that one day she would find a way out of all this. She felt trapped, as if she were sinking in quicksand with no one to pull her out of it.

'Will yer stop day-dreamin' an' get some spuds peeled!' Kate's thunderous voice brought her back to reality.

'Yeah alright Mam.'

She brushed some breadcrumbs from the table into her cupped hand, then she peeled some potatoes and a large swede, and put them to boil in the large iron pan. She placed some clean sheets of the Liverpool Echo on the table to serve as a tablecloth, and on top of that she put an enamel plate with a lump of rock salt, five cracked dinner plates of different designs, and an assortment of bent and twisted tablespoons.

Just then Willie arrived on the scene, puffing and panting, 'What you been doin'?' he asked casually, pointing to Jimmie's bandaged hand. Then, without waiting for an answer, asked Mary, 'What's fer dinner, I'm starving.'

By this time their meal was ready, and as Mary dished out the mashed vegetables, she announced, 'Scouse without meat, call it what yer like, it's all there is, so eat up.'

The meagre meal was wolfishly despatched by the hungry, sniffing children, and as they ate silence reigned in the MacLean house. Each child was engrossed in his or her own reverie. Mary wondered what work would be like in the morning? Jimmie speculated about his new teacher, and Willie clicked his spoon against his teeth, thinking of St. Augustine's and the notorious Corky Green. Ah! well! They would all have to wait and see.

CHAPTER TEN
'Neddy' and Miss Lowe

'New every morning is the love,
Our waking and uprising proof,
Through sleep and darkness safely brought ...'

The tall, dark-haired, young woman pointed and tapped out each word of the hymn that was written on the blackboard, occasionally turning to face the mixed class of boys and girls, her brown eyes sparkling beneath her neat, shiny fringe.

'Through sleep and darkness safely brought,
Restored to life and power and thought.'

After the hymn was finished, she turned and addressed the class. 'Right, please sit down. My name is Miss Lowe and I live in Liverpool, not Everton.'

'Aw! She's a red,' whispered Arthur, who was sitting next to his pal, 'but she's a bit of alright. Wouldn't mind laying 'lowe' with 'er!' he sniggered.

'And,' continued Miss Lowe, 'if any of you boys pass any uncomplimentary remarks, or try to get smart, verbal or otherwise, you'll be sorry you ever clapped eyes on me. I'm not a tart, I'm not a bit of skirt, I'm here to educate you. Help me to help you,' she smiled, exposing two rows of beautiful white teeth.

Next the register was called, and the children who had health problems were escorted, in lines of two, up Everton

Brow, to the school clinic in Plumpton Street, by a health visitor.

Jimmie gazed up at the jolly-faced nurse, and as he gazed, yellow eye drops were administered, causing him to blink rapidly.

'Keep your head back, there's a good lad,' advised the nurse. She took a length of bandage, and threaded it through two pieces of dark brown card, then tied the bandage around his head, adjusting the cards to shield his eyes, like blinkers on a horse.

'Cor! Miss!' complained Jimmie, 'do I 'ave ter 'ave these on? I'll look like a bloomin' 'orse.'

'Never mind what you look like,' said the kindly woman, 'your eyes are very precious, so we've got to look after them. What would you do if you couldn't see? It doesn't matter what others say, you look after yourself, my lad. And now,' she added, with a smile, 'let's have a look at that hand while we're at it.'

Jimmie studied the nurse as she dressed his hand; her face seemed to shine in the brightly-lit surgery, reminding him of the advertisement for starch, with a lady in her brilliant white, starched uniform, tenderly smiling at him.

'There you are, how does that feel?'

'It feels good, Miss.'

'Now don't forget what I said about your eyes, will you?'

'No, Miss, I won't ferget. Ta-ra.'

The children were marched back to school, looking like wounded soldiers returning from battle. As they entered the classroom, they were met with titters of laughter, girls holding their hands over their mouths, trying to hide their sniggers.

'You can shut that up right now,' warned Miss Lowe, 'I can't see anything amusing!'

'Feel a right bloody idiot,' muttered Jimmie to Art, as he tried to bury his face behind an exercise book. 'What yer been doin' while I've been away?'

'Aw! Summat about farm animals, sheep, pigs an' cows, an' where they live,' mumbled Arthur, vaguely.

'Right, Mather, you seem to have plenty to say for yourself, what have you written about this morning? Stand up!'

Arthur got to his feet and blurted out, 'Cows, Miss!'

'Well, let's hear about them then. Quiet everyone, Arthur's going to tell us about cows. Right Arthur, away you go!' Miss Lowe announced, with a twinkle in her eye.

'Please Miss, cows are big animals with horns and four legs, an' they've got a big bag that 'angs down underneath, near its tail.'

'It's not a big bag, Arthur, it's an udder.'

'Oh yes Miss, an udder, an' it lives in a field. The boy hesitated.

'Yes Mather, what is it?' asked Miss Lowe.

'So, do all cows come from 'Uddersfield then?'

A howl of laughter erupted around the classroom. Miss Lowe lifted her desk lid to hide her face, and the laughter that she couldn't control, and pretended to be searching for a hankie.

'Alright, alright!' she bellowed, having recovered from the laughing fit. Down came the desk lid with a bang, immediately quietening the children.

'Sit down, Arthur.'

He responded immediately. 'What's up? Did I say summat funny?'

'Don't know,' Jimmie said, 'all I know about 'uddersfield is what our Willie told me. 'e thought they were in the second division.'

The milkman's head could be seen over the screen of the door, 'Jimmie, Arthur, bring the milk in, please.'

The boys were delighted at this privilege, and executed the order without hesitation. Straws were then distributed to the undernourished children, who promptly popped the cardboard tops off the milk bottles, by pushing their fingers through the holes in the middle and inserting the straws to siphon up the creamy liquid. Arthur pushed his thumb into the lid and a fountain of cream splattered all over him, covering his cheeky face. The sight was all too much for Miss Lowe, who beat a hasty retreat from the room, her hand over her mouth.

'Think she's pissed her bloomers,' commented Arthur.

'Don't be vulgar,' Jimmie spluttered, as he sucked at the straw greedily, 'she's just gone ter get 'er tea.'

The morning was soon over, then it was a rush outside and a race along Netherfield Road, to China Street. There was always a queue outside the dinner house, and usually a fight or two in progress.

Jimmie slipped off his cardboard blinkers as he ran, he didn't want anyone making fun of him, or calling him a horse. They were lucky, there was no queue when they arrived, so they went straight into the dismal hall, with its long line of tables and benches.

'Wonder what's on terday, Art? Oh no, bleedin' yeller-belly. Blimey, finish up lookin' like Charlie Chan the Chinaman. Not so much, Miss.'

The woman behind the long, green, counter ladled the food into soup plates, 'Here's yer spoon, an' bring 'em back when yer've done. No slopin' off wi' 'em,' she warned.

The two boys were not impressed by their meal, even though they were hungry.

'Ah well! I suppose we'll 'ave ter force it down,' sighed Jimmie, 'might be all we get terday. Swaller it wi'out breathin', yer won't taste it then.'

'Aye an' shut yer eyes,' agreed Arthur.

'Come on, 'urry up before it gets crowded, yer know what 'appens in 'ere when they serve this stuff up,' said Jimmie, 'there y'are, what did I tell yer?'

The boys jumped up, as bits of curried potato, onion and carrot were flicked across the table by rival gangs.

'Here y'are, Miss,' cried the lads, flinging their plates and spoons down on the counter. 'Ta-ra, see yer termorrer,' and with that they shot out of the door, adding, 'if we 'aven't been poisoned!'

'Cheeky little bleeders,' called back one of the dinner ladies.

The boys ambled back to school, and the cardboard shades were slipped back as discreetly as possible, over Jimmie's eyes.

'What yer doin' ternight, Art?'

'Don't know yet. See if the gang will 'ave us. Don't see why they shouldn't, we're as good as them. Still got that seashell from Aigburth?'

'Yeah, thought I'd give it ter Tess after school.' Jimmie prised the shell out of his pocket and held it to his ear, 'Tide's goin' out!'

'Gerraway, giz it 'ere, let's listen.'

Arthur put the shell to his ear. He heard a whooshing sound, 'Ow d'yer know it's goin' out?'

'What?'

'The tide!'

''Ave a look at yer neck when yer get 'ome,' chuckled Jimmie, 'there's a dirty, big tidemark all the way round!'

'Cheeky devil! At least I 'aven't been left out in the rain all night, an' gone rusty!'

As they entered the playground, groups of girls, with their frocks tucked inside their knickers, were skipping.

'Look over there Art, she's got 'oles in 'er knickers!'

'Who? Where?'

'That big tart from the top class.'

Arthur's eyes scanned the rows of girls, 'Yer 'avin' me on.'

'No I'm not. She's got two 'oles where she puts 'er legs through, ha ha!'

'Aw, gerraway wi' yer!'

Art seemed disappointed.

'Thought yer were goin' ter get yer eye full, didn't yer?' laughed Jimmie.

'The big ship sails through the Alley-Alley-O,
The Alley-Alley-O,
The Alley-Alley-O.'

The girls chorused as they jumped in and out of the long turning rope.

'On the last day of September.'

'Which one d'yer fancy, Jimmie?'

'None of 'em. Not interested in girls. Only like Tess, 'cos she's different, doesn't mix wi' the other kids, an' she talks nice.'

'What! Yer like 'er? After she trapped yer bleedin' 'and in the door?' Art couldn't believe his ears.

'Well! She didn't know. It couldn't be 'elped, it was an accident. Besides, 'er mam's sick, an' she was upset an' cryin'.'

'Yeah I suppose yer right,' agreed Arthur. 'Jean's not a bad lookin' judy, is she? Gorra lorra work on wi' 'er mam. She 'as ter look after 'er. I never see 'er playin' out these days.'

The bell rang and all the children filed into class. It was a warm afternoon, and so after the geography lesson, they were allowed to lay their heads down on their folded arms across the desk tops, and soon many of the children fell asleep. It was so peaceful. Miss Lowe walked up and down the aisles between the desks, her lovely fragrance drifting towards Jimmie and Art.

They had never smelled that kind of perfume before. The only one they had experienced was at the Pop picture-house on a Saturday afternoon, when the attendant sprayed the air with a cheap, sickly-smelling, vapour. Sweaty little bodies had squeezed in to see their idol, Flash Gordon, or the famous Clyde Beatty the lion-tamer, and the air soon became stale and fetid. When the attendant squirted the spray, the howling audience would chant.

'Squirt some on me, Mister, squirt some on me!'

The attendant would retort, 'Why? Are yer lousy or summat?'

Someone would shout, 'Well, stick yer spray, point first!'

'I'll 'ave the lot of yers out. Quick, smart, now watch it!' and he'd shine his torch up and down the rows of noisy, fidgeting kids.

'Put yer torch out, Mister, we've come ter see Flash Gordon, not yer flippin' flashlight!'

And so it went on.

All these thoughts were swimming through Jimmie's mind as he lay, head down, on his desk. Art was sound asleep and was dribbling from the corner of his mouth. Jimmie stared at him for a while, then went back to his day-dreaming again.

He thought of Art's dad, and wondered where he was, and what he would be doing? He'd probably be on the high seas by now, or chasing some hula girl along a tropical beach. Or maybe cannibals were chasing him instead, with big spears to make scouse out of him.

Then there was his own old feller, probably not out of the Mersey Bar yet, that's if he got his ship alright. Anyway he must have, because he didn't come home last night.

The rumble of a tram brought his attention back to the classroom, and from the corner of his eye, he noticed a trickle of water creeping across the floorboards by his desk and he nudged Arthur.

'Wadder yer want?' protested Art, drowsily.

'I think someone 'as peed themselves,' he whispered.

'As long as it's not me,' Art turned his head away, still half asleep.

The teacher had already spotted the flow. 'Come on, dear, you'd better go home.' Miss Lowe shook the girl who was still asleep, 'Come on now, Lilian, you can go.'

'It's Lily Jones, Art, it's Lily Jones, she's wet 'er pants.'

Art yawned lazily, 'Tell 'er ter gera washer on.'

The girl left the classroom, scratching her head and hardly aware of what had happened, except tor the trickle down her legs and her wet pants.

'Jimmie go and get Mr Harris to bring his mop. Quietly, now, don't wake the others.'

The caretaker arrived with his long mop and bucket, grumbling and grousing to himself, clanging his mop bucket as he mopped up the pee with Aunt Sally, and making rude gestures behind the teacher's back.

Jimmie saw this and was angry. Miss Lowe was a lovely lady and treated them well, 'Ignorant sod,' he mumbled, under his breath, 'that wasn't called for, it's his job to mop up the pee.'

Mr Harris was obviously annoyed at having his tea-break disturbed, and he left the classroom still deliberately banging and clanking the bucket as he went.

'Alright now, children,' said Miss Lowe to her sleepy class, looking across the room from her large desk, 'I'm sure you're all awake by now, especially after that noise. Those who are still sleepy, I would suggest that you go to bed earlier. You must get your sleep as you can't learn if you're tired, so remember: early to bed, early to rise, makes children healthy, wealthy and wise.'

She made the children repeat the verse after her until they had memorised it. At the same time, she looked around her class of poor, bedraggled, youngsters, and wondered what she had let herself in for? The sight of these waifs, some of whom had no seat in their pants, untidy and uncared for, most with head lice, filled her with compassion. Inside she felt sick, and once again took shelter behind her desk lid; this time to wipe the tears away from the corners of her eyes. She hadn't known these children very long, yet already she felt a certain closeness to them.

'I'll be back in a moment,' she announced, 'and no talking.' She knocked on the door of the headmistress's office and entered.

Miss Bolt could see that she was upset. 'It's alright, my dear, I know how you feel. I wondered what I was coming to when I left my home in Harrogate. Here drink this,' and she handed Miss Lowe a cup of tea. 'I've been here nearly twenty years, but it's surprising how you learn to cope. They're good children, dirty maybe, and smelly, but I'm sure you'll grow to love them as I do.'

'But why? Why? It's not fair. I've never seen anything like it before. They don't stand a chance,' sobbed Miss Lowe, in between sips of hot tea.

'But we've got to give them that chance. If we don't, who will?'

'But what are the authorities doing to help? Dear God, some of them are starving, sick, and at best, neglected.'

'Yes, I know, and it will be the same for their children and their children's children, unless someone helps them to find a way out. It may seem a thankless task that we have here at Netherfield Road School; Everton Ridge is probably the poorest and dirtiest part of the city, but if just a handful make it in life, that's a reward for us. We need you here, the children need you. I think you've got what it takes, that's why I offered you the job. Do you feel a bit better now?'

'Yes I do, thank you.'

'I can't hear any noise from your classroom,' observed the head, 'seems like they're showing you respect already.'

Miss Lowe smiled, 'I do hope so. Thank you once again, I hope I grow to be as wise as you. No, I'll not leave them. How can I? The poor little mites.'

The headmistress smiled back sympathetically, having recognised a little of her young self, in her new recruit.

Miss Lowe returned to her class pleased that she had overcome her first hurdle, and feeling much happier and more confident. She was encouraged by Miss Bolt's little talk, and was determined to live up to her expectations.

'Right, now,' she said brightly, 'let's have some nice clean faces in the morning. And for being good whilst I've been out, I'm going to let you go home fifteen minutes earlier.'

'Hurrah!' cheered all the kids.

Miss Lowe dismissed them without further ado. 'Bye now, children.'

'Bye, now?' queried Jimmie, 'what does she mean, bye?'

'Yer dumb sod,' scoffed Arthur, 'it's the posh way of sayin' ta-ra.'

The two lads waited outside the school gates for their new teacher, 'Your tram's comin' Miss,' they cried, as they saw her crossing the schoolyard.

The tall, slim Miss Lowe sprinted and jumped on the tram.

'Cor! Did yer see 'er run Arthur?' Jimmie gasped, impressed by her athletic performance.

'Yeah , I bet she could beat Sydney Woodison!'

The teacher waved and smiled at the boys as she dropped her fare into the conductor's hand. Then she turned to inspect the Liverpool Coat of Arms, on the side of a passing tram; Neptune and the Liver Bird, accompanied by the motto *'Deus Nobis Haec Utia Fecit',* which means 'God made these blessings for us.'

Miss Lowe was disgusted, she felt it was an insult to the suffering humanity she had witnessed that day. 'Blessings from the devil, more like!' she fumed, as she stared fixedly out of the tram window.

So absorbed was she with these thoughts, that she seemed unaware of where she was as the tram swayed along at a steady pace, ferrying her homeward, away from the grime and poverty. Her emotions had been stirred by the children in her care, who were trapped in a hopeless world, and unable to find a way out.

CHAPTER ELEVEN
Mary's New Job

As Jimmie and Arthur strolled home from school in a leisurely fashion, the familiar sights of their neighbourhood met their eyes. Women, young and old, carried heavy bundles of laundry on their heads, as they emerged from the wash-house, and bedraggled toddlers clung onto their mothers' aprons or shawls. Men in their dozens loitered about the streets, leaning on the landing railings, desperate for whatever work they could find, and in the meantime, hoping that Thursday would soon come, so that they could draw their Unemployed Assistance Benefit. Whatever money they did get, was barely enough to keep body and soul together, yet despite their despair, they could usually manage a witty remark, or tell a funny joke.

It was this humour and wit which helped them to survive, helped them to keep on hoping when their lives seemed pointless and bleak. To bring a smile to a sad face seemed to be their aim, and there was always someone to share their last few pennies with, or a pan of scouse, if it was needed. As they walked along, they shared the day's experiences with each other.

'Didn't like the way Charlie Harris gave our new teacher the fingers up sign, Art. I'll make 'im pay, the frigger!'

'Think yer a bit sweet on 'er, Jimmie Mac,' laughed Art.

'Well she doesn't deserve it, she's new an' all that,' his face reddened slightly, 'an' besides, it's 'is job to mop up the pee, that's what 'e's paid for.'

Arthur eyed his mate suspiciously, and could see that he was deep in thought. 'Got any ideas?'

'We'll 'ave ter wait an' see what we can come up wi'!'

Just at that moment, a Hindu sweet-seller passed by, carrying a large tin box in front of him, which was supported by a leather strap around his neck. He wore a spotless white turban around his head.

'Got plenty o' Indian toffee Sam?' asked Jimmie.

'Yes,' came the reply.

'Serves yer right fer makin' so much!' laughed Jimmie.

'An' I 'ope yer 'ead gets better soon,' added Art, only too willing to join in the fun.

The two boys passed Spot's sweet shop and turned into India Street. They stopped abruptly, and their mood immediately turned sober, as they were confronted by the sinister green ambulance, parked outside the Magee's house.

Both boys trembled with fear, for they knew that it was serious if an ambulance was called.

'Makes me blood run cold,' shuddered Arthur.

'Me too!' said Jimmie, 'got the shivers all over me.'

They headed straight for Art's house, without glancing back. Groups of women were standing at their doors, curious to see what was going to happen.

'Here they come!' one of them shouted, eagerly, 'they're takin' 'er away!'

'Shut yer bleedin' mouth, Missus. Ger'ome an' mind yer own business.' Jimmie shouted angrily at them.

The frail Mrs Magee was gingerly stretchered into the waiting ambulance. Gerry carried some of her belongings in a carrier bag, and accompanied her in the ambulance. No bell or siren sounded as they sped off, and Tess and Jean were left sitting in stunned silence on the doorstep, tears streaming down their faces.

The two boys went across to them, 'Yer alright, Tess?' asked Jimmie, softly, desperately trying to find some way of comforting her. 'They'll look after yer mam, don't worry.'

The girl sobbed, uncontrollably.

Arthur patted Jean on the shoulder, trying to console her in his clumsy, childish way.

'I've got summat fer yer Tess, 'ang on,' Jimmie awkwardly fished the shell out of his pocket. 'I tried ter give this ter yer before, 'ere take it now. I found it at Aigburth, in the sand.'

The young lad offered her his one and only possession, 'Yer can 'ear the sea if yer listen, 'old it ter yer ear!'

'No! Don't want it!' she sobbed, 'Don't belong to you, so it's not yours to give away!'

'But it is mine. I found it on the seashore,' Jimmie insisted.

'No!' she protested, tearfully. 'Don't belong to anyone, only God! It's His - God's.'

'But it was there fer anybody ter pick up, so I picked it up!'

'Thank you all the same but I can't. How's yer hand? I'm sorry you've hurt it because of me,' Tess snuffled, changing the subject.

'It's not so bad now,' Jimmie assured her, shuffling uneasily, and hiding his bruised hand behind his back, 'it'll soon be better.'

The girls had stopped crying now, but anxiety and despair were clearly etched on their faces.

'Dad won't be comin' back for us, he's staying at the hospital with mammy,' Jean explained.

'What will yer do, then? Who's lookin' after yer?' Art asked.

'Father Flynne. He's coming to fetch us, to look after us,' said Tess.

'We'll have to go now,' put in Jean, 'we'll have to get Moira ready, she's asleep just now. She'll probably cry when she wakes up and mammy isn't there.' Jean and Tess stood up to go back into the house.

'Yer'll come ter see us, won't yer?' asked Art, his head bowed down with sadness at the thought of losing his girl.

'Yes of course we will, won't we, Tess?'

Jimmie's eyes accidentally caught sight of Tess, and they both blushed and turned away. The four of them started to laugh at the blushes.

On that happier note, the girls reassured them, 'Don't worry, we'll see yer again.' Then they ran off up the stairs to their house, giggling and showing their pale blue knickers as they reached the top.

'Glad they're feeling okay now. We must 'ave cheered 'em up,' said Art, then he turned and noticed a group of old women watching them.

'An' what the 'ell d'yer think you're gawpin' at?' he yelled across the street.

The women tucked their shawls around them, then turned to walk away, complaining loudly to one another, 'Want their arses tannin' - cheeky young devils!'

'When yer big enough, yer'll be too old!' shouted Jimmie, cheekily. 'Got nothin' better ter do than 'ang around, waitin' fer people ter die, watchin' an' waitin' ter see who'll be next. Bleedin' banshees, that's what you are!'

As Jimmie's anger subsided, his thoughts reverted to Tess and her refusal to accept his shell. A strange feeling crept over him, bothering him as he examined the shell.

'Hey!' Art grabbed his pal's arm, 'hey look!'

Turning to where Art was indicating, Jimmie saw two nuns walking down the street towards them.

'Quick! Nuns! Spit out,' urged Art, anxiously, 'or yer'll get bad luck.'

The tall, lean, figures in black habits glided gracefully towards them, looking like two giant swans, with their white head-dresses gently flapping. Dangling from their waists were identical silver chains, bearing crucifixes, which swayed from side to side as they moved.

'Hello boys, and how are you today?' one of them enquired, cheerfully.

'Er, er fine, Miss,' Jimmie stammered, embarrassed.

Arthur just sniffed pointedly and remained sullenly silent.

The nuns entered the Magee's home, and it wasn't long before they reappeared with Moira and Tess holding onto their hands. Jean followed along behind, carrying a small battered case, and a brown paper parcel tied up with string, no doubt containing a few items of the girls' clothing.

'Goodbye boys,' the nuns said, smiling as they closed the door.

The two boys spat out across the cobbled street, as before. They didn't want to risk bringing bad luck on themselves.

The girls waved as they were escorted away by the nuns, until they were out of sight.

'D'yer think we'll ever see 'em again, Art?'

'Who knows, 'ope so,' Art sighed, dejectedly.

Mr Magee called just once to empty his house of its contents and Jimmie caught his last sight of him. Gerry waved to him as he left, and Jimmie noticed that he was wearing a black tie, the obvious giveaway that he had lost his wife.

'Well it was a way out for them,' Jimmie commented sadly to his pal. 'There's a way out fer everyone, though it's not always the one that they hope for.' His thoughts raced on, and he thought of Tess and her sisters, hoping that at least they would be able to stay together, and that they would be better off at the convent, than in this filthy rat hole.

The house remained empty for weeks before an elderly couple, the Grimbles, moved in. They appeared to be a quiet, polite pair, keeping themselves very much to themselves, and hardly moving outside the house. Jimmie sometimes ran errands for them. Mrs Grimble, who was never a well woman, sat in her dimly-lit room, and her husband read books most of the day. Occasionally he could be seen returning from the library, with a new stash of books under his arm, touching his cap in salutation to any of the female neighbours who happened to be about at the time. Such an unaccustomed show of good manners always produced astonishment.

Time passed by, until eventually Kate gave birth to another son, Eric. Meg Gilbert and Bessie Mather attended her, and the doctor was present for the actual birth. Much against Mary's wishes, she was forced to stay at home to look after Lily, and attend to all the household chores.

She was missing from work for three days and she was sacked upon her return. She pleaded with the oversized forewoman to reinstate her, but it was to no avail, there were plenty of girls waiting to step into her shoes. Nellie even tried to persuade the manager, giving him one of her best smiles and a wicked wink, as if promising him a favour, if he could see his way to keeping Mary on, but that didn't work either.

Poor Mary trudged dejectedly all the way home that morning from Wavertree. She anxiously thought of her mam, and what she would say when she told her what had happened? At least it wasn't Mary's fault, it was Kate's, for making her stay at home.

'She'll just have ter like it, or lump it,' stated Mary out loud.

At last Mary arrived home, and her mother, surprised to see her back so soon, and noticing her miserable expression, demanded, 'What you doin' 'ome? An' what 'ave yer got a cob on fer?'

'I got finished fer stoppin' off me work.'

This prompted a tirade of abuse from Kate, first directed at her, and then at the factory.

Mary interrupted her, not wanting to have to listen to the bad language, 'It's alright Mam, I'll go ter the Labour this mornin'. I'll get somethin.'

'See that yer do then,' grumbled Kate, 'enough mouths ter feed, an' I'm not feeding one that isn't workin'.'

Mary immediately set about preparing herself for the job hunt. She combed her hair and rubbed her shoes over with an old rag. She'd have to look as respectable as she could to get a decent job, that's if there were any available.

'Did they pay yer up?' asked Kate.

'Nellie said she'd bring it fer me. It won't be much though, about eight or nine bob for last week. I'll be off now, but I'll be back as soon as I can.'

'See that yer do, you'll 'ave ter get the tea fer the others.'

Mary's stomach was rumbling for want of food, she had left her carry out at work. 'Never mind, there's plenty of people worse off than I am,' she consoled herself, though with little conviction.

She walked briskly along, trying to make the best of things. As she passed the school, she could hear, through the open window, children's voices singing. She had loved school, and cherished many happy memories. She quickened her pace, as it upset her to think of the better times she had spent there.

Mary's brow glistened with little beads of sweat as she sat opposite a bald, bespectacled little man at the Labour Exchange. He had friendly blue eyes and was clean-shaven, though the collar of his shirt was frayed along the edges. This was probably the only working shirt he owned. His dark, pin-striped suit was neatly pressed, and he leaned towards her in a friendly manner to put her at her ease, sensing instinctively that she was very nervous.

Mary proceeded to explain to him, in her best English, how and why she had lost her job.

'Good gracious me!' he exclaimed, sympathetically, 'that was a bit harsh, lass.'

Mary didn't comment, she just listened apprehensively, her eyes never straying from her interviewer.

'You know,' he went on, in his broad Lancashire accent, 'where I come from, I've seen youngsters like yourself, working in t' cotton mills, frae early mornin' till late at night, five and a half days a week, for only a few shillings. Little lads working in t' coal mines, an' then they talk about the negro slaves in America, working in the cotton fields. The children here are just as much in slavery.'

Mary listened enthralled. They were her views exactly, but she had never been able to express them properly to anyone else.

'Aye,' he continued, 'and they call this a free society. It's a mockery to civilisation, a disgrace to humanity.' Then he suddenly recalled that he was interviewing this girl for a job and handed her a form, 'Here lass, fill this in. If you've any problems with the questions, I'll give you a hand. Use my pen, it's better than a pencil.'

Mary reflected that she had never met such a kind, helpful, man in her life before. She took the pen that he held out to her, and completed the questionnaire in her very best handwriting.

'My, that's neat writing!' he exclaimed admiringly, as she handed it back to him. 'Sit in the waiting room now until your name is called.'

Still feeling nervous, she joined a group of other girls, wondering what kind of job she would be offered, if any. She thought of big, fat, Bess, the forewoman at the sweet factory, and prayed that her next boss would be kind and helpful, like the gentleman she had met earlier. Despite her dress being old, Mary looked quite neat, and her fresh complexion and golden shiny hair had impressed him. She was startled at hearing her name being called.

'This way, dear.'

She was ushered into a large room, where she had the feeling of being cut off from the outside world. There was a frosted glass window high up in the wall, making it impossible for her to see outside. She could hear the noise of trams in the distance, and a paper boy shouting his wares. She absorbed all this in a matter of seconds, as she was being introduced to a little man who was seated at a large desk.

He stood up and shook her hand. 'I am Mr Beiber, how do you do?' He sat down again and smiled at Mary, then he asked for Mr Tomlinson, Mary's interviewer, to come in. Mr Beiber called for tea and biscuits to be brought in saying, 'This girl is cold. Would you like some tea, Mary?'

After Mr Tomlinson had left the room he turned to her and began, 'Now tell me all about yourself, and which school you attended.'

Mary explained how she had come to be out of work, and how she cared for her young brothers and sister, supplying any details she thought he would be interested in.

'Well my dear, my mother's maid has left after fifteen years with the family, and we urgently need someone reliable, with good manners and a willingness to learn. Age doesn't matter, I can see by what you have just told me that you are quite capable of managing.'

Mr Tomlinson reappeared carrying a tray which he set down on the desk.

'Help yourself, Mary,' invited Mr Beiber.

Remembering her manners, Mary said, 'Shall I pour, Sir?'

'Please do,' he replied, approvingly.

She put the milk into the cups, then poured the tea. Sugar, Sir?'

'Er, no thank you, Mary.'

She handed him the cup, then sat down, having taken an arrowroot biscuit and put it on the side of her saucer. As she was nibbling at the biscuit, Mr Beiber sipped his tea, scrutinising Mary as he did so. He was ready for a cup of tea, as he had been interviewing all morning.

'Now then, my dear,' he continued quietly, 'I've already made up my mind.'

As he spoke, he pressed a bell on the desk and Mr Tomlinson popped his head round the door.

'No more interviews, we've found a suitable applicant, that's if Miss MacLean would like the position?'

'Would she like the position?' Mary was overcome, and could hardly believe her ears. 'Was Mr Beiber seriously telling her that she could have the job?'

'Oh! Yes, Mr Beiber! Thank you for offering the job to me. Oh! Yes, I would like to take it!' She was so excited that she didn't notice the two men smiling at each other, knowingly, agreeing silently that their plan had worked.

Mr Tomlinson was especially pleased, for he had discerned the girl's character in the first place and had recommended her for the job. The kindly man wished her all the best as he left the room and gave her a wink.

Mr Beiber then turned to Mary, 'Now Miss MacLean, here is a contract of your employment. Would you just care to read it?'

Mary glanced at it, knowing instinctively, that everything would be alright. Mr Beiber then took out his wallet and handed her a ten shilling note, saying, 'Take this, dear, you will need to get black stockings and any other items you may require. Your uniform will be at the house when you arrive. Oh! yes, of course, you'll want the address!' He gave Mary his business card.

She studied it and read, Mossley Hill, printed in gold letters.

'We shall expect you to live in, of course. You will have your own room with a wireless, and you'll take your meals with cook, in her kitchen. We will arrange for you to have three days off every two weeks, and a salary of two pounds each calendar month. 1 hope all that will be satisfactory?'

'Oh! Yes, Sir! That will be fine.' As she signed the contract, she wondered if this was all a dream? Was it really happening to her?

'Now then,' Mr Beiber said, 'when can you start? We really need you as soon as possible.'

'Will Wednesday be alright, Sir?'

'Yes, yes that will be fine. Oh! Here's your fare home. Mr Tomlinson told me that you had walked here,' and he handed her twopence.

Mary accepted the money and gave a little bob, 'Might as well get used to doing that,' she thought, then smiled and said, 'Thank you, Sir. Goodbye.'

After her departure, Mr Tomlinson congratulated Mr Beiber, 'I think you've made a wise choice, Sir.'

'Yes, indeed we have, haven't we? And such fine manners too, for a working-class girl!' replied Mr Beiber, highly-delighted with their morning's work.

In spite of feeling tired, Mary didn't take the tram home, she was so happy that she forgot her hunger and weariness. She clenched the ten shilling note in her hand, with the twopence wrapped up inside it, and felt like a millionaire.

'Wonder what Nellie will say when I tell 'er?' she pondered, as she made her way home. 'She'll be glad fer me, but we're goin' ter miss each other.' Her mind suddenly clouded over at the thought of what her mother's reaction would be?

'Would she be agreeable to her living out? Perhaps she should have asked for a day job, but she didn't want to miss this wonderful opportunity. Positions like this one were few and far between. 'Be positive, Mary,' she urged herself out loud, 'I'll get round her, have ter be tactful, but not deceitful.'

She looked about her, passers-by were looking at her strangely, as if they thought, 'Poor kid, talkin' to 'erself!'

'Well did yer get a job?' her mother barked, as soon as she entered the house, 'took yer long enough.'

Mary nervously crossed her fingers behind her back, 'I've to go back in the morning, it's a maid's job with a Jewish family. Very nice respectable people. If I get it, I've got to live in,' then she hurriedly added, 'so you won't have to keep me, and I'll be able to give you some money as well, an' there's a new uniform an' shoes.'

Kate was quiet, weighing up the pros and cons of the situation as she breast-fed Eric. 'She wouldn't be any worse off if Mary got this job, and she wouldn't have to keep her, and there would be money besides. She also considered how she would be able to brag to Meg and Bessie about her Mary, in service to a posh well-to-do family, and wearing a uniform as well. Better get down there in the morning, then. Don't go an' miss it. Do yer think yer'll get it?' she asked, eyeing her daughter with something akin to respect.

'Yes, Mam, I think I will.'

Mary couldn't believe what she was hearing. Was her mother really anxious that she should get the job, or did she see it as a step up the social ladder, even though it was only in a small way?

'Ere,' said Kate, handing the baby to her, unceremoniously, 'take yer baby brother, an' get 'is wind up.'

Mary took him and laid him over her shoulder, gently patting his back.

Meanwhile, Kate couldn't wait to race across to Bessie Mather's house and shout up the stairs, 'Can't come in Bessie, you know I 'aven't been churched yet. Just thought I'd let you know that our Mary's got a posh job, in a big mansion, see yer later, ta-ra.' She trotted off in an excitable state, feeling like a Rhode Island Red hen, that had just laid the world's largest egg, and cocking her head at passers-by. She was eager now to get back to Mary, to make her repeat the story, supplying all the details, so she could relate them to her friends and convince herself that it really was true.

Mary drew her face close to her baby brother's and kissed his soft cheek, 'Poor little lad,' she murmured. 'I've found a way out, and you're just starting out in life. I hope it's better fer you than it 'as been fer me.'

117

She paced to and fro with him across the kitchen floor, rocking him and humming a tune until, at last, he fell asleep.

CHAPTER TWELVE
Ten Green Bottles

Mary and Nellie were standing outside Travis's fruit shop.

'Yes,' Mary was saying, 'I start on Wednesday morning.' Her excitement was tinged with very real sadness at having to leave her friend.

'Gosh I'm goin' ter miss you, Nellie,' she took her pal's hand.

'Go on, soft girl, gerraway wi' yer, yer'll 'ave me bawlin' in a minute!' Nellie half-laughed, giving her pal a friendly shove, 'I'm really pleased fer yer, Mary.' She was sincere in her pleasure at her friend's good fortune.

'I'll not ferget ter get yer money on Friday, from fat-arse Bess.'

It always made Mary laugh when Nellie called the forewoman by that name. 'Thanks, Nellie, yer a good pal.'

At that moment, Jimmie and Arthur appeared, and Mary called over to them, 'Come on, let's go an' celebrate with a Vantas.'

'Celebrate?' queried Jimmie. 'Why? 'ave yer won summat?'

Mary explained to her brother about her new job, then added with an anxious frown, 'Don't tell me mam that I've already got it though, will yer?'

As the four of them sat on a long wooden bench savouring their bottles of fizzy pop, Mary went through all the details of her coming venture. Jimmie looked forlorn at hearing the news; he was certainly going to miss his sister, though he was genuinely glad that her life was changing for the better.

'Don't be sad lar, I'll be comin' ter see yer every month. Besides, you've still got Arthur an' Nellie.'

Nellie, who was sitting next to Jimmie, put her arm around him and said, 'It's okay, I'll look after yer.'

'Yeah, I bet yer will!' Jimmie carelessly wiped his mouth with his sleeve, and simultaneously shrugged Nellie's arm away. 'Come on, Art, let's go. Thanks fer the drink, kid.'

Arthur belched loudly as they plonked the empty bottles down on the counter.

'Don't be late 'ome either of yer,' Nellie called after them, 'an' say "excuse me", yer little pig,' she added, for Arthur's benefit.

The boys ran out of the shop and into the crisp autumn air, Smoke was ascending from the many chimneys, drifting and curling up into the sky like grey ribbons. The gang had assembled on the hollow waste ground between Roscommon Street, and the bottom of Bala Terrace. It had grown quite dark, and there were no street lamps near the wasteground.

Hambone was shouting out instructions to his mates, like a General drawing up battle plans for his officers. 'Now! Are yer all clear on what yer 'ave ter do? 'ave yer got yer bags?'

'Yeah!' each one answered in turn.

'Well then. Why the 'ell don't yer answer me?' Hambone turned to the small lads, 'youse two can keep watch. Yer can whistle I s'pose? Right then, whistle like 'ell if old Cocky, the watchman, comes prowling around, then run like 'ell!'

Arthur and Jimmie were despatched round to the front entrance of the haulage warehouse owned by Bout's, grumbling all the way.

'Aw! On the bleedin' watch again, it's always us,' Art moaned, angrily kicking a large stone along the ground. He rattled the big sliding door, obviously locked, then they positioned themselves in the shadows, keeping watch as they had been instructed.

'Ow the 'eck are they goin' ter get in 'ere?' Art asked his mate.

'Dunno. You tell me.'

The gang, one by one, had scaled the twelve foot wall, using foot holes that had been chipped out of the grey mortar in the wall, then they slid under three rows of barbed wire, edging their way precariously along the sloping roof. Occasionally a bat fluttered past startling them, and making the more nervous ones jump.

'Ell!' someone shouted, 'vampires!'

'Shut yer flamin' gob!' ordered their leader sternly. 'Right,' he said, 'who's goin' in first? Come on, Cleggie, it's not far ter drop!'

There was only a drop of a few feet to a landing which led to a wooden staircase, at the bottom of which were four huge lorries, loaded up and ready to be driven to their various destinations the following morning. The gang members descended silently in pairs, and made their way to their assigned vehicles. The smell of diesel permeated the whole atmosphere.

Hambone sat on the roof and waited, having tied a thick rope around his waist, ready to haul up their loot, and finally the gang.

The lads clambered up the bales of goods, holding firmly onto the rope that secured them, and selected bales that were in the centre of the load, so as to avoid any immediate tell-tale signs of a break-in the following day. The corners of the hessian bales were split open, and the contents scooped into waiting carrier-bags, the boys fumbled in the darkness, being careful not to spill anything.

The raid lasted twenty minutes, then Hambone, as arranged, hauled the bags up to the roof. The gang followed, one by one.

'Right!' hissed their leader, 'don't hang about, back to our house!'

With that, they all sped off down Lower India Street. No one was home, and the gang members emptied out their loot, one at a time, onto a large round table. There were dried apricots, prunes, currants, raisins and monkey nuts. They were shared out into equal parcels for each member of the gang. Leaving the house in pairs, they disappeared into the gloomy night to their various homes.

Kate didn't question where the goods had come from, with two carrier bags full, she was only too glad to receive her share of the luxury foodstuff. 'Don't eat too many of them nuts ternight,' she cautioned Jimmie and Willie, 'they'll bung yer up, an' chew 'em properly. They'll make yer belly bulge if yer don't.'

As she gloated over the supplies she added, 'I'll make some apricot tart termorrer, an stew some prunes, yer'll need the prunes ter loosen yer up after that lot!'

She decanted the produce into some empty jam jars, feeling quite smug at her good fortune. 'First her Mary getting the chance of a fine job, then all this stuff fer nothing. It had been a very eventful day.'

Jimmie poked his fingers into some empty monkey nut shells, like the fingers of a glove, and tapped them on the table top, 'Look,' he chuckled with his mouth full of soggy, half-chewed up nuts, 'Fred and Ginger doin' their stuff, dum diddly dum dum, diddly dum.'

'Knock it off, yer'll make yerself sick!' Willie complained. 'Tell 'im Mam, tell 'im ter pack it in!'

'Right, that's enough!' Kate ordered. 'Get up them dancers. You too, our Willie, move yerself.'

'Aw! Blinkin' 'eck! It's not fair!' Willie pinched his young brother's bottom as they climbed the dark staircase. 'See what yer've done, yer should 'ave kept yer soddin' mouth shut.'

'Yer did yer share o' moaning,' Jimmie retorted.

Willie dropped his trousers, ready to climb into bed, and Jimmie seized his opportunity and clawed at his brother's bare behind.

'Ouch! Yer little sod!'

Jimmie didn't hear anything else, because of the ringing in his ear from the heavy blow that he got in return.

Kate, her patience wearing very thin, yelled from the foot of the stairs, 'Be up there in a minute, if yer don't quieten it. Now get ter sleep the pair of yer!'

'It's not me Mam, it's soft lad 'ere,' shouted Willie.

Kate tapped her foot on the bottom step, pretending to go up, then everything went quiet.

The two lads were dozing off, but Jimmie couldn't resist having the last word, 'Ave ter change yer name, our Willie, 'ave ter call yer Jack.'

Willie took the bait, 'Why?' he asked, 'why Jack?'

'Cos yer jumped like a jack-in-a-box when I pinched yer bum,' laughed Jimmie. He got thumped for his effort, which quietened him down at last.

Mary stayed up with her mother, tidying up after the bags of dried fruit had been put away. The dying embers flared up as the empty nut shells were thrown into the fire.

'Better not be late in the morning,' said Kate to her daughter, 'yer gotta go an' see about that job.'

It had slipped Mary's mind that she had said she must go for the interview. She wanted the morning to herself to buy her stockings and a few other things. She knew that if Kate had discovered the ten bob, she wouldn't have had it for long. She hated lying, and turned away, her face reddening as she folded the baby's nappies. She was like Jimmie, her blushes always gave her away.

'What's the matter?' asked Kate, 'yer look flushed, not gettin' a cold are yer?'

'No Mam, er, I'll be fine,' she managed, 'I'll take the lads ter school in the mornin' an' go right after.'

Thankfully, her mother seemed satisfied, and Mary decided to make her escape while the going was good, 'I'll go up now Mam, g'night.'

She was taken aback by her mother's unusually gentle voice as she wished her goodnight in turn.

Silence finally reigned in the ever-bustling MacLean household, and Kate sat by the dying fire, the baby on her knee, sucking hungrily at her breast, as she reflected on the day's events, and wondered where her husband would be at this time?

'Probably sweatin' his guts out firin' the ship's boilers,' she said aloud.

Then she sang and rocked her child tenderly. '*Go ter sleep, my little pickaninny.*'

The following morning, Mary walked to school with Jimmie and Arthur, waving them goodbye as they walked through the gates. The boys sauntered into the school yard, mingling with the other boys.

'What yer got in yer pocket, Art?'

'Just brought a few prunes ter chew on.'

'Don't want ter eat too many o' them, they'll give yer the trots.'

It was at this point that Jimmie had what he considered to be a brilliant idea. 'Tell yer what, let's give some of 'em out ter them judies in Mrs Metcalfe's class.'

'Why? What yer up to?'

'Never mind, just give us an 'andful.'

Arthur still looked puzzled, but as he studied Jimmie's face, he slowly began to understand what his pal meant, and smiled slyly in anticipation of the fun they were going to have. They handed the prunes out to the gullible girls in the lower class, who took the bait eagerly and ate gluttonously, unaware that in a little while nature would inevitably take its course, and they would all be making a bee-line for the lavatory.

The school bell rang, and as they lined up, Mrs Metcalfe said sternly, 'You girls finish what you're eating. I don't want anyone eating in my classroom.'

Then they all filed past and into school. The two inseparables, marched smartly past Miss Lowe, 'Mornin', Miss,' they chanted in unison, smiling sweetly.

'Good morning, boys.'

The caretaker, Charlie Harris, was ambling idly past, carrying a wastepaper basket.

'Look at 'im,' sneered Art, 'tryin' ter look busy.'

'He will be in a bit,' replied Jimmie, sniggering at the thought.

The morning had dragged on slowly. Miss Lowe had asked the class to draw and colour a picture of their favourite fruit. As she walked up and down the aisles, she stopped at Art's desk.

'What's that supposed to be, Arthur?'

'A banana Miss,' then, under his breath to his pal, 'Charlie Harris'll go bananas in a bit.'

'And what are you drawing, Jimmie?'

'Dried prunes Miss. They're my favourite fruit.' He tried to sound innocent, but was unable to suppress a smirk. He suddenly realised that Miss Lowe was looking at him in a very strange way.

'You're not up to anything, you two, are you?'

'No Miss,' they replied, keeping their heads down and struggling to suppress their giggles.

'Right then, Jimmie and Arthur, do your little job now, take the milk round the class will you?'

Most of the bottles had been warming on the hot pipes, and it was distributed to the other children, along with the straws.

'Shouldn't be long now,' Art said, out of the corner of his mouth, as he passed Jimmie in the aisle, 'they've got it on the pipes in Mrs Metcalfe's class too!'

'I don't want an orchestra this morning,' Miss Lowe warned the noisy drinkers.

'What's she mean?' asked Art, opening his bottle gingerly.

'I mean,' said Miss Lowe, 'I don't want any slurping and noisy drinking. Just watch your manners and do it quietly.'

The empty bottles rattled and clanked as they were dropped back into the crates, and soon the classroom was vacated for playtime.

'Aw! We're always last out when we take the milk round,' moaned Art.

'Shurrup!' said Jimmie, 'stop yer moanin' an' look over there.'

Jimmie directed Art's gaze to the girls across the yard where they had resumed their game of skipping.

'Yeah, that's some of 'em,' agreed Art, pointing to the girls who had partaken of the forbidden fruit. The girls had their frocks tucked into their knickers and, as they jumped, they sang,

'Wallflowers, wallflowers, growing up so high,
We're all little children, we all have to die.'

They skipped and sang merrily, unaware of their onlookers.

'What yer thinkin', Jimmie?'

Jimmie's smile widened into a laugh, 'I was just thinkin' about them chewed-up prunes bein' swished about with the warm milk inside their bellies.'

The skipping and the song continued.

'Excepting little Betty and she's the youngest child.
Half a shame, half a shame,
Turn your face to the wall again.'

'Aye, yer'll 'ave ter turn yer face, when yer starts blowin' off,' guffawed the mischievous pair.

They had stopped laughing and were watching the girls carefully for any tell-tale signs, when it happened.

One of the girls suddenly let go of the turning rope as if it was red hot, and ran, clutching her backside, to the confinement of the playground toilet.

'It's started, they've got the rumbles.'

The two conspirators were highly delighted that their plan was working, and as a diversionary tactic, pretended to jump over an imaginary trench, throwing invisible grenades at an unseen enemy.

'Rat-tat-tat! Gotcher! Bang! Bang!' they shouted at each other, as they fired their imaginary machine-guns. Then they collapsed on top of one another, laughing hysterically.

The rest of the girls carried on with their skipping, taking no notice of their friend who had run off.

'Blue-bells, cockle-shells.'

The two boys watched intently, their disappointment growing that they had only got one of them, and as they were all called back into their classrooms, they wondered if that was all the excitement they were going to get?

'Ten green bottles standing on a wall.' Miss Lowe beat time with her ruler on the desk as the children sang along in class.

'And if one green bottle should accidentally fall.'

Art noticed the shadow of a girl as she hurtled past their door, and gave Jimmie a sharp prod with his elbow. Immediately afterwards, the tall figure of Charlie Harris ran the opposite way, to Mrs Metcalfe's classroom, awkwardly banging his mop bucket as he ran.

'There'll be nine green bottles, standing on a wall.'

And so the song went on, the children singing loudly, Miss Lowe walked down the aisles, conducting with one hand and pulling the window wide open by its cord, with the other hand.

'Must be sailin' a bit near the wind,' Art whispered.

As he spoke, the waving ruler in Miss Lowe's hand came down on his head with a loud thwack. Art resumed his singing.

'Eight green bottles standing on a wall,
Eight green bottles standing on a wall.'

The tall teacher peered over the partition into the next classroom, and spied Mrs Metcalfe holding a handkerchief firmly to her nose, and Charlie Harris mopping the floor furiously.

Miss Lowe turned and stared at the two mischief-makers, who were grinning and smirking at each other, and wondered suspiciously if they had anything to do with the events in the adjacent classroom? At the same time, she kept her makeshift baton beating in time to the groaning voices.

Soon other girls could be seen hurrying past, clutching their backsides, hoping and praying that they would reach their destination before catastrophe struck, but not praying as hard as Charlie Harris!

The caretaker looked hot and bothered, and rivers of sweat ran down his bald head and dripped off the end of his long nose, as he ran to and from the classroom, carrying fresh buckets of hot water and Aunt Sally and sawdust. In some cases tragedy had struck instantly, without warning, and the unfortunate girls had had accidents on the seats of their desks and were promptly sent home.

'And if one green bottle should accidentally fall,
There'll be nothing but the smell left
Hanging on the wall.'

'Glad we've got the inshore wind,' sniggered Jimmie.

There was a further commotion, as Mrs Metcalfe herded some of the girls outside the classroom, and Miss Bolt arrived on the scene to see for herself what all the fuss was about?

As soon as the pungent smell reached her nostrils she hastily retreated to her office, shouting as she ran, 'Send them home, Mrs Metcalfe will you?'

'What, all of them?'

'Yes! Yes! Let them all go home until tomorrow!'

'Cor! They're all goin' 'ome!' groaned Art.

'Yeah, an' it's not even dinnertime yet!' exclaimed Jimmie, 'but I'll tell yer what, I know someone who'll be too busy to get 'is dinner.'

Charlie Harris had his work cut out that day, he couldn't ever remember working so hard before, continually mopping and disinfecting the floors and desks, until all the nauseating smell had gone, replaced by the powerful odour of Aunt Sally.

The twelve o'clock bell rang shortly afterwards, and there was so much interesting activity, that Art and Jimmie were almost sorry to hear it. In fact, the whole school seemed to be involved, for that was the sole topic of discussion among the children.

Miss Lowe dabbed at her wrists and neck with perfume, 'Right,' she announced, appearing to be greatly relieved, 'you can all go now. I'll see you after lunch.'

The children poured out happily into the playground, Jimmie and Art shouting a cheeky ta-ra to their teacher. They chased after each other, singing at the top of their voices.

'Charlie, Charlie, chuck, chuck, chuck,
Went to bed with three young ducks,
One died, Charlie cried,
Charlie-Charlie, chuck, chuck, chuck.'

Miss Lowe watched the two rascals suspiciously as they ran out of the building but had no evidence to support her misgivings.

CHAPTER THIRTEEN
Poor Maggie

'There's a toothbrush and some Gibb's dentifrice,' said Mary, handing the gift to Jimmie, 'now brush yer teeth every mornin' and night. Don't ferget will yer? I've got the same fer meself, so when yer use it, think of me will yer?'

Then, turning to her mother she said, 'Here Mam, I got some scenty soap fer yer.'

Mary had spent the morning walking and browsing around the big stores, TJ Hughes, Lewis's and others. She was aware at times that she was being watched by floor walkers, but she was no thief, so she didn't worry, just kept her hands off the merchandise, until she had made her choice, then approached an assistant.

She bought her black stockings, artificial silk, but very smart, and three white handkerchieves. Then a little bit of luxury, a small jar of Pond's face cream.

'So you got the job, then?' enquired Kate.

'Yes Mam.' Mary waited apprehensively for her mother's next remark.

'Well I'm very pleased fer yer,' was her unexpected comment.

Mary breathed a sigh of relief. 'I start at ten in the morning; just thought yer'd like a little gift, it's not much, but I hope yer like it?'

'Yeah, yeah thanks,' and Kate put the soap to her nose, 'Mmm smells nice, ta, I'm sure yer dad'll be pleased fer yer as well.'

Jimmie had removed the pink cellophane paper from the toothpaste, and was peering through it at the sky outside, 'Cor! The sky's all pink.'

Then he set about brushing his teeth, 'Tastes nice, good enough to eat.'

'Well don't, it's fer brushing yer teeth with,' Mary warned him, 'so don't swallow it. Rinse yer mouth with water, then spit it out down the sink!'

'Hmm! What a waste,' Jimmie muttered.

'Might as well 'ave some mix fer tea,' chipped in Kate, her mood improving to match the occasion. 'Got yer dad's allowance terday; long overdue as well, 'ere get yerself a fish if yer like, the usual fer the others.' She handed Mary half-a-crown.

Jimmie looked on in disbelief, 'First at his sister, then at Kate, and wondered if his mam was going soft in the head, or was it old age or summat like that?'

'Don't bother gettin' our Bobby any, never know when 'e's comin' 'ome these days,' Kate added, frowning disapprovingly.

'Yeah,' agreed Jimmie, getting his little dig in as usual. 'It's ages since I clapped eyes on 'im, I've fergotten what 'e looks like.'

'Cor, just look at yerself in the mirror sometime!' Kate scoffed, 'that's who 'e looks like, at least 'e did, the last time I saw 'im.'

'I'd like to 'ave seen 'im before I go termorrer,' said Mary. 'Still never mind. Come on, Jimmie, let's go an' fetch the chips.'

Tea was soon over, and there was no washing-up, for they ate out of the papers, so there were only three chipped cups and a jam jar to rinse out.

Turning to Mary, Kate uncharacteristically suggested that she should go out. 'Go on then, yer can go out. I know yer dyin' ter go across ter Nellie's.'

For Jimmie this was all the proof he needed that his mother had finally flipped, especially when she then offered to do Mary's bit of ironing.

Mary had gone with Nellie up to Travis's to say goodbye to Tom, while the two mischief-makers squatted on Art's doorstep, discussing the day's events under their breath, laughing and sniggering as they recalled all the best bits. Then they started to sing:

'Our Sally's new drawers,
Our Sally's new drawers,
There's a hole in the middle, for Sally ter piddle,
In Sally's new drawers.'

'Wonder 'ow many cacked their knickers?' Art asked, nearly splitting his sides, with laughter.

Tears streamed down Jimmie's cheeks, 'I'll bet yer, ha ha! I'll bet yer they've been washin' an' dryin' 'em by the fire fer termorrer. Ha ha, ha!' and he was convulsed by another fit of uncontrollable laughter.

Bessie, Art's mother, shouted from indoors, 'Alright, we've 'eard yer, that's enough, yer like a couple o' mockin' birds.'

'What's mockin' birds?' Jimmie asked, with feigned innocence.

'A bird that mocks,' came Bessie's exasperated reply.

'Yer mean like the girls at school, that mocked their knickers?' asked Art.'

'Muckin' birds, ha ha, ha!' and the two boys roared all the more.

'It taught old Charlie Harris a lesson,' smirked Jimmie, 'bet 'e's still moppin' up.'

And so it went on between the two, joking as only Liverpool lads can do, until Bessie got fed up with it and shouted at them both angrily, 'Come on youse two, I told yer ter pack it in. Shut it now, or I'll shut it fer yer.'

'Aw Mam! We're only 'avin' a laugh. It's better than cryin' isn't it?'

'Aye, only at someone else's misfortunes, yer'll come ter a bad end the pair of yer. Ole Nick'll be rubbin' 'is 'orny 'ands, knowin' 'e's got yer in 'is 'orrible grip,' persisted Bessie, trying to frighten the two boys.

She had certainly succeeded with Jimmie, for his eyes widened, 'Hell!' he whispered to Art, 'what the 'ell d'yer think she means?'

'Take no bloody notice of 'er, the silly old cow,' Art assured him, 'reads too many tea-cups; gazes at 'em all day long, an' the way she oops, lookout! She'll change 'er tune in a minute, 'ere's Mrs Parry, the moneylender, ter get me mam's club. She'll reckon ter be out, that'll quieten 'er down.'

Suddenly all hell broke loose, as someone started shouting loudly, followed by a terrible screaming. It appeared to come from the lower part of India Street.

'Come on Art, let's go!'

The two raced off down the dark street, in the direction of the screams, and to the spot where a crowd had now gathered, They halted abruptly, and Arthur asked a woman bystander what had happened?

She didn't bother to answer, because just then Maggie Hislop was carried out of her shop on a stretcher, and lifted into the waiting ambulance. Her grey hair was matted with blood and the side of her face was bruised and swollen, as if she'd fallen heavily.

'Poor old soul!' a toothless old hag was heard to mutter, 'never did anyone any harm, she didn't deserve that, poor ol' queen.'

'An' robbed as well!' another woman exclaimed.

The lads listened intently, and watched as the policeman took statements from potential witnesses.

'Crikey! Robbed!' gasped Art. 'Hope the gang didn't 'ave anythin' to do with it, and got greedy an' raided the shop!'

'Move along then, the show's over.' One of the policemen tried to marshall the crowd that were hanging around, hoping to pick up some more juicy tit-bits to relate to their pals.

'Come on, go back to your homes,' he repeated impatiently.

'I saw 'im runnin' off!' came a voice from an open window, 'I saw 'im!'

The policeman looked up as the woman continued, 'Yeah, I saw 'im, 'e was a big feller. I can't walk, so I just sit at the winder an' watch people go by, or the kids playin' in the street.'

By this time, most of the sightseers had left the scene, so the policeman asked the woman, 'Is there was anything else you can tell me?'

'He was as big as a 'ouse side,' said the woman, gesticulating and enjoying herself immensely, 'he'd been angin' around the shop fer ages.'

The two boys stood within earshot. It was better than being at the pictures watching a serial, but they were very much relieved to hear that particular piece of information. It couldn't have been any of the gang, as none of them could be described as being as big as a house side.

'Yeah, at first I thought 'e was waiting fer somebody, but nobody else came, so I thought 'e must 'ave been up to no good, the big get.' At this point, the old woman paused for breath and folded her arms, delighted that she was being considered as an important witness. 'Then 'e went inside Maggie's shop. I saw 'im go in, then there was a thud and a scream. Maggie's scream, and 'e came dashin' out like a whippet, an' 'igh-tailed it down towards Greaty. Yeah, 'ands like shovels 'e 'ad, 'ands like shovels, stoker's shovels,' she added, for good measure.

'What's a whippet?' asked Jimmie.

'Sh! Sh! It's a grey'ound yer know!'

'Well, that's all I need for now,' said the policeman, closing his notebook, realising that that was all he was going to get at the moment, 'I'll send someone round in the morning to see you, so if you can remember anything else that might be important, you can tell them tomorrow. Goodnight to all of you, and lock your doors won't you?'

'Can't be any of the gang,' said Art, when the policeman had left, 'they can run, but they 'aven't got 'ands like shovels, none of 'em. Thank goodness for that!'

The two pals returned home and sat in the stairway, pondering who was home from sea and who had hands like shovels.

Arthur said, 'Who did it, Watson?'

'I'm not Watson, I want ter be Sherlock 'Olmes.'

'Alright then Sherlock, who did it?'

'Did what?'

'Bashed old Maggie's 'ead.'

Sherlock had no idea, and nor had Watson! So they both went to bed to sleep on it.

Time went by, and no one was ever brought to trial, or convicted of the robbery and violent attack on poor Maggie Hislop. Thankfully she made a remarkable recovery, but sold her business and retired to Southport, choosing the popular seaside resort, so that she could keep in touch with her friends, especially on the Twelfth of July.

Tim Cranley had also left the area, having moved right away from Everton in a hurry. The finger of suspicion pointed in his direction, but nothing was ever proven. It was also claimed that he had raped a girl in a back entry one dark night and given her a child, and desperately needed money to get away, so perhaps he had a stronger motive than anyone to rob old Maggie, but for what? Two pounds and ten shillings!

Jimmie and Arthur were aware of all the gossip going around about Cranley, and discussed it together, just as their heroes, Sherlock Holmes and Dr Watson would have done.

'I wonder if it was Tim?' Art pondered. 'But why?'

'I dunno, 'e didn't need ter pinch, 'e could 'ave boxed fer money, 'e was big an' strong enough, 'e'd 'ave taken anybody on anytime fer a few quid.'

'Maybe 'e's gone scrappin' in some fairground,' was Art's suggestion.

Jimmie was confused to say the least, all the ifs, whys, wheres and hows remained unanswered. 'It'll come out in the wash someday,' he sighed, exasperated.

'I was wonderin' when yer was comin' back down ter earth,' laughed Art, 'been watchin' smoke come out of yer ears fer the last ten minutes. Yer want ter tell yer mam ter give yer salt fish, fer it'll give yer brains.'

'If I 'ad plenty o' them, I wouldn't be 'angin' around 'ere,' he said, 'I'd be famous; manage Everton, an' Dixie Dean, or buy Aintree Racecourse, an' own a lorra 'orses. Maybe be boss over the docks an' ships, makin' lots o' dough, an' do yer know what I'd do? I'd give it ter poor people ter buy proper food an clothes.'

He was off on his daydreaming again. Art was used to this, and wondered if Jimmie would ever succeed in doing any of those things?

Arthur sniffed noisily, 'Yer goin' ter do a lot wi' yer money, if yer gets some aren't yer?' he asked. 'Yer'll 'ave nowt left fer yerself if yer give it all away.'

'What I do wi' me own money is my business, an' wipe yer snotty nose,' Jimmie retorted, haughtily.

Arthur chuckled, 'Ope yer do 'ave lots o' money one day, an' I 'ope I do too!'

CHAPTER FOURTEEN
Farewell Denny

Autumn turned to winter, and the cold, dark, nights were exciting and adventurous, especially now that the boys were accepted as gang members. Sometimes there would be an unexpected raid on a rival gang, resulting one night in Jimmie and Willie coming home with their heads split open. They had fallen through a skylight, but fortunately, had landed on some rubber tyres and heaps of sacking.

'Glad we made a soft landing,' Willie said, relieved.

'Soft landin'?' Jimmie screeched, 'I fell on top of you, you bony sod!'

Willie laughed, thankful that his young brother hadn't hurt himself, well not too much anyway.

One night the gang decided to take a ride on one of Bout's lorries, as it left the garage. They clung precariously onto the back by the rope that bound up the load, the same rope that they had climbed up to steal the dried goods the night they broke in. However this was different, this was fun. The lorry sped along at breakneck speed.

Hambone shouted, 'Okay you can let go now. All jump off!'

'Can't!' shrieked Jimmie in panic, 'it's goin' too fast!'

They had all jumped clear except Jimmie and Willie, and the gang watched helplessly as the loaded vehicle gathered speed and headed off down Walton Road and out towards Aintree, with Jimmie clinging on for dear life to the back of the lorry, Willie having dropped off at the last corner.

'Me mam'll kill 'im when 'e gets 'ome,' Willie wailed to the others, 'that's if 'e ever does get 'ome.'

Then, turning to Art, he added, 'don't blame me, it's not my fault, 'e should 'ave let go like the rest of us. Daft little sod, only 'ope 'e makes it fer school in the morning!'

They were all amused by that possibility, though Art and Willie were secretly worried.

The lorry eventually came to a road junction and it slowed down, which gave Jimmie the opportunity that he needed, as well as the courage to release his hold on the greasy rope, to which he had stuck like glue. He dropped off, painfully slapping his hands on the cobbles, and tumbling over as he fell. He immediately sprang to his feet, blowing into his cupped hands to relieve the stinging, then set off to walk back in the opposite direction.

Willie usually covered for him with his mam, but this time it didn't work. Kate waited up anxiously and it was past midnight when he finally showed his face, and got a leathering with the strap.

'Ow far did yer get?' asked Willie.

'Not far enough,' came the reply. 'Should've kept goin.'

Willie tried to comfort Jimmie, by reminding him that it would soon be Christmas, though they both knew it wouldn't be the kind of Christmas that most people would be having. The only indication that the festive season had arrived, was that Goodfellows sent round their parcels for poor families, each according to the size of the family. They were seven (six now that Mary was no longer with them), so they usually received a decent-sized parcel. The contents usually consisted of fresh fruit, a duck or a chicken, tinned fruit, evaporated milk and other items of food very rarely seen in thousands of poor homes, and of course, the ever-popular Christmas pudding.

Jimmie and Art and their families had their bit of fun trying to crack nuts with the heavy end of a poker, which sent the nuts and their shells flying all over the tiled floor.

That year, a few toys were included in the parcel, so Jimmie took possession of a toy motor car, Malcolm Campbell's 'Bluebird'. This was the only toy he ever owned, something that was really his, but eventually even that disappeared, never to be seen again.

Christmas was soon over, and in January 1939, Rob came home from sea. He had registered initially as a trimmer, sailing first down to Tiger Bay, Cardiff, from where he should have been home after six weeks, but because of an accident to one of the stokers, he was kept on in his place. So it was several months before he made his reappearance in India Street.

Rob was delighted with their new baby. He and Kate had chosen the name Eric, before he had gone away to sea. Rob talked of his adventures and experiences to Kate like a typical old salt, especially when he'd had one over the eight. It was at times like these, that Jimmie would hide under the big table to listen to his father's tales of foreign lands, far away. Perhaps one day he would go there too! Then, when his parents had fallen asleep in their chairs, Jimmie would creep up to bed unnoticed.

Willie had taken possession of Mary's small bed whilst she was away, so they all enjoyed a bit more sleeping space. Jimmie missed Mary very keenly, but at least she was happy in her new position with the kindly Jewish family. She had visited them only twice in four months, and then only for the day, but she always brought the money that she had promised to her mam.

Kate was glad to see her and called her queen, but Jimmie often questioned if it was really Mary that his mother eagerly awaited, or the money that she brought with her? Maybe it was a bit of both.

Jimmie often used to think of his favourite sister as he lay in bed and wondered what she was doing? Winter was always very cold, and he didn't know which was the lesser of the two evils. Shivering in the chilly bedroom, which he hated, or getting too hot and being bitten by the bugs in summer.

Art and Jimmie visited little Denny Rodgers on several occasions, but on one of these, Mrs Rodgers asked them not to come again, out of concern for the two lads, as Denny's condition had worsened considerably. Jimmie had tried to give the seashell to Denny the last time they saw him, but he didn't want it either.

Jimmie thought it very strange, and he gazed at the object for a long time. The sea had owned it for perhaps centuries, so maybe it wanted to be back home where it belonged, the little lad reasoned. It didn't want to be here among all the dirt and filth.

'Y'know,' Jimmie said to Art, 'Tess must 'ave been right when she said, "it doesn't belong to us, it's God's". Yeah, it's fer folk ter look at, but not ter take away.'

Jimmie became a little fearful of the shell, in case he had offended God, so he wrapped it up in a piece of cloth until he had decided what to do about it.

It was late January, and Art and Jimmie had been shopping with Jimmie's nin, then had delivered her safely home to China Street. It was bitterly cold, and the freezing mist rolled in from the Mersey. The sun had deserted the sky that day, and as the two boys made their way home, they watched their warm breath drift out into the cold, dank air. From somewhere behind them, they heard the clip clopping of horses' hooves. They turned around and were confronted by two large black horses, looking almost ghostly in the deserted streets, and behind them, they pulled a glass hearse.

The pair stood still, petrified, as the black-plumed horses and their sad train passed by. Another coach followed, again pulled by sombre-looking black beasts. The horses' eyes bulged alarmingly, as they glared angrily ahead; the whites of their eyes clearly visible, as they noisily clattered and clanked their polished hooves on the cobblestones. Occasionally, sparks darted from their shoes, as if they were trying to dig up the road beneath them.

The driver of the hearse was a sinister figure, haunched over his chargers, constantly tugging hard at the reins to keep the restless animals in check. It was difficult to discern his features, as his black-ribboned top hat was pulled down over his eyes, and a thick, dark, woollen scarf encircled his neck and mouth, keeping the wintry fog at bay. Only his long, sharp nose was visible.

The two boys made their way towards Bala Terrace, and Jimmie turned to his pal, feeling sick, 'See yer later Art,' he said, solemnly. 'Won't be goin' out again terday. Got summat ter do.'

The boys parted, each having realised instinctively that the funeral train was for their friend, Denny Rodgers.

Jimmie wondered why people didn't have white horses for funerals, like Hopalong Cassidy's horse Topper, and Ken Maynard's horse; that was white too. In the boy's mind, everything connected with black was sinister. He thought of the Pop matinee, and how the cowboy baddies were always dressed in black, and sneaky Ming, in Flash Gordon's *'Trip to Mars'*. Yes, Ming wore a long, dark cloak with a tight-fitting skull cap. They were all black, and even the droopy moustache and pointed beard were black. 'It must be the sure sign of a villain.'

Jimmie's thoughts then turned to his dad, and where he was and what he would be doing? 'Maybe he could explain all this to him?'

As he thought of his dad, he suddenly recalled, the silly coloured flowers, and their day out in Sefton Park, and he laughed. He decided he would stay in for the rest of the day, or 'rest on his oars', as the old salts would say. However he couldn't shake off a restless, agitated feeling, and he took the shell, still wrapped in its rag, from its hiding place under the bed. He went to the front door, and as if aroused from an awful nightmare, he sprinted off through the swirling fog.

How long he waited for the tram he never knew, he didn't even remember getting his connection to Aigburth from the Pier Head. Instinct directed him towards the cliff tops. His plimsoles squelched noisily through the sodden grass, and he stumbled and jolted himself repeatedly as he traversed the uneven ground.

Visibility was very poor, and the clinging fog rolled heavily inland from the river, engulfing him. The continuous wailing of fog-horns sent shivers down his spine, and once more his imagination took control over him. He envisaged men struggling, as they were sucked down into the murky waters, trapped in the wreckage of some stricken vessel. It was only when he caught sight of a small, bright light moving towards him, that these imaginings faded, and brought him back to the present.

As the light moved closer to him, he looked up and was confronted by a huge dark shape, like a giant bat, which seemed to hover over the light source. His heart thumped against his ribcage, and his tongue seemed as if it was glued to the roof of his mouth, so that he was unable to shout out, or call for help.

Then a broad Liverpudlian accent bellowed out, almost threateningly, 'What the Dickens are yer doin' lad? Yer'll be goin' over the edge, look just there,' and he pointed with his torch, which was the light that Jimmie had seen earlier.

Jimmie's fear melted away as he recognised the tall figure of a policeman, his cape spread out behind him. His eyes followed the torch beam to the place the policeman was indicating.

'See!' said the policeman, 'there's no fencing around this area. Some idiots must 'ave torn it down.'

Jimmie realised that this was the place below which the gang had been trapped and he shuddered. He unwrapped the shell, almost reverently, holding it close to him for a moment, as if saying a prayer, then flung it with all the strength he could muster, out into the darkness, and back to the sea.

'There yer are,' he whispered, 'yer back 'ome now, where yer belong. Yer out of it now, just like Denny is out of it, an Tess, our Mary, an' old Maggie Hislop.'

The policeman stood and silently watched this strange ceremony, his bicycle leaning awkwardly against his hip. He fingered the chin-strap of his helmet to get relief from it cutting into his red, chapped face. His grey eyes glinted, and tiny droplets of moisture clung to his brown, walrus moustache, and he wondered at this small lad.

'Where yer from, lad?'

'Everton. India Street, Sir,' croaked the boy.

'Yer've come far enough. Couldn't yer pick a better day than this? Yer scared me stiff; I thought I was seein' things. Just look at the state of yer, wet through yer are, 'ow yer gettin' 'ome?'

'Aye, yer scared me as well, I thought yer were a blinkin' bat. Yer gave me the shivers.' As he spoke, he extracted two crumpled, damp, tram tickets from his trouser pocket. 'That's how I'm gettin' 'ome,' he said, in answer to the policeman's question. 'The red one's fer the Pier Head, an' the yeller one takes me ter Neddy Road. I 'ad ter come. I 'ad ter put the shell back where it belonged, in the sea, that's where it lives.'

'Right yer are then, lad,' nodded his new-found friend, 'let's get yer 'ome. Come on heave ho!' He put his arm out and lifted the small boy onto the crossbar of his bicycle. 'Hang onto the 'andle-bars, yer can ring the bell if yer see anything comin', though I doubt it very much as it's a real pea-souper terday.'

He threw his own leg over the saddle and off they cycled, the policeman chatting to Jimmie as they rode along together.

'Wish I had a penny piece fer every lad I've taken 'ome on me bike. Aye taken off ships as well, so don't you be gettin' any ideas, me lad.'

The bright beam of the bicycle lamp penetrated the darkness and the fog, and soon they reached the tram terminus, much to Jimmie's disappointment, for he was enjoying the ride and liked the policeman.

He thought to himself, 'I've never met such a kind man, an' a bobby at that!'

The policeman waited with him until the tram arrived, and indeed, it was a good thing that he did, for the tram wouldn't have stopped but for the policeman shining his torch at the driver.

Jimmie turned to his friend, 'Thank you, Sir. Thanks fer the ride.'

'Get along 'ome wi' yer, an' pick a good day next time.' Then, turning to the conductor he said, 'See that this lad gets 'is connection at the Pier Head, will yer?'

'Sure, sure,' the conductor replied.

As the tram moved off, the policeman called after him, 'What's yer name, lad?'

'Jimmie Mac. Jimmie MacLean.'

The policeman was swallowed up by the mist as the tram glided away.

By the time Jimmie had almost reached home, his hands and legs were blue with cold. As he walked along near Denny's house, he passed a group of old women, huddled together, wrapped in black shawls. They were the moaning minnies, who attended funerals, and who were supposed to comfort the bereaved.

'Like a lot o' bleedin' ravens waitin' ter pounce,' he muttered scathingly, as he reached the door of his house. 'Can do wi'out that whingein' lot o' cows.' Jimmie crossed the threshold to be greeted immediately by his mother's scolding.

'W'here've yer bin? Just look at yer, yer wet through an' freezin.'

Kate turned the lump of coal over on the fire, so that it blazed cheerily, then she pushed aside some steaming nappies that were drying on the fireguard. 'Ere,' she said, 'come an' get them wet clothes off, an' warm yersef.'

Jimmie's face gradually grew ruddy as he started to thaw out, and as he stared into the flames, tears appeared and rolled down his cheeks and into his mouth leaving a salty taste. He thought of poor Denny, all alone in the cold ground.

Kate looked up as she mopped the floor, 'It's alright now, 'e's not sufferin' anymore.'

'Think so Mam?' Jimmie sobbed, mopping up his tears with the rough towel.

'Yeah, course 'e's alright,' Kate went on, 'e's got no pain now.'

'Tell yer one thing Mam,' Jimmie said, as he turned to warm his bottom.

'What?'

'e won't be pestered wi' bedbugs anymore.'

'Come on now, let's 'ave yer face washed. Yer look as if yer've been follerin' the pigs up Plumpton Street.'

They both laughed.

Jimmie felt that his mother, for once, was showing some sympathy, and that she really understood his feelings. 'Yes perhaps she did, perhaps it was the life she'd had to endure that had made her seem hard. Perhaps she was afraid of getting hurt, which happened if you were soft, especially in the poor area in which they lived. He had seen another side to his mother today.'

After the cold winter, the warm spring sunshine was a welcome sight indeed. People emerged from their homes like animals reappearing from hibernation. They didn't get much out of life these poor people, but those of them who were a bit better off owned a wireless set, complete with accumulators, which Jimmie and Arthur would take to the nearest garage for recharging, and earn a ha'penny or two for their trouble.

Art's mother, Bessie, had a wireless. Of course, she didn't have as many mouths to feed, so her husband had been able to buy her this luxury item, on his last leave.

One day Bessie commented about something she had heard on the wireless set that she felt was quite important. 'Lucky if any of us get to Southport this year,' she said to Kate.

'Why? Whadder yer mean?'

'Why, 'aven't yer 'eard the news?' asked Bessie, knowing full well that Kate hadn't. So she proceeded to tell her. 'It's that German feller - Hitler, causin' a lot o' trouble in Europe, an' 'is stooge, Mussolini.' She became quite animated as she related the latest events. 'Yeah, killin' and lockin' away a lot o' Jews in prison camps, smashin' all their shops, breakin' into their 'ouses, an' wreckin' things. It's terrible!'

Kate listened intently, as Bessie made the most of her opportunity and rambled on about the invasion of Poland, Czechoslovakia, and other places that Kate had never even heard of.

'Hope Rob gets 'ome before anything starts up 'ere,' she said, 'the last one was bad enough. Our Mary works fer some Jews, and very nice people they are too. It's a shame!'

Mary came home for a day in April, and was able to tell them of the personal suffering of the Beiber family, who had lots of relatives in Germany. The Beibers hadn't heard from them recently, so naturally they were very anxious and feared the worst.

'Ow nice you look, princess,' Kate said to Mary, 'an' 'ow grown up you're gettin'.' Kate was so very proud of her daughter.

Mary took off her coat.

'Ere, let me put it over the chair fer yer. Ooh what a lovely coat!' exclaimed Kate admiringly, stroking the garment, as she laid it carefully over the chair. 'So, 'ow 'ave yer been keepin', chuck?'

'Fine Mam, just fine. It's a very good job, an' the Beibers are very nice to me. I get plenty to eat, my own room, and even a wireless.'

'Wireless! A wireless! 'ave yer really got a wireless of yer very own?'

Mary laughed, 'Of course I have Mam. The Beibers have three wirelesses in the house, as well as mine and cook's, an' when I've finished work at night, usually around seven thirty, unless they have friends in, I have a hot bath…'

At this point, Kate interrupted her with, 'A bath? Do yer get one every night?'

'Let me finish Mam,' Mary smiled at her mother's simplicity, though she would never ever look down on her, or her family; Mary wasn't that kind of girl. 'I listen to stories on the wireless and poetry and music. Perhaps I'll write some stories myself one day. I'd like to. Mrs Beiber is so kind to me. She has given me some nice things to keep, like this handbag. She loves my hair too! Hers is jet black, and I brush it every night for her…'

Once again Mary was stopped from continuing her tale, this time by her friend, Nellie, who had just heard of her friend's visit.

'Hiya kiddo!'

The two girls hugged each other, 'Well, just look at yer,' said Nellie, holding her friend at arm's length and inspecting her, approvingly, 'Yer've put a bit o' weight on, an' yer've grown. It must be all that good food, an' what a posh dress. An' just smell that scent!'

Mary was amused by Nellie's comments but protested, 'Hey! hang on, I'm still the same Mary.'

'Yeah,' agreed Nellie, 'but look 'ow posh yer are. Isn't she, Mrs Mac?'

Kate proudly surveyed her daughter and nodded her assent. 'Ow long are yer 'ere for?' she asked.

'Well, I'm meeting Mrs Beiber in town at Bunny's.'

'Cor!' exclaimed Nellie very impressed, 'that's a snooty place. Yer've ter pay just ter go in there!'

'Mr Beiber is picking us up in his car later,' Mary added, for good measure, enjoying the effect all this was having on her audience.

Kate's chest visibly expanded. She was so proud of her daughter, and wanted the whole world to know it! She poured out the tea she had just made and handed Mary the best cup, 'Ere y'are, queen,' she said to Mary, 'yer don't take sugar do yer?'

Then she turned to Nellie, 'I'll just go an' 'ave a word wi' yer mother,' and she handed Nellie her tea, then left the girls together.

Kate ran out of the house, clutching Eric under her arm, anxious to get across to Bessie's to brag about her Mary's good fortune. Meanwhile, the girls talked and laughed and also cried a little, over the times they had shared together.

Suddenly Mary leapt to her feet, 'I'll have to get going, Nell.' She glanced at her watch, 'I'll try and stop a bit longer next time.' Then she grabbed her black leather handbag and took something out for Nellie. It was a small, gift-wrapped package.

Nellie couldn't believe her eyes when she opened it, for inside the wrappings was a bottle of Evening in Paris perfume. She was delighted and gave Mary a big kiss.

Mary put her coat over her arm and, as they reached the doorstep, was staggered to find that all the neighbours had gathered to see her off.

'Gosh!' Mary cried to Nellie, 'look at all that lot!'

They heard someone comment, 'Isn't she a nice girl?'

Another said, 'She's a real smart lass. I always knew she would be.'

Kate's heart was bursting with pride.

'Come on youse two,' called the tram conductor, smiling, 'let go of one another if yer wants ter get on. Don't know what yer'll do if war comes.'

Jimmie and Art arrived just in time to see everyone waving Mary off, and poor Nellie sobbing and crying into her cupped hands.

'Gosh!' Jimmie cried, 'it's our kid, an' I've missed 'er.'

He was quite upset and Art seeing this, grabbed Jimmie's arm and yelled, 'Come on run!'

They ran along Netherfield Road, trying to keep up with the tram and Art whistled noisily.

An old man tapped Mary on the shoulder, 'Think them two lads are tryin' ter catch yer attention.'

Mary turned and looked, just in time to see the breathless pair. They had stopped running. She waved back furiously as Jimmie and Art stood gasping for breath. She struggled to hold back the tears that sprung into her eyes and wondered when she'd see Jimmie again?

CHAPTER FIFTEEN
Ta-ra

'But it's the Isle of Man sign,' protested Jimmie.

Art was trying to explain to Jimmie the significance of the swastika signs that someone had daubed on the doors of Santini's garage.

'Yeah, but it's got another leg on it,' Jimmie argued.

'Slimy bloody I-ties! Get back ter I-tie land, an' Musso, where yer belong!' people would shout at the Italian immigrants, as they passed by the door.

All this didn't make sense to Jimmie, and he couldn't understand what was going on and continually asked questions of Art.

'Why 'ave people written that on their door? 'ow do you know about all this?'

'Me mam tells me everything,' Art replied, 'she 'ears things on the wireless.'

'Santinis sell blinkin' good ice-cream any road,' Jimmie added positively.

'Better not let the gang 'ear yer say that, scatterbrain!' Art looked very serious as he spoke, 'they'll bloody well kill yer!'

'I don't care,' retorted Jimmie, defiantly, 'it's not right. The Santinis 'ave lived 'ere a long time; they don't cause any bother. It's our lot that fight, not them.'

As war approached, two policemen patrolled Roscommon Street more often than they used to do, in case of any trouble over the immigrants. Despite this, one night Santini's garage was raided and wrecked. Their ice-cream vans were destroyed, and tins of diesel oil were poured into the cream.

Sacks of cornflour were ripped open, and the contents scattered around.

Kate was bothered by the news, keenly aware of the general feeling among young and old at that time.

'You 'aven't been round there, wrecking that garage, an' doin' all that damage 'ave yer?' She glowered at Willie, 'an' you too, Snooks, you weren't there I 'ope?'

'No we weren't there Mam,' the boys assured her.'

'See that yer don't then. Them I-ties'll cut yer tails off. They've long knives down their socks; don't trust them lot!'

If Kate had wanted to frighten them, she had certainly succeeded, as far as Jimmie was concerned, but Willie just laughed.

It was only a matter of days before the Italian family moved away, loading a big lorry with freezers, electric generators and other equipment. Another van came for their furniture and away they went. Nobody knew where to, but they weren't really interested; they'd got rid of the enemy just as they'd intended.

Jimmie and Art enjoyed the summer months in Miss Lowe's class. She often took them on afternoon trips around Liverpool, to the Museum or the Walker Art Gallery. They also played football at Club Moor, or went to Sefton Park or Stanley Park, and she always took an enormous bag of assorted biscuits with her as her treat for the children.

Miss Lowe was a popular teacher, well-liked by all, not just because of the outings and the biscuits, but because she took a genuine interest in her pupils, and possessed a kind of magnetic charm which attracted them to her.

On one such trip to Sefton Park, as the kids were romping and playing on the grass, a rag-tatter yelled out noisily across from the big houses, that were on his patch.

'Rag bone! Rag bone!' Other words were called too, but they were incoherent.

The incident made Jimmie remember when he was over in Sefton Park with his old feller, trying to sell the gaudy flower-pots and he chuckled at the thought.

The rag-tatter called again.

'Poor old sod,' Jimmie commented out loud, 'it's just a labour o' love ter 'im, that's all it is.'

The people of Liverpool waited with the rest of the world for the outcome of what seemed inevitable, and wondered how it would affect Britain?

The Orange Day march on the Twelfth of July 1939, helped the locals to forget, for a while, the forthcoming troubles, as the threat of war loomed ever closer.

Everything passed off just as in previous years, with everyone determined to have a damn good time There were the usual dancing, singing, merriment and laughter, and also the drinking which led to the inevitable fights.

Kate and Bessie didn't go to Southport this time and only watched the parade. Kate, of course, now had Eric to look after and Rob was away at sea. Bessie's husband, too, was with his ship, and so the two women comforted each other, as good friends do.

Jimmie and Art were due to go up into Prince Edwin Street School, which was annexed to Netherfield Road. They were both very sad, as were all the class, at the prospect of having to leave Miss Lowe.

Towards the end of August, the world news became more and more serious, and Bessie had her ears glued permanently to her wireless, straining every ounce of energy out of it until the machine fell silent, and the accumulator had to be recharged.

Jimmie and Arthur had to walk very carefully with their heavy containers, so as not to spill the acid onto their socks, or worse still, their legs. They regarded it as a dangerous mission, but a very necessary one.

'Yer know Art,'said Jimmie on one of these missions. 'Yer mam reminds me of a wireless operator on a sinking ship, waiting to pick up signals, and the signals getting weaker an' weaker.'

It became obvious that war was imminent, and on the 28th August, gas masks were issued. People were then told how to build shelters, though not supplied with either the tools, or the equipment to do the job, at least not in Jimmie and Art's area.

The two pals leaned on the railings on the landings, they had an excellent view of what was going on, and observed the events in India Street and Bala Terrace, not appreciating the seriousness of the situation.

Men, women and children all joined together, like an army of ants, digging away, making big holes in the dry earth with shovels, picks, pokers or anything that would serve to prod or scrape a hole in the ground.

'Just look at the silly devils,' scoffed Art, 'more Irish navvies around 'ere than I thought. Them 'oles'll be full o' water if it rains.'

That was as far as the building of their air raid shelters proceeded, at least until they were built on a large scale by the authorities, or until proper equipment was made available. It looked as though giant moles had invaded the streets, or a team of archeologists had discovered some ancient ruins. Still it kept people busy, and alerted them to the imminence of war and the need to protect their families.

Jimmie's dad came home on the 30th August and immediately set off to join the Royal Navy. He was prepared to serve King and country once more, as he had already done in the Great War.

Kate returned from shopping late one Friday afternoon, having bought white plimsoles, a blue jersey and navy-blue trousers.

'Boy! Them's great Mam! Are they fer me?'

'Yeah,' she answered, 'an 'ere's a new toothbrush fer yer. Yer needed a new one, looks as if yer've been sweepin' the chimney wi' that one our Mary bought yer!'

Jimmie wondered what was going on as he stood and examined his old toothbrush. He thought of Mary and wished that she was here. She would explain to him the significance of all the hustle and bustle in the household.

'I'm goin' across ter see Art,' he told his mother, 'be back soon.'

'Art would know what was happening,' he thought, 'because if his mother didn't tell him, Nellie would.' He met Arthur coming out of his house, and before he even asked, Art blurted out the news.

'Yer'll be goin' ter the countryside pal, out of all the trouble, an' the Germans.'

'What d'yer mean, the countryside. Where's that?'

'Don't rightly know, Jim.'

'Are you comin' as well?'

'No,' came the sad reply, 'yer goin' wi' your Lily.'

'Well I'm not goin' then, I'm stoppin' wi' you an' the gang. We'll show them Germans, we'll get our poles, an' catapults, an' wait fer 'em comin', an' we'll fight 'em,' he stated emphatically.

'Come on, now youse two,' put in Bessie, who had overheard their conversation and was feeling upset, 'it'll all be over in a few months, might not even start at all.' She didn't feel at all confident of that herself, but tried to console them by saying, 'Yer'll be back tergether again before yer can wink.'

'But I want you to come, Art.' Jimmie was bewildered, and couldn't understand why his best pal wouldn't be going away with him?

'Me mam said, yer stoppin' 'ere wi' me, an' that's flat!' Art mimicked his mother's voice and mannerisms, and succeeded in making Jimmie laugh.

'There yer are, I made yer laugh. Come on don't worry, me mam says it'll all be over with soon.'

Jimmie was crestfallen, and could not believe that he was unable to persuade Art to come to the countryside with him, 'Okay then Art. See yer around mate, so long,' and he walked off, feeling totally lost.

'Yer'll 'ave ter look after Lily,' Kate was saying to Jimmie.

'But she's only seven Mam. I can't look after 'er,' he protested.

'Then yer'll 'ave ter learn! It's best fer youse two, an' best fer us,' she insisted, 'it won't be long before our Willie leaves school, so it's no good 'im goin'. I'll only 'ave Eric ter look after 'ere, an' it'll be safer where you're goin'. There's 'undreds goin' from your school, an' St Augustine's, an' all over Liverpool, an' all over England, so yer won't be on yer own. Yer'll make new friends.'

'Are we all goin' ter one place, then? There's goin' ter be a heck of a lot of us.'

'No, yer'll be goin' ter different places.'

'How far is it then? 'ow long will we be stoppin'?'

'Yer ask too many questions. Go out an' play wi' Arthur.'

Kate turned away to hide a tear, but Jimmie saw it, so didn't ask any more questions.

Jimmie and Arthur went to the Pop matinee on Saturday 2nd September. There were the usual scraps and skirmishes in the queue outside, as well as the inevitable shoving and pushing. It was a nightmare for the old man whose job it was to hold back the howling kids, and prevent them from stampeding into the cinema, without paying.

'If I'm not 'ere next week, will yer let me know 'ow Flash Gordon gets on wi' the Claymen?' asked Jimmie.

'Yeah sure, course I will,' promised Art, with a lump in his throat. 'We'll go up ter Spot's when we've 'ad us tea, an get a ha'penny punch. I'll treat yer.'

'No, it's my treat. I'll 'ave a penny left, an' it's me what's goin' away, so it's me what's buyin,' insisted Jimmie, feeling grown-up all at once, and rattling the money in his pocket.

'Okay then,' agreed Arthur glumly, dreading what would be their last time together.

As they walked home from the cinema, they hardly spoke to each other. Everything still seemed to be just the same; women were coming out of the wash-house carrying bundles of clothes, their hessian aprons tied around their middles.

Art shouted across the road to a tall woman, 'Got yer old feller's drawers clean, Missus?'

But somehow the wisecracks and funny jokes didn't seem to be quite so funny anymore. All the sparkle had gone out of their good-natured teasing. Even the women who were being teased sensed this and didn't curse them back.

As they dawdled along, they kicked at a piece of orange peel between them, until it dropped down a drain. They trudged solemnly back to India Street, fully aware that this might be their last Saturday afternoon together for a very long time.

'Are yer goin' across ter see yer pal?' Kate asked Jimmie, without looking up from her ironing. 'Yer'll be goin' termorrer.'

'No, I don't feel like it. Besides our Mary might come.'

Jimmie rolled the Hotspur, Rover and Knockout comics that Willie had given him, into a tube, 'Ave yer got a garter, ter put round me comics, Mam?'

'No. 'Ere, tie 'em up wi' this,' and she handed him a piece of string.

She carefully folded the children's clothes that she had just ironed, and placed them in the bottom of two pillowcases, 'Now look after these won't yer?' All yer clothes are in 'ere, an' yer comics as well.'

Kate wetted an indelible pencil with her lips, then wrote her children's names, and the names of their schools, on the brown labels that they had been given for that purpose.

Jimmie managed to raise a smile at seeing his mother with the blue marker, as he recalled how he and Art had scribbled a game of Oxo on Bobby Gilbert's pot leg.

'Yer can still smile then?' Kate asked, as she noticed him chuckling to himself.

He looked up to see his mam tying a label to the half-empty pillowcase.

'There,' she said, 'an' there's another label ter tie on yer jersey termorrer, so's they'll know who yer are.'

Sunday 3rd September was a beautiful, warm day, and hundreds of children were assembled at Netherfield Road, Prince Edwin Street, and St Augustine's schools. Each child was labelled and clad in the best clothes they were able to muster.

Kate said to Jimmie, 'Yer know yer should 'ave gone ter see Art before yer left, ter say ta-ra.'

But that would have been too much of an ordeal for the little lad. It was bad enough having to go away at all, but to have to say goodbye to his best pal, especially when they didn't know if they would ever see each other again, was just too much to ask, and he knew that Art would feel just the same.

The assembled children were given a packet of biscuits and a half pound bar of Cadbury's milk chocolate, and told to save them for the journey.

Jimmie packed his and Lily's away into the white cotton pillowcase that he carried saying, 'Hope they won't melt!'

Some of the kids had eaten theirs before they'd even left the assembly point, with the result that many of them were sick either before, or on the journey.

Jimmie caught sight of Miss Bolt, and Mrs Metcalfe, along with his new teacher, Jock Marshall. They were counting and re-counting, checking and re-checking the parade of children.

'Please Miss,' said Jimmie, addressing Miss Bolt.

'Yes, Jimmie, what is it? Be quick lad.'

'Where's Miss Lowe? I can't see 'er.'

'Oh! Miss Lowe's not coming, she's staying behind.'

Jimmie's heart sank with yet another disappointment. It wouldn't have felt quite so bad if Miss Lowe had been coming with them.

'Now stay in line children,' called one of the teachers, but Jimmie wasn't listening.

'What's up wi' you, our Jimmie?' Lily asked him.

'Aw shurrup! It's bad enough you taggin' along wi' me,' he snapped.

Lily immediately started to cry at her brother's sharp words, 'Gonna tell me mam when we get 'ome, you'll see!' Lily must have thought she was off on a day out to Southport or somewhere. She was too young to understand.

'Yer not goin' ter start yellin' are yer?' Jimmie pleaded, less harshly, and hastily grasped her hand in his, 'Come on, we're goin' now!'

The large army of schoolchildren filed out of the schoolyard, four abreast. They carried an assortment of pillowcases, battered suitcases, brown paper parcels, in fact anything at all that would hold their meagre belongings; each one was labelled clearly. Each child had their gas mask, in its easily-recognised square box, carefully slung around their neck on a piece of string. They were all highly-excited, and chattered away fifteen to the dozen, many not realising that this wasn't a holiday, but a serious evacuation in case of trouble, or at worst, a bombing.

The evacuation had been well-planned, and those children who were struggling with their loads, were assisted by attendants, school staff, welfare workers and officials. The convoy of children swayed along Shaw Street, like a giant snake, then traversed down through the great city. The noise was deafening, but above the screaming, laughing and crying crowds, someone had started to sing:

'Wish me luck as you wave me goodbye.'

'Wish they'd shurrup,' Jimmie complained, turning to his sister. 'Silly devils, don't know what they've got ter warble about?'

He sniffed loudly, trying not to show his feelings in front of his young sister, as he didn't want her crying again.

'Look, we're here now,' he said, nudging Lily, 'that didn't take long did it?'

Megaphones echoed throughout the station, calling out teachers' names and classes. Then excited youngsters were helped onto the LNWR train, its big engine waiting like some huge, mythical dragon, hissing and spurting out steam from its nostrils, ready to take its unusual cargo to a safe destination.

Jimmie turned and glanced back at the barriers. Crowds of women were waving frantically, almost climbing over one another in their desperate efforts to catch a last glimpse of their departing children.

Suddenly he grabbed his sister's arm, 'Look! It's me mam! There she is! There! She's come ter see us off!' He waved back to his mother. He wasn't really sure whether or not Lily had spotted her, but she waved all the same.

Kate's eyes were red and puffy, and tears were streaming down her cheeks. It was impossible to hear her voice above the deafening noise of the crowd, and besides she was too far away anyway.

She waved sadly, 'Goodbye Jimmie, ta-ra, son, I love you,' at least that's what she seemed to be saying, though Jimmie couldn't be sure.

At last they had all boarded the train, and Jimmie sat morosely, silently staring out of the window. He was longing to see his pal, and fervently wished that he was coming too. 'Wonder what Arthur's up to?' he muttered to himself.

The train whistled loudly as it left Lime Street Station, and as it rolled and gathered up speed, and the carriages clanked noisily over the lines and points, it seemed to be chanting.

'A way out at last, a way out at last.' He spoke the words out loud, and Lily studied him as though he was daft.

But he repeated them, this time with more conviction, 'Yeah it is, this is the way out.'

Part Two
WELSH SCOUSE

CHAPTER ONE
The Journey
September 3rd 1939

Clouds of dirty, grey smoke belched from the black locomotive as it laboriously and deliberately dragged its eight, heavily-laden coaches along the North Wales Coast. Its piercing whistle could barely be heard above the din of the children on board, who were enjoying a once-in-a-lifetime experience. For some it was an adventure, for others a holiday, yet no doubt all of them were apprehensive about their future.

The war had come suddenly, rescuing many from their small, dark, terraced homes in the slums, with their dirty back streets and entries. That squalor was now far behind them.

They hadn't known any other way of life, never before having ventured over the boundary of the inner city. Poverty and filth had been their inevitable lot. None of these children were aware at this moment in time, that fate had intervened, and each of them was now heading for an entirely new way of life, a way out, away from Liverpool.

The city had made thousands of people very prosperous, but had also left hundreds of thousands poor, miserable, hungry and without hope.

The teachers and volunteers accompanying the vociferous, whining juveniles, hadn't anticipated the amount of work that would be involved in caring for such large numbers. Their day had started early, not only packing and preparing for the journey, but mustering the children at their various schools and assembly points, counting and checking their enormous brood, which had been no easy task. They also had to take the place of mothers, nursemaids and lavatory assistants when necessary, using their limited medical skills to cope with cases of travel sickness, or overindulgence in the free chocolate, biscuits and drinks. Whatever the cause, the staff were stretched to the limit.

Some of the little ones fretted and cried, and wanted to get off the train to walk back home, whereas the unruly and hard-necked brats thought it was all a game, and did their best to harass their carers and make their task more arduous.

As the train thundered noisily along, Lily stirred uneasily in her sleep. She opened her eyes, then slowly realised where she was, as she glimpsed telegraph poles seemingly whizzing by. She scratched her mop of auburn hair, then tried to smooth it down with both hands, to the sides of her tear-stained face.

'Gosh! It's about time yer woke up. Yer've bin leanin' on me, an' I've got cramp, an' pins an' needles in me arms,' complained Jimmie, rubbing his freckled arm. 'Are yer okay? Do yer want a biscuit, Lil?

Cor, look at the sea, it's blue! Different colour to the Mersey isn't it?' He soon forgot his aching arm, as he excitedly took in the new sights out of the carriage windows, 'Look over there,' he shouted, pointing to the other side of the carriage. 'Look, cows an' 'orses, an' look at dem fellers stickin' big forks in the grass an' pilin' it up, bet dat's good fun, doin' dat. Warra they doin', Miss?' Jimmie bounded over to the opposite window to get a better view.

Miss Crosby, who was in charge of the group in her carriage, smiled at the excited lad, 'Why, they're haymaking, Jimmie, getting all the dried grass in for the winter to feed the cattle.'

'There's piles of it!' he gasped. 'Where are dey gonna purrit all?'

'They put it into huge buildings called barns, then it's pressed well down, so don't worry, they'll get it all in to be sure. Tell you what,' said Miss Crosby, changing the subject, 'can you keep an eye on this little feller for me? I'll only be a few minutes, there's something I need to see to.'

Jimmie stuck out his chest at being asked to do something for Miss Crosby. 'Come on, lad, yer can squeeze in 'ere wi' me,' he coaxed the lad in a friendly fashion, as he made room for the small boy. The headmistress gave the child a gentle push towards the beckoning Jimmie.

Then, turning to the rest of the children, ordered in an authoritative voice, which her charges instantly recognised must be obeyed, 'No noise now, and stay in your seats. D'you hear me?'

'Yes Miss Crosby!' came the childish chorus from the twelve kids in her care.

She then steered her broad backside through the sliding doors, drew them together behind her, and waddled off down the corridor, in the direction of the toilet. She smiled and waved to the staff and children in the other compartments, and awkwardly tried to keep her balance as the train swayed from side to side, then she lunged through the narrow door of the WC.

'Thank goodness it's vacant,' she sighed, puffing and panting after her ordeal. After relieving herself, she washed her hands and splashed them with cologne, as she gazed into the dusty oblong mirror. She looked at herself critically, then addressed her reflection, 'Good gracious. What a wreck, is that really me?'

She then adjusted her thick, lisle, stockings, arranged her grey hair, then pinched her cheeks to bring a little colour into them. It was good to be alone for a few minutes, even in this tiny, smelly cubicle. She sighed again, tucked her pink silk blouse into the waistband of her black tailored skirt, and in an undertone, muttered, 'Once more into the breach ...!'

Her blue eyes, the dominant feature of her round, friendly, face, seemed to lack their usual sparkle. 'Come on now Gertie, pull yourself together, this war's going to upset a lot of people, but at least we can try to be pleasant.'

With one last look in the cloudy mirror, she pressed with her finger the unsightly mole on the side of her chin. Then hurriedly as an afterthought, she applied a pale pink lipstick, almost smudging the side of her face as the carriage suddenly jerked, momentarily causing her to lose her balance. She arduously manoeuvred her bulky, rotund body back down the narrow corridor. She reached her compartment and heaved back the doors with renewed vigour. She took a deep breath, then resumed her command.

'Come on, you lot,' she barked across to a couple of girls playing imaginary hopscotch, 'back to your seats.'

Everyone who knew Miss Crosby held her in respect, and she was greatly admired for her untiring work with the poorer classes of people in Liverpool. Her attitude was not affected by colour, race or religion, and her unstinting efforts stemmed from her Christian principles and love of humanity.

No one seemed to know anything about her origins but, an old Irish woman once said of her, 'From Heaven.. Aye from Heaven itself. She floated down to us, sent by the good Lord Himself.'

Once, she was asked if she had a family of her own, and she replied, 'Of course I have, just look around you! All these are my family, wonderful people they are and I love them all, and they love me. Why, I can walk the streets of Chinatown day or night without fear. I've lived with these people for the past thirty years, and the Scousers love me.'

During those thirty years she had acted as peacemaker in many a neighbourhood, and had stood defiantly between both Catholic and Protestant families. Against the odds, she had managed to bring out the best in them, relieving tense situations, and even creating friendships between people of different religions. Yes, these were definitely Miss Crosby's family!

She settled herself comfortably in the carriage, 'Ah! That's better! Now then, little Edward, what have you been up to while I've been away?'

'Is that 'is name, Miss?' asked Jimmie. 'He wouldn't say his name, an' he's lost 'is label from 'is jersey. I've been tryin' ter get 'im ter say summat, 'e's not dumb is 'e?'

Lily calmly made a suggestion, 'Maybe he's peed 'imself.' Then, straightening her dress over her knees, and looking at Miss Crosby with a sweet smile on her face, she giggled behind her hand, as little girls often do.

'No, I don't think so,' laughed Miss Crosby. 'At any rate, he'll be alright with you two. He has no brothers and sisters, and he's only seven-years old.'

Jimmie, who couldn't help feeling sorry for the underdog, patted Edward on the shoulder in almost a fatherly fashion, 'Come on now Eddie, 'ere, 'ave a chunk o' this,' and he handed him some milk chocolate.

At the crinkling sound of the silver wrapping paper, ten pairs of greedy eyes surveyed the delicious offering.

'You lot can take your beady little eyes elsewhere, you've guzzled all yours,' Miss Crosby warned.

All the eyes immediately focused back on their comic books. Two girls, who had found a piece of string, reverted to their game of cat's cradle, and the rest just whispered and sniggered amongst themselves.

Jimmie then piped up, 'What shall I call yer? Eddie or Edward?' his voice muffled by his mouthful of chocolate.

'Edward, call me Edward. I don't like that name Eddie. Besides, me mam calls me Edward,' came back the small voice, sniffling.

Jimmie was taken aback by the quiet but firm reply. Miss Crosby, who had been checking documents relating to the evacuation, had also been observing this little scene from the corner of her eye and interjected, 'That's alright, Jimmie, his name is Edward. Edward Eric Jones, and with a surname like that, he's going to live in the right place.'

'A place like what, Miss? What place are we going to?' Jimmie's vocal chords were still clagged with the contents of his mouth sticking to his tonsils.

'Bangor, in North Wales,' announced Miss Crosby.

She gazed around at the group of tired little faces, each one displaying a puzzled look, for they had obviously never heard of such a place.

'Wales?' murmured Lily, nibbling on an arrowroot biscuit, 'I thought whales were big fish that swam in the sea.'

Her feet were swinging to and fro and she was eager to get involved in the conversation. Now and again, she pulled at the tight elastic on the legs of her knickers, as they were causing her some discomfort. They were really a size too small, but they were the only ones available that her mother had been able to buy at the last minute.

'No dear,' corrected Miss Crosby, 'Bangor, in North Wales, is a very nice city, and I'm sure you're all going to like living there.'

She smiled reassuringly at the children, and tried to refocus her thoughts onto the problem of getting all of them housed with decent families before nightfall.

'Is it as big as Liverpool, that city, Bang-er?' chirped one curious lad. 'Is it Miss?'

'It's not Bang-er; we're not talking about firecrackers lad, it's Bang-or, Bangor,' came the patient explanation.

To herself she thought, 'Hell! I'm going to have a right job on, educating this little lot.'

'Right, Miss. Bang-er, Banger, I gerrit.'

Sensing a challenge to her authority in this cheeky repetition, Miss Crosby decided to dismiss the matter before it got any further out of hand. She shook her white, scented, hankie in the boy's direction, and gave him a long, withering, look, which threatened retaliation should he start up again. It did the trick, and the matter was closed forever.

Lily, who by now had finished her biscuit, was still thinking of Welsh Wales in terms of huge fish, and cried out with a flurry of biscuit crumbs cascading from her open mouth, 'Wonder if yer can get salt fish in Bang-er? We used to 'ave salt fish every Sunday fer our dinner.'

'That's nice, I'm sure,' came the reply from the harassed Miss Crosby.

Suddenly Lily broke into song, spattering everyone within reach, with the remains of her biscuit crumbs,

'Sally Army, salt fish,
Three ha'pence a dish,
If yer don't like it, don't buy it.
Sally Army, salt fish.'

Miss Crosby seized this opportunity as a cue for getting the children involved in a song. The long journey had left them all, including herself, very tired.

'Let's have a sing-song,' she suggested, trying to sound jollier than she actually felt, 'how about *Old MacDonald*?'

'Aw! It goes on too long,' moaned the 'Bang-er' boy. Then, turning to his mate, suggested, *Ten Green Bottles.*

Miss Crosby readily agreed. Anything to keep them amused, she thought, and she proceeded to lead them in song.

Jimmie's mind instantly raced back to the time when he and Art had had Netherfield Road Junior school in chaos. The lovable Miss Lowe had had them singing the same song, when the notorious prune incident caused uproar in the next class. Jimmie was propelled back to the present by Miss Crosby's chirpy voice.

'Come on lad, sing up!'

The happy group sang on, each bottle accidentally falling in each verse. They were, for the moment, contented and excited, as the train raced along the Welsh coastline to its destination.

CHAPTER TWO
Bangor - North Wales

It was almost 2.30pm when the monstrous engine finally ground to a halt, crunching, hissing and groaning like a wounded leviathan. The platform had been deserted, but not for long, as the children started to disembark from the packed carriages.

A cacophony of sound replaced the tranquillity of the station, as the evacuees tumbled sleepily from the train. With pillowcases over their shoulders; some carried battered suitcases tied round with string, whilst others, more fortunate, carried haversacks. Round each young neck hung the inevitable gas mask, on string which chafed and throttled. The little army was marched, in some disorder, into the station yard. They had finally arrived in the city of Bangor!

The train driver and his mate, with sweaty, coal-smudged, faces, leaned over the side of the engine, 'Wouldn't like the job of sorting that lot out 'Arry. God bless the little mites, there'll be more than a few tears flowing tonight, both 'ere and in the Pool.'

The driver turned away sniffing.

Harry, his mate, tapped the steam pressure gauge, trying to look busy, a lump coming up into his throat. 'We'll take 'er away into the sidings, 'Arry, 'till we get the go-ahead. We'll 'ave a bit of tucker 'till they're ready for us.' His voice was sad and quavered with emotion.

'Are yer okay, Bill?' asked Harry. 'Got a cold comin' on?'

'Yeah, I'm okay, bit of a sore throat as well, be right when I've 'ad me brew,' Bill said gruffly.

The two women teachers scanned the length of the train to make sure that no one had been left behind, and that all packages and parcels had been removed. Apparently everyone had been accounted for, so now the job of sorting the milling throng of bewildered children into smaller groups, was to be put into operation. Once that had been completed, these groups, together with the people in charge, headed out of the station yard for various locations around the Welsh towns, villages and mountain farms. Those groups who were going to the more isolated locations travelled by green Crosville buses.

The train driver, who had been observing all these goings on with his mate, sounded a final farewell blast on his whistle and a hoot from his engine, and everyone responded by laughing, cheering and waving as they departed for their unknown destinations. Most of them would be likely to be placed in the outlying areas around Bangor, such as Bethesda, Rhiwlas, Tregarth and Mynydd Llandegai.

Miss Crosby and her staff had been met by officials from the Bangor Council, and were now guided by these along Deiniol Road, to Garth Road, in the direction of the pier, wishing that public transport had also been provided for them, but at least the children seemed relatively happy to be off the train and using their legs again.

'Hurry up, gerra move on, Lil,' Jimmie called out to his sister. 'Yer marched better than this wi' the Orange Lodge.'

He was holding onto young Edward's hand, as he had been ordered to by Miss Crosby, though he would have done so anyway, as he had taken on the role of big brother, and had become attached to him.

He humourously nagged his two charges, 'Cor! Of all the kids I've gorra look after, an' I've got youse two.'

'Aw! Look what you've done, our Jimmie, yer've trod on me new pumps. Me mam'll kill yer, she blancoed 'em last night. Yer did it on purpose,' Lily accused him.

'Shut yer face, an' get goin', or yer'll be left behind in a foreign country or summat,' snapped Jimmie, as he slid the sleeve of his new jersey across his runny nose.

He certainly was weary, and two other kids to keep an eye on, after all, he was only ten-years old himself, but he never felt sorry for himself, and always tried his best to be a man.

'Come along now, children, we haven't got very far to go,' said Mrs Metcalfe, trying to sound as cheerful as she could.

Her voice was barely audible above the hullabaloo, and she could see the children were tired and beginning to drag their feet and lag behind. In fact she was worn out herself, and would be glad of a sit down.

Jimmie was so anxious about his responsibilities, that he didn't notice at first, that tears were streaming down Edward's face. He squeezed his hand reassuringly, and whispered kindly, 'Come on now, lar, if yer don't like it 'ere, I'll take yer back termorrer. How's that?'

Then, trying to distract him he added, 'See that big 'ill over there?' nodding his head in the direction of the Cathedral, 'well, we'll go an' climb up there if yer want to. Yer'd like that wouldn't yer? Bet yer can see the Liverbirds from up there, an' can yer smell that? Breathe in, breathe out. Yer can breathe in can't yer?'

'Smell what?' sniffled the younger boy, who by now had forgotten what he was crying about, 'can't smell nuttin.'

'The sea, the sea, can't yer smell the sea? If yer lick yer lips yer can taste the salt. That's gonna be the gear, we'll be able ter watch the biguns come an' go,' said Jimmie excitedly.

'Biguns? Whadder yer mean?' asked Edward, his tears now completely dried up.

'Big ships an' all dat. Cor, don't know much do yer, Eddie lad? Oops! Sorry Edward!' Jimmie corrected himself.

'Anyway, yer'll feel better termorrer when yer've got used ter things an' all dat.' Jimmie was issuing directions as if he had lived in the area all his life.

Miss Crosby noticed this and smiled approvingly, knowing that she had made a good match with these two lads. A green Crosville bus passed by and she called out, 'Wave, children! Wave!'

The driver tooted his horn, and the kids waved back at them through the windows, and cheered at the top of their voices, some of them making rude gestures, until the bus was out of sight.

'Cheeky young so-and-sos, I only hope I get my hands on some of them in school. I'll teach them a few manners!' spouted Miss Crosby, to a scarlet-faced Mrs Metcalfe. 'Mind you,' she continued, defensively, 'I don't think they're any of our lot, but whether they are or not, I'll give 'em some earache if I do come across them again.' She giggled to herself like a schoolgirl, after all, they were only having a bit of fun after being cooped up for so long on the train.

The afternoon sun was uncomfortably hot as the band of evacuees turned right off Garth Road and into Glynne Road, stopping at St Mary's Church House.

Miss Crosby flicked her cologned hankie across her face and urged, 'Come on now, try to smarten yourselves up a bit, neat marching lines please.' She sounded like a company sergeant major and she knew it!

They did look a sorry sight, as they shuffled along in their badly-fitting shoes. Some of them had flopped to the ground with their meagre belongings through sheer exhaustion. Some slouched awkwardly against pebble-dashed walls, others sat in the shade, trying to cool their little bottoms on the hard pavements.

By this time, some groups of local women were gathering opposite in Orme Road, eyeing the unsightly cavalcade, and conversing with each other in a strange tongue, obviously discussing these little strangers, which the war had brought so suddenly to their city.

It seemed like hours to the kids, yet it was only a few minutes before a tall, lean woman by the name of Miss Davies, the supervisor of the WVS, emerged from a semi-detached house across the road.

She wore a grey uniform which matched her hair, and carried a black leather briefcase. She marched, hand outstretched, towards her old friend Miss Crosby, and greeted her warmly, 'You finally made it then, Gertie?'

After speaking to Miss Davies in like manner, the headmistress then introduced her staff.

Whereupon, Miss Davies said, 'My own staff will be here shortly to assist in the billeting. It's choir practice you know. I knew they'd be cutting it fine for your arrival,' she tutted.

'Cor! There's a bleedin' war on, an' all they can talk about is choir practice,' blurted out one cheeky boy, who got a swift slap on the head from Mrs Metcalfe for his trouble.

Five more women, obviously Miss Davies' staff, straight from choir practice, didn't look too happy, as they converged on the group. After all, they had had to cut their practice short, having had only an hour, instead of the usual hour and a half, which was a sin in itself in Welsh Wales.

Each member of staff sorted her own group according to their ages and sex. Brothers, sisters and family members were kept together, as far as possible. Some of the bystanders, who had been watching with interest, eagerly consented to take some of the better-dressed children into their homes, having first pick so to speak. This being approved of course, by the WVS.

Unfortunately, Lily was placed in a different group from her brother, and though she sobbed that she wanted to be with Jimmie, she was persuaded when he reassured her, 'Go on Lil, yer'll be alright, I'll see yer termorrer when yer gets settled in.'

Although he didn't know where he would be himself at that point, he knew that Lily would be in Orme Road, and he would knock on every door until he found her the next day. Jimmie and Edward were the last of Miss Crosby's group still to be billeted.

They were led from house to house, in and out of garden gates, but just one look at the scruffy little urchins was enough for the householders to say a polite, but firm, 'no thank you.' They even resented the fact that they had dared to trespass in their gardens. In some cases, curtains were pulled discreetly aside, and the occupants wouldn't even come to the door.

'Don't worry now, lads,' Miss Crosby consoled them, 'if we don't get anywhere for you to stay, you can come and stay with me for a little while until we manage to get you fixed up.'

The mere mention of staying in the same house as Miss Crosby frightened Edward out of his wits, and he turned pale at the thought.

'What's up, lar?' asked Jimmie, 'feelin' sick or summat?'

'No, I'm alright but I'm goin' ter keep me fingers crossed fer the next house.'

Miss Crosby led the boys through the next wrought-iron gate and down the path. Little squares of garden, containing fragrant, brightly-coloured wallflowers, bordered the crazy-paving pathway; their scent was always associated with wartime memories by Jimmie, in later life.

The strange-looking trio halted in its tracks as the front door suddenly opened. A hazel-eyed, auburn-haired, woman in her early thirties, stood and stared in amazement at the three strangers. She slowly wiped her hands on her multi-coloured apron.

'Good afternoon, my dear,' said Miss Crosby, politely, 'I'm sorry if I caught you at an inconvenient time. My name is Crosby - Miss Crosby. My mission is to find a home for these two boys who are the last of my group. They are evacuees from Liverpool. It would be very kind of you if you could agree to have them. That is of course, if you have a spare bedroom. They are exhausted, and I must admit, rather dishevelled, but they have had such a long and tiring journey and need a rest, a meal and a good sleep.'

The young woman didn't reply, but instead called out for her husband, in a strong Welsh accent, 'Hywel! Hywel! Can you come here for a minute?' She brushed her short hair back from her forehead as she called again, 'Hywel! Oh! There you are!'

A large, bald-headed, man loomed over the small boys; his brown, sun-tanned, chest was covered in dark hair, and he was dressed in shorts. It seemed likely that he had been sun-bathing in the back garden. He apologised to Miss Crosby for his appearance, as his wife put him in the picture.

'Hywel, they're evacuees, looking for accommodation, just for the two boys. Oh! and this is Miss Crosby who is in charge of them.'

The young woman had a beautiful voice, soft and melodious, quite different from that of her husband when he caught sight of the lads.

'My God! Heavens above! Where on earth have you found these two?' He scratched his bald head and muttered, 'God forbid, bechod!' Then, 'yw eich enw?'

'Hywel please, they're not Welsh, they don't understand,' interrupted his wife.

'I'm sorry, please forgive me, Miss Crosby.' He found it difficult to take in the situation and the spectacle before him.

Miss Crosby smiled her sweetest smile and said, 'We have travelled from Liverpool today. There's been quite a large evacuation, and no doubt many more children will be following. Not all of them will be coming to Bangor, of course. My main concern is to get these two housed before nightfall. They're the only ones left in my group. I can tell you, we're desperate!' Miss Crosby stressed these last three words with vehemence.

'And I can understand why!' exclaimed Hywel.

'Just a minute del, bach,' his wife chipped in, 'let the lady finish what she's saying, dear.'

Then, turning to Miss Crosby, 'please excuse him, he's upset to see the state of the children. It really is heart-breaking.'

'Well,' said Miss Crosby, on the defensive, 'you can't go off looks you know, these two are good boys. All they want is a good hot bath, a meal and a change of clothes, then even their own mother wouldn't know them.'

She also told the couple that there would be an allowance for each child, and eventually parcels of clothing and shoes would be distributed for them.

'We don't know how long this war is going to last and it's a big responsibility to have the children to care for. In a way, their future is in your hands and people like you, the Welsh people, so far, have shown great hospitality to the new arrivals, but I expected that. I know many Welsh people myself.'

To herself she thought, 'Gertie, you are soft-soaping again,' but she just smiled and wrapped her arms around the boys' shoulders, like a mother hen protecting her chicks.

It was Hywel who spoke first, having digested Miss Crosby's little speech, 'You are a very persuasive woman, Miss Crosby. I'll tell you what, as you are so desperate, we'll take them for a few days, until you can get them fixed up somewhere else. I don't think we can take them on a permanent basis.'

Hywel looked at his wife, helplessly. She responded, 'Oh! I think we can give them a trial. Don't you think so, bach?'

'Right you are then, del.'

Then speaking to Miss Crosby, He said, 'Leave them here.'

Miss Crosby's heart jumped for joy, and, without any hesitation, in case these nice people changed their minds, she produced a fountain pen and thrust it into Hywel's big hand, 'Sign here, please. Oh! and thank you so much,' she gushed.

The official papers were signed, the simple formality was over. She then turned to the youngsters and, reverting to the Scouse tongue that the boys knew so well.

She warned them, 'Now youse two, behave yerselves. Don't let me down, or yer'll get it good and proper, Ta-ra now. See yer at school.' She patted each boy on the head in an affectionate gesture, then hurriedly made for the garden gate, as if afraid that the young couple might have a change of heart.

She waved a cheery good-bye, very relieved that she had succeeded in housing her last two charges. On her way up Glynne Road she muttered to herself under her breath, 'Cor! I'm gasping for a brew. I'm parched.'

On nearing Miss Davies' residence, she spotted her friend in the garden, watching her as she came up the road.

'I see you've done it, Gertie. Well done!' Obviously referring to the absence of the last two of her charges.

'Phew!' gasped Gertie, puffing and blowing, her chubby cheeks rosy as apples. 'Aw! My feet are killing me, well not so much my feet as my new shoes. I'll give 'em a good soaking later. My feet I mean,' she laughed, easing off the offending shoes, as she sank into an easy chair in the comfortable parlour.

'You poor dear,' sympathised Miss Davies, 'it's been a long day for you, hasn't it?'

'Too long,' agreed Miss Crosby, 'and maybe it's not over yet for some poor kids.'

She sipped the hot tea from the china cup that her friend had placed in her hand, feeling satisfied with a job well done.

Miss Davies, after sitting quietly with Gertie for a few minutes, left the room. She would run a nice hot bath for her dear friend, who by this time, had dropped off to sleep, her tea only half drunk.

CHAPTER THREE
Settling In

'Leave your bags there,' the big hairy man instructed Jimmie and Edward as he stepped outside, his sandalled feet slapping the concrete drive as he walked. He ushered them down the side path of the house and called out to his next door neighbour.

'Bob! Are you there, Bob? Have you got a few minutes?'

'Be with you in a jiffy, Hywel,' came Bob's voice from behind a huge, neatly-trimmed, privet hedge.

The boys followed Hywel through a tall wooden gate, to a small, recently-cut, lawned area, with pretty flower borders. A long, grey-coloured shed, dominated the bottom of the garden and matched the surrounding trellis fencing and gate.

Jimmie, eyes were everywhere, taking in everything at once, spotting a well-laden apple tree, and directly opposite, a young pear tree bearing a few pears.

'There you are now, my beauties,' came the voice from next door.

'Must be Bob,' thought Jimmie, and wondered why this Bob was calling them 'his beauties'. He soon realised that his words were not directed at them but at his pets; two wire-haired fox terriers, as they scurried noisily around their master's legs, playing and jumping with excitement, fresh and lively, feeling good after being clipped, brushed and powdered. Bob Jones was proud of his dogs and possessed many certificates and rosettes for his earnest efforts at dog shows.

'Stay now, stay!' he commanded, but the frivolous animals were too fidgety to obey their master, and sped off towards Bob's house, disappearing through the back door.

'Silly little buggers they are at times,' he laughed, as he approached his neighbours. 'Now! what have we got here, boyo? Evacuees is it? Well, well, well!'

'Want you to do a little job for me,' said Hywel. 'Can you cut the boys' hair, Bob?'

'Certainly,' he replied, smiling from ear to ear like a wide-mouthed clown, and without further hesitation, he drew his steel grooming clippers from the breast pocket of his brown smock.

'Now, who's first?' he asked, waving the clippers menacingly in the air.

Jimmie and Edward were made to strip to the waist, and a tall wooden stool was brought out of the shed. Edward shivered and shook at the prospect of his hair being cut by this strange man, wielding the horrid-looking clippers, and he slunk behind Jimmie, hoping that no one would notice him.

'Righto, we'll have the oldest first then.' Bob smiled at Jimmie, as he lifted him up onto the tall stool. A 'doggy' smell wafted from him into Jimmie's nostrils. He blew on the shears and clicked them, as would a Spanish dancer with his castanets, doing the flamenco.

'Ah! Shame! Bechod!' commented Bob, as Hywel explained the boys' situation. The big rough hand clutched Jimmie's forehead to hold it steady, as locks of auburn hair descended onto the grass.

'Ouch! Ouch!' came Jimmie's painful cries, muttering under his breath all the while, something about 'bloody foreigners.'

The teeth of the clippers didn't always nestle into their original grooves when the handles were squeezed together. So they plucked and pulled, leaving ugly red patches on Jimmie's scalp.

Meanwhile Edward, on witnessing the operation, and so much hair falling onto the grass, started to cry, thinking to himself that there was hardly a cow's lick left.

'There now, boyo. That's better! You look like a new man now,' Bob declared, proudly, as he lifted Jimmie off the stool.

Jimmie felt his head. It tingled and he muttered angrily, 'Hell! What a crop!'

Bob laughed as he clicked his shears in joyful anticipation of his next customer, 'Next please!' he called, ignoring Edward's reaction.

There was a struggle when Edward was lifted up by Hywel, his legs kicking furiously in all directions, and he was forcefully held still by Hywel, whilst the hair-cutting ceremony commenced. The youngest customer had more red blotches on his scalp than his predecessor, because in addition to Bob's uncontrollable clippers, he struggled and jerked his head all the way through the proceedings.

In the meantime, Jimmie was preoccupied with trying to alleviate the itching on his neck and back, as tiny loose hairs were now clinging with sweat to his little body. He also had to contend with the flies which were busy flitting around him.

It was hard work for both men to hold Edward still. His face was red and hot, and wet with sweat and tears, but his ordeal finally came to an end and Bob gave him a playful tap on the head, 'There you are, bach!'

The small lad was swung from his perch, and after Hywel had thanked Bob profusely, he led the boys into the house, through the hallway and into the kitchen, which overlooked the garden, or was it the barber's shop?

'My! That's better, isn't it?' said Beth. 'Come on lads, sit down,' she clucked, like a mother hen.

She pushed a plate of neatly-cut sandwiches in front of them. 'Come and eat,' she invited them.

Jimmie thought he had never seen such luxury as this ham on the sandwiches. Cups and saucers were on the table, with plates to match them; cream-coloured, with a green edging. There were also spring onions and tomatoes, thinly-sliced, no doubt grown by Mr Hughes, for that was the name of the people whose house the boys were to live in.

'There you are now, boys,' coaxed Beth. 'Bechod! Poor lads, shame!' This last expression she murmured in a soft voice as she patted both little bald heads. Then, as an afterthought, she rubbed her hands on her apron, just in case!

Beth and her husband had eaten earlier, so they just had a cup of tea each. Hywel rubbed his hairy arms. He sported a Hitler-type moustache, which twitched from side to side whenever he was excited, or about to speak.

Beth sat opposite her husband with her back to the sink, Jimmie was on her right, with Edward on Hywel's left and next to Jimmie. Both boys faced the window. This was to be their seating arrangement for the next three years.

'Come on, boys, eat up, get cracking. You'll never be able to box if you don't eat,' said Hywel, clenching his fists and folding them under his large biceps.

Jimmie thought he was a big show off. In fact, Mr Hughes' biceps were nowhere near as big as Tim Cranley's. Jimmie ate ravenously, and he remembered his pillowcase still at the front door and the remains of his chocolate, which by now would probably be melted.

'Me bloomin' gassie as well.' They had been told never to go anywhere without their gas masks, not even to the lavatory.

Edward still hadn't moved, except to hang his head on his chest. So far he hadn't eaten a thing. Hywel stood up, drained his cup, then walked over to the sink and put it down on the draining board.

'You drink your tea too hot, Hywel bach,' Beth scolded, 'not good for you.'

'Ooh! it's not too bad,' he replied, dismissively, leaving the kitchen. 'See you later, Beth.'

It was only then, as Hywel left the room, that Edward reached shyly for a sandwich and tentatively took a small bite.

'Good, isn't it?' Jimmie said, finishing his third one.

'Now then lads, eat up, there's fruit and jelly to finish off with,' said Beth, as she busied herself in the kitchen.

'Can't eat any more, Missus, thank yer,' said the older boy, patting his belly. 'I'm f'lup.'

'Surely not, you'll have to eat more than that,' Beth said to Jimmie, as she placed her cup and saucer on the draining-board.

'Me too Missus, I'm full too.'

As if it was an afterthought, Edward pushed his plate away, leaving half a sandwich hanging over the edge and touching the table.

'Put yer buttie on yer plate properly, an' just look at all them crumbs,' admonished Jimmie, giving him a sharp nudge.

Edward was annoyed at Jimmie's attitude, and gave him a withering look, 'Aw! shurrup!'

Jimmie responded with another elbow dig, 'I'll shurrup yer cheeky little sod. Looks as though I'm gonna have ter look after youse, so yer'd better behave yersel. D'yer 'ere?'

'That 'urt me,' complained Edward, rubbing his arm and looking at Beth for sympathy, but Beth ignored this.

Instead she said, 'Well, I expect it's all the excitement of the day and you've travelled such a long way now, haven't you?' She stared at the tired boys for a moment, then a gentleness welled up in her and tears appeared in her soft hazel eyes. How she had longed for children of her own, only to be denied them, having lost two babies in early pregnancy. She instantly restrained her emotions and quickly composed herself, she had two now, even if they were only lent to her for a short time.

'Let me see,' she announced on an impulse, 'you can both call us Auntie and Uncle, that would be nice, wouldn't it now?'

The boys looked at each other approvingly. Jimmie thought it would be nice, although he did have his aunties Mollie, Joanna and Maggie back home in Liverpool, but it was only on rare occasions that he saw them.

Just then, he let out an uncontrollable burp at the most inopportune time, 'Sorry! The onions were a bit strong, Missus, er Auntie. I only 'ad two an' all!'

'That's alright, but you must say 'excuse me' and place your hand over your mouth when you are about to repeat. It's good manners, maybe we'll give you both a dose of castor oil, your little tummies must be upset at not having a proper meal all day,' said Beth kindly.

She went over to the cupboard and began rummaging in the medical drawer, 'Now then,' she mused, 'I have it here somewhere. Ah! yes! here it is!' and she withdrew a half bottle of the cure-all. 'I'll just give you both a teaspoon each for now, and we'll see how you are tomorrow?'

Beth held the spoon close to Jimmie's mouth. He hadn't a clue what was in store, for he'd never sampled castor oil before, so he gulped down the oily liquid in anticipation of something pleasant, only to almost bring back his tea.

'Cor! What's that? 'Eck it's 'orrible!' and his face went into all kinds of distortions.

Beth turned to Edward, who had been watching the proceedings with interest, 'Right you are, Edward. Your turn now. Come on, there's a good boy.' She poured the spoonful of oil down the small boy's throat.

He tried hard not to flinch and held his breath so he wouldn't taste the awful stuff, 'Gosh! Eck! It's awful! Phew!'

'It's 'orrible, isn't it, Eddie lad?' Jimmie laughed as his pal grimaced.

'Nuttin' ter laugh at!' grumbled Edward. 'In future, yer wanna keep yer gob shut, then we won't 'ave ter take medicine an' all that.' Edward stood his ground against his senior, and was proud of not making too much fuss.

Beth went upstairs to the bathroom. She giggled as she turned the hot and cold taps on over the bath and sprinkled some Dettol into the water, swishing it around several times with her hand.

Still chuckling to herself, she called the boys to come upstairs. Jimmie had never seen a bathroom before, and wondered where all the water had come from?

'Get undressed both of you. Come on now, there's no need to be shy.'

Edward's pants were whipped down by his new auntie, his jersey and vest pulled unceremoniously over his head.

'In you get.'

Meanwhile, Jimmie had his ganzy half over his head, when his pants were also quickly removed, leaving him so surprised that he almost toppled into the huge white bath.

'There now, lads,' Beth said, dousing their heads by pouring a large jugful of water over them.

Coal-tar soap was next applied to both napless pates, which she then scrubbed vigorously. Her long fingernails dug deeply into the boys' scalps.

'My heavens!' exclaimed Beth, 'this will get rid of any unwanted visitors. Shut your eyes, both of you, I'm going to rinse you off.' This she did, with lovely clean water.

Edward, spluttered and wriggled and got a mouthful, 'Eck, gorra bleedin' mouthful!' he complained, when he got his breath back.

Beth tapped him on the head, 'Close your eyes and mouth in future, and don't use that kind of expression. It's not nice. What if you did swallow some of the water? There's plenty more.' She giggled at cracking a humorous remark.

'Must be rubbing off from these lads,' she thought, as she towelled them both dry. 'Finish yourselves off now. There's someone at the front door.'

She gathered their clothes into a bundle, and trundled off downstairs, holding them out in front of her at arm's length, and quickly depositing them in the back garden. 'That's that!' she declared with satisfaction.

She then rushed to the front door, 'Oh! Hello, Gwenda! How are you, del?' She let her niece into the house.

'Not too bad, Auntie,' came the reply from the young lady, who smiled pleasantly revealing her even white teeth.

Her face was tanned, and small freckles were dotted over her slightly upturned nose. Her eyes were a deep blue, and a neat fringe almost touched her shapely eyebrows.

Beth gave her niece a kiss on her cheek, but only as a gesture, and she looked at her in a rather patronising way. Gwenda's modest pale blue dress flattered her petite figure.

'Your hair looks nice,' commented Beth, looking her niece up and down, 'yes really nice, del.'

'Heard you got two little evacuees,' Gwenda said, as she straightened her hair where her aunt had ruffled it up.

'My! Word gets round very quickly, doesn't it? Come upstairs a minute, the boys have just had a bath and they're going to bed.'

Gwenda followed her aunt up the stairs.

'Good! I see you've finished drying yourselves,' Beth remarked, on entering the bathroom, 'though your hair's still wet.'

Jimmie was wondering about his bald head and lack of hair, and thought it strange that Beth should say this. She whipped the towel off Edward, to dry his head, and his face coloured up at the sight of Gwenda.

'Mine's dry Missus, er Auntie,' said Jimmie, as he ran the cold tap and splashed the side of the bath, trying to remove the tidemark.

'Leave that now, Let's get you into bed.'

Both lads looked at each other, then Jimmie also caught sight of Gwenda, and his face turned a bright crimson.

'Bechod! Aren't they nice lads,' she commented.

The boys hastily followed Beth into the back bedroom, and scrambled into the big double bed. Jimmie claimed the window side; he could see the sunlight still creeping through the ill-fitting roller blind. The clean, white cotton sheets felt good to their tired little bodies, and their heads sank deep into the huge, soft, pillows.

It was sheer luxury to Jimmie to have only one other person sharing the same bed. At home in Everton, the first occupants always arranged the flocks into their own particular area. The last one in, slept on the woven spring, covered only by the tick covering.

Jimmie pushed his hand into the soft, sprung mattress, and jerked his bottom up and down to test the comfort. 'This is the gear, Eddie lad, isn't it?' he said, as he pulled the cool sheet up to his chin. 'Are yer still with us, lar? Are yer alright?'

'Yeah,' came the quiet, muffled reply. His little shoulders were shaking, and he gave a sniffle and shoved his head under the sheets and wept silently.

'Aw! Yer'll be okay termorrer lar, yer'll see. Tell yer what, yer can give me a first wet - hey? An' what about that nice judy?'

'No! Leave me alone,' cried the young lad, 'leave me alone!' The sobbing continued.

Beth could be faintly heard as she chatted to Gwenda, together with the gushing water from the bath as it swirled down the plughole.

'Sounds like me old feller when 'e's 'avin' a few,' joked Jimmie, as he heard the gurgling sound.

'Nos da, lads, good night,' Beth whispered, popping her head round the door. 'Sleep well now.'

'Good night Auntie,' Jimmie responded, 'and thank you.'

There was no reply from Edward, as she silently closed the door.

He continued to sniffle, and Jimmie tried to cheer him up. 'Can I tell yer a joke, Eddie? Listen it's about a lad called Mustard. That's a daft name isn't it? Well, anyway, this lad lived with 'is ma down Rossie, you know where Rossie is, don't you? Roscommon Street.'

Edward sighed, then yawned, 'Go on then, carry on, let's 'ear it.'

Jimmie continued with the tale, 'Well, this lad, Mustard, got took short one day just as he got home from school, and was almost doing it in his kecks, but when 'e got to the closet, his ma was perched on the throne, wi' 'er drawers 'angin' round 'er ankles.'

Mustard paced backwards and forwards, jumpin' up an' down. 'Urry up, Mam,' 'e shouted, 'I'm nearly doin' it!'

Is ma shouted back over the top of the lavvie door, 'yer'll 'ave to do what yer always do.'

Mustard called back, 'can't do that, Ma.'

The joke rambled on and on until Edward was fast asleep.

Jimmie patted his head, then turned towards the window, his eyes nearly closed. There wasn't really an end to the joke, as he had made it up as he was going along, to take Edward's mind off fretting for his mam.

A thrush sang sweetly in the garden below, and in the distance, he could hear a dog barking. He wondered what Art and the gang would be up to? Still running the entries and streets, or playing White Horse? Then he thought about his Mam, Mary and Bobby; at his tart's house probably. Then of course, he wondered about his Dad, and where he was at this moment? Gone to fight the Jerries? He had boasted that him and his mates would see all the Jerries off!

There were lots of tears that night in Liverpool. Kate rocked Eric in the wooden rocking chair, tears streaming down her face. What with Rob having joined the Royal Navy, and Mary away in domestic service, she was lonely, and wished fervently that she could have done more for Jimmie and Lily. But of course, that's the way life goes. You couldn't give it, if you hadn't got it. Her thoughts rambled on, and she suddenly sat up, as she realised the date, 'Eck! It's the third of September, what a nice pressie, the kids 'ave all left. It's a day I'll never forget. What a birthday!'

Back in Bangor, Jimmie slept, drained by the day's events and a long way from his home in Liverpool, as he would be for some time to come.

CHAPTER FOUR
Thanks Mr Mayor

While Beth was seeing to the boys, Hywel, was on his way up Glynne Road on a most important errand, telling his wife he wouldn't be long, but also acting in a very mysterious way, and smiling to himself for the bright idea he had just had. He walked briskly until he reached the house of Miss Davies, the WVS supervisor, and he rang the doorbell, several times in fact, before the lady of the house appeared.

'Hope you don't mind, Miss Davies,' said Hywel, smiling what he judged to be his most attractive smile at the flustered woman, on finding her neighbour on the doorstep, 'I need to use the telephone urgently. Could you oblige? I would be most grateful.'

'Why, certainly, Mr Hughes! Come right in,' gushed Miss Davies. She felt so privileged that such a man would deign to ask her a favour, and she indicated the telephone on the hall table, then disappeared into her sitting room, closing the door discreetly behind her.

Hywel lifted the telephone. He was about to make a very important call, 'Hello! Hello! Is that His Worship the Mayor?'

Only a buzzing noise came from the annoying machine, followed hy a loud clicking, which caused him to move the earpiece away from his ear. He tapped the receiver and eventually made contact with the party concerned.

'Hello! Hello! Yes, this is His Worship speaking. To whom am I speaking?'

Hywel embarked on a lengthy explanation of who he was and his reason for ringing, stating the plight of the two boys, who had been billeted on him. 'Almost in rags!' he said. 'They are badly in need of clothing and anything else that young boys need.'

His Worship pooh-poohed and tutted, rattling on and on with all kinds of excuses, He reminded Hywel, 'The boys billeted in your home are not the only children in need, and stressed that the welfare funds were extremely low, but I'll treat the matter with the utmost urgency at the very next council meeting, and promise to give it careful consideration.'

At this point, Hywel's plan came into action. 'There's no need to consider it for the future, these two small boys need to be seen to now,' bellowed Hywel. 'Come and see for yourself. Good gracious me man, do I have to spell it out for you?'

There was no reply from His Worship, so Hywel verbally hit him below his chain, so to speak, with his next comment, 'By the way,' he added slyly, 'you didn't acknowledge me the other night when I saw you coming out of the Liverpool Arms. Was that Ellen Roberts with you?' Hywel chose his words carefully and continued, 'I said hello to you, but you didn't speak. Maybe you didn't see me?'

His Worship quickly interrupted, 'Ah! Yes, Hywel, er yes, it was Ellen Roberts. She's one of the staff at the town hall, y'know. Just mixing a little pleasure with business. You know how it is. It was mostly business. Look, I'll tell you what, Hywel, pop up and see me, I'll get something arranged for those boys. Yes, pop up. And thanks for ringing me on such an important matter.'

Hywel looked at himself in the hall mirror and gave himself a foxy smirk, then replaced the earpiece, without even acknowledging the mayor.

'Got the bleeder over a barrel now, haven't I?' he sniggered, smugly congratulating himself. 'Never did like him, or get on with him, with his self-important attitude, and always thinking that he was better than everyone else.'

Hywel shouted out to Miss Davies a 'thank you' for the use of the telephone, and closed the door rather noisily, half-arousing Gertie Crosby, who had just turned over in her sleep.

She had retired early after a lovely bath. She wriggled contentedly like a huge cat, who had just finished a large saucer of cream, and half awake, she sighed happily at all that she had achieved on that very tiring day, then drifted back to sleep.

The radio was quite low, and Beth was singing along to Cwm Rhondda, with a male voice choir. She had a soprano voice, and occasionally entered festivals and sometimes gave a song or two at the local hotels, but only on request.

'Hello, del bach, my, you've been a long time. The boys are well asleep by now and I was wondering where on earth you had got to?'

She continued humming softly.

'Glad we got that lot sorted out, del,' her husband went on. 'His Worship, the bloody Mayor! Can't stick the bleeder!' He eased his feet into his slippers, 'tried to fob me off, didn't he now? but I told him a thing or two, clever little dick!'

It was obvious to Beth that her husband was quite agitated and she placed a cushion behind his head, 'Here, drink this. It will make you feel better.'

She handed him a large glass of pale sherry; their usual Sunday night tipple. Sometimes it would even stretch to a second glass, if her sister Meg, visited them.

Hywel ranted on ceaselessly in his native tongue, calling His Worship some very impolite and unmentionable names. Instead of sipping his sherry, he had unwittingly tossed back the glass and swallowed it in one go, almost choking himself in the process.

Beth poured him another drink, and this made him feel more cheerful, even making him consider the possibility of a third glass! His moustache twitched as he put the glass to his lips, he pondered for a moment, sniffed the delightful liquid, then took a small sip.

Suddenly Beth roared out, 'My heavens! It's His Worship, the Mayor. He's coming down our garden path!'

Again, her husband almost choked on his sherry.

'Quickly! Show him in!' exclaimed Beth in agitation, as she hurriedly hid the bottle in the sideboard and rushed into the kitchen with both their glasses, spilling some of their contents as she went.

'Dash it! Damn it!' she tutted in her annoyance, not so much for her clumsy actions, but for the unnecessary loss of the sherry.

By this time, His Worship was being ushered in through the door by Hywel, and he commented that he could smell something burning in their garden.

'Why, yes,' replied Hywel forcefully, 'it's the rags belonging to the evacuees. They haven't a stitch to wear. Disgusting situation!'

He indicated the easy chair by the window, inviting his visitor to sit, and then proceeded to give another lengthy explanation of the boys' circumstances.

Beth appeared at this very opportune time, bearing a tray laden with tea and biscuits. She poured the tea and handed one of her best china cups to the mayor, at the same time holding her breath, for fear he might smell the drink. She wouldn't want him to think that she was a wicked woman. No! Very respectable she was!

'Thank you kindly, Mrs Hughes, no biscuits for me, diolch, not long since I had my evening meal,' he said, patting his stomach. 'Do you know,' he continued, 'we've had several calls from various areas about children needing clothing.'

After taking a sip of tea, he slid a long brown envelope from his inside pocket.

'Here take this,' he said, handing it to Hywel, 'there should be more than enough to cover the necessities. Let me know if there isn't? Must do our bit for the poor little mites!'

Again he sipped his tea, at the same time carefully scrutinising Hywel and Beth's faces, as the latter glanced approvingly over her husband's shoulder, at the very generous cheque. Hywel's moustache twitched more rapidly than ever, and he thanked his Worship several times. Then Beth joined in, also expressing her thanks, and offering their guest another cup of tea.

'No, must go now, Mrs Hughes, but thank you both.' He prised his paunchy frame from the chair, pressed open his gold pocket watch, eyed the time, then clicked the cover back into place, swung it on its chain and neatly flipped it into his waistcoat pocket. He gave Hywel a lengthy, penetrating stare, and raised his bushy eyebrows questioningly.

Hywel winked at him, nodded, half-closed his eyes and shook his hand, as if to say, 'Don't worry, your secret is safe with me. It'll be alright now!'

Without further ado, the mayor quickly but courteously, squeezed Beth's hand and bid them both 'nos da'.

After leaving the house, he strode down the path, not looking back, closed the iron gate behind him, then placed his bicycle clips around his ankles, and as they say in cowboy films, rode off into the sunset.

Beth patted Hywel on the back and laughed, 'Good for you, del, good for you! And now we'll finish that tipple.'

It was very late when the couple finally retired. They busied themselves calculating the price of clothing, and the sizes the boys would require. Hywel had measured the soles of the boys' plimsoles before they were consigned to the incinerator. Only their gas masks had survived the inferno, and even they were sprayed with insecticide, just in case some unwelcome visitors should be hiding in the crevices.

'Nos da, del bach,' Beth said to her husband.

'Sweet dreams, sweetheart,' came the reply.

They kissed goodnight and embraced.

'Go to sleep now, Hywel,' Beth said softly. 'Big day tomorrow. They won't mind you being an hour late, will they, under the circumstances?'

'Good heavens, no, del. Not with all the time I put in at work,' Hywel yawned, and with that, they kissed again and went to sleep.

CHAPTER FIVE
First Outings

Hywel Hughes had waited only five minutes, when Mr Ellis the manager of EB Jones, Men's and Boy's Outfitters, appeared. 'My, you're an early bird, Mr Hughes,' he commented, as he opened the shop.

'Yes, haven't got much time to spare. Can you serve me quickly?' replied Hywel.

He handed over the list of items required, and as Mr Ellis switched on the lights, he scanned the list. 'Why, yes, of course.' The manager's eyes gleamed at the prospect of such a large sale so early in the morning, and he anticipated a nice commission at the end of it.

'Now,' he said, 'shirts; grey cotton, sizes - yes, we have these, vests and underpants; four pairs. Suits, his eyes lit up at these items, four suits; stockings, four pairs, caps, two, sandals; two pairs.'

The list seemed endless. Yes! Mr Mayor had been very generous indeed! Hywel sorted the sizes easily, having dealt with the boys at Friars College, where he instructed in physical exercise in the evenings. He was particularly good at judging measurements, human or inanimate. He made the comment that no doubt there would be other potential customers that day, for the same kind of items.

Mr Ellis quickly and neatly wrapped the sizes separately, saying, 'It's a shame that children so young should be dragged away from their parents, and all because of a bloody madman in Germany.' On the whole, it was just shop talk and he continued the idle conversation without let-up.

He itemised everything twice over, and on instructions from Hywel, placed two boxed shirts with loose collars in front of him saying, 'These are your size, I believe, Mr Hughes.'

'Yes! Diolch, Mr Ellis,' said Hywel, feeling very pleased with himself.

Mr Ellis wiped his long nose with a large white hankie, 'Hope your new refugees settle in alright,' and again he bemoaned the fact that these children had to be separated from their parents.

He had no children of his own, not being married, and he had become a rather miserly character, and to be honest, he wasn't bothered whether such kids were separated or not, or who looked after them, or why such perplexities ever happened, least of all, Hywel's new brood. All he was interested in was sales and making money. However Mr Ellis thanked Hywel profusely, and the shop bell clanged noisily as he opened the door for his departing purchaser, who was laden with parcels and packages.

'Da bo chi, Mr Hughes.'

Hywel thanked him for his quick and efficient service, and after wishing him a pleasant 'hwyl', he strode from the shop with his booty, eager to get back to display them to Beth and the boys; well satisfied with his morning's work.

It had turned 10:00am and the boys awakened to the rustling of brown paper parcels and boxes, which were piled high at the foot of the bed.

'Come now, boys. My you have slept! My goodness, look at the time!' Beth gasped in an excited voice, 'Right, out you jump!'

Her voice seemed extremely loud to Jimmie as he had hardly had time to recollect where he was, or what had happened the previous day? He needed to gather his thoughts.

He was thinking that it was all a dream and that he would wake up in India Street. He was ready to lie down again, when the sharpness of Beth's voice again echoed round the small room. He scratched his bald head which brought him abruptly back to the reality of the situation. Then he caught sight of the parcels.

He was about to jump out of the warm sheets, when he suddenly became aware that he and Edward were stark naked. He was shy and not accustomed to exhibit himself, especially to a strange woman.

'Here now Edward, try these on, new underpants and vests, indeed, and there's new shirts, yes lovely grey shirts and two suits each. See some sandals and socks, indeed aren't you lucky boys now? My goodness! My heavens!' Beth's voice rose and fell in varying degrees, almost singing she was, as she excitedly unwrapped the packages, impatient to inspect their contents. 'My, and aren't you lucky boys?'

Hywel, who had been hovering nearby, was so proud of his achievement and whispered quietly to Beth, 'So glad you're all pleased. Got to dash off to work now, have a nice time sorting this lot out, ta- ra!'

Beth was bubbling over with happiness for her evacuees! 'Uncle Hywel has bought all these for you, and ties and caps too!'

Both boys scrambled out of bed, almost knocking each other over in a frenzy to inspect all the new apparel laid out in front of them and ready to wear. It was better than Christmas! They had forgotten their embarrassment in their haste to dress, first in the lovely white underpants; a priority for Jimmie.

In his haste, Edward had squashed two legs into one slot. Beth and Jimmie laughed uproariously, and Edward, blushing, withdrew both legs and started again, getting agitated in his frantic efforts to cover his nakedness.

'Yer've gorrem on back ter front anyway,' Jimmie laughed, pointing to the label. Of course, even he hadn't realised that there was another way to tell that they were back to front. It was more by luck than good management that he had succeeded in getting his on the right way round, and he could easily have made the same mistake; he wasn't used to such luxuries back home in Everton.

The newness and softness of the clothes felt so good to their skin. The cotton shirts fitted well, though the trousers had to be hoisted up a little with the aid of braces, another of Hywel's purchases, but were at knee-level, nevertheless.

'You'll soon grow into everything lads, besides they'll last longer,' said Beth wisely, as she neatly rolled up the sleeves of Edward's shirt.

'Don't bother putting your socks on today, you'll not need them, it's lovely outside, warm and sunny, just put on the sandals.'

She was as excited as the boys, and kept breaking into the Welsh language, mingled with English, forgetting that the boys knew no Welsh. She was amused by their puzzled faces, 'Never mind,' she grinned, 'you'll soon pick it up, and understand what I say.' Then, as an afterthought she added, 'Gwenda will be taking you both out later when you've eaten, I'll leave you to finish off. Have a wash now, won't you?'

She began to wrap up the sheets of brown paper, folding them neatly and winding the lengths of string around them, saying as she left the bedroom, 'Never throw anything away. It always comes in handy, and besides there's a war on now!'

'Thank you Auntie!' called out Edward, blushing bright red.

Beth was surprised to hear Edward speak.

Then Jimmie followed suit, 'Me too Missus, I mean Auntie. Thanks a lot fer the clothes an' everything.'

Beth was so touched by their gratitude that she felt quite choked. She popped her head round the door, 'You're most welcome, I'm sure,' she smiled, then hurried down to the kitchen and busied herself making a pot of tea. Strawberry jam sandwiches were quickly lined up on two plates in readiness for the new residents. Beth had scarcely poured the tea when they both entered, transformed by their new outfits, and took the places that had been assigned to them the day before.

'Good boys, I see you've washed. We'll go to the High Street after lunch for toothbrushes, and anything else you might need, and maybe spend a few pennies that you've both collected. There they are on the fireplace,' Beth said, pointing to the two piles of coppers.

'Thank you, Auntie,' said Jimmie, his mouth bulging with strawberry jam butty, and sluicing the contents of his mouth with the warm, sweet tea, then taking another gluttonous bite when Beth wasn't looking.

Edward nibbled away like a little hamster, first removing the crusts which he was unable to eat because of his missing teeth at the front.

'Dip it into yer tea lar,' Jimmie advised him. 'Go on do it when she's not lookin.'

Edward ignored his friend's advice, and continued to eat daintily, tucking into his sandwiches in his own way, despite the comments from his partner. Now and then he would lick his sticky fingers, oblivious of the world around him, and staring fixedly at his plate.

Jimmie had already devoured his, and was waiting for Edward to finish. 'Come on gerra move on, get yer jaws bangin'. Me nin could eat crusts, an' raw carrots, an' she didn't even 'ave a tooth in 'er tunnel.' Jimmie reinforced his message by giving Edward an impatient dig with his elbow. 'We're supposed ter be goin' out, aren't we?'

Beth had been listening to the conversation, and chuckled at hearing the broad Liverpool dialect. She turned from her chores and faced the boys, trying to control the laughter that bubbled up inside her. She urged Edward to hurry up, 'Gwenda will be coming anytime to take you out.'

'Finished now Auntie, had enough thank you,' Edward announced quietly, as he slid from his chair.

'You will have to start eating all your crusts in future. We can't waste anything now.' She reminded the boys, yet again, that there was a war on, which seemed very funny to them, since that was the reason why they were here, in her house, sitting at her table, eating her food, away from their families, living in a strange land, where the people spoke a different language.

Beth felt sorry for the two boys, so cheered them up by saying, 'We'll feed the birds, just this once, with the leftovers,' which made Edward breathe a sigh of relief.

Jimmie was glad to see Gwenda make an appearance at that moment through the kitchen door, calling out in a sweet voice, 'I did knock and call out Auntie Beth, but you must not have heard me, sut dach chi (how are you)?'

'Da iawn, diolch, Gwenda, (very well thank you),' Beth replied.

Both lads hurriedly pushed their chairs under the table, eager to get outside and explore their new environment. It was all so strange to them, like a big adventure, and they were full of anticipation for the morning with their new friend, Gwenda.

'Be good, all of you, enjoy your walk. I'll expect you back at 12.30. We'll have a cold lunch, that will be nice now, won't it?' Beth said, as she placed the dirty crockery into the washing-up bowl in the sink.

The boys said ta-ra to Auntie, and Gwenda said something to her in Welsh and kissed her on the cheek, 'I'll look after them, don't worry,' she promised, as she walked out of the door.

Jimmie and Edward were already at the garden gate and Jimmie, remembering his manners, stood holding the gate open, as Edward and Gwen walked out. They all walked briskly down Glynne Road and along Garth Road.

'That's the school you'll be going to, Jimmie bach,' Gwen remarked, as they passed a dark, grey, stone building.

'It doesn't look very big. How many kids go to it? How many classrooms are there? Where's the playground?'

'My, all these questions! I wouldn't know, but you'll see for yourself when you start there. It's bigger than it looks from the outside, but enough of school talk for now, that can come later, you're out to enjoy yourselves today!' declared their charming hostess, cheerfully.

She quickened her pace and the boys broke into a trot.

'You'll have to walk quicker than that if you want to see the pier,' said Gwen, as they hurried along. 'Who knows, we may have an ice-cream.'

Gwen chuckled to herself, it wasn't every day that she had two young lads as escorts, and admiring ones at that! The boys raced past her, but not too far ahead.

Soon, a beautiful panorama of the Menai Straits came into view, with Bangor Pier, which Gwen had just mentioned, stretching well out into the narrow strip of sea. Sailing boats were dotted here and there; it was a truly wonderful sight to the awe-struck Liverpool lads.

The boats skimmed along, their sails dipping and bobbing, tossing and blowing and reflecting in the clear, blue-green, waters. They had never seen anything so magnificent in all their young lives!

Hungry gulls swooped over the silent, glassy sea in search of food. They cried out in their hunger as they raced along, scavenging and dipping low over the surface of the water. Morsels of fish, not fit for human consumption, were thrown overboard by fishermen; rewards for the swiftest of wing, who were then chased and pecked by the not-so-fortunate. Everything looked so peaceful and calm, and the salty air was fresh and good to breathe.

There was no one in attendance at the pier entrance, so the little party barged its way through the turnstile and hurried along the wooden boards. As they passed by the little domed kiosks, the newly-painted rails on either side of the pier, glistened in the morning sunlight. It was thrilling for both lads, especially when they caught sight of the ferry leaving Beaumaris.

Jimmie ran to the rails and would have gone headlong over the edge of the landing stage, if it hadn't been for Gwenda, who grabbed the collar of his shirt.

'Heavens lad, don't do that again. I had visions of diving in after you; steady up now, take it easy!'

Jimmie's face reddened at being chastised, especially by a girl, and he looked around self-consciously, to see what Edward was doing, only to find him with his head between the top two rails, peering into the still, green sea.

'What yer lookin' at?' he asked.

Edward withdrew, at the same time bumping his head. 'Aw nuttin', just jelly fish an' all dat - dat's all,' he muttered, rubbing his bald head.

'Come on now boys, time's getting on,' chivvied Gwen. 'There'll be a lot of people here before long, coming off the ferry, usually get a lot on Monday mornings, with shoppers going into Bangor. We'll do this again though,' she promised.

She pointed out all the landmarks along the coastline, 'See,' she said, 'that's Great Orme, then there's Llandudno and Little Orme.' She pointed out Puffin Island, and across to Penmaenmawr. 'Look over there, Penrhyn Castle, and of course, the mountains.'

Gwen had her arm around the two boys, and the three of them strolled back casually along the pier.

'It's been good fun, yer takin' us 'ere, Gwen. Wish some of me mates could 'ave been 'ere, they'd 'ave liked it! There's so much to do and see, isn't there? Yeah, I think I'm goin' ter like it 'ere. Me mam will be glad too. Mind yer, she wouldn't know us all toffed up an' dat, an' wid us 'aircuts as well.' Jimmie laughed, tapping Edward's baldy head.

'Gerroff will yer! Leave me alone!' Edward had his own thoughts about being away from his mother, and it seemed as if he was about to give way to tears again.

A warm friendly pat on his shoulder from Gwen, and a caressing arm about him, soothed his troubled thoughts.

'You have a nice name now, haven't you? Edward Jones, though I never could understand why the name Jones is Welsh, as there's no J in the Welsh alphabet.'

'Cor!' chipped in Jimmie. 'Might be Irish, Gwen; Paddy Jones. Aye that's what I'll call yer, Eddie lad!' Then he burst into song.

'Yer'll never go to heaven - wid Paddy Jones,
'Cos Paddy Jones, is a lazy bones!'

Gwen suppressed her laughter as they raced along Garth Road and down by Avon Adda, along the black cinder path and past the putting greens.

'Gosh! Don't it stink dat river? Phew!' Jimmie held his nose with his thumb and forefinger.

Edward buried his in his arm. Gwen just smiled at them, she was accustomed to the foul smell of the open sewer, and warned the boys not to go anywhere near it, especially when it rained, as the water reached the top of the banking and could be very dangerous. There was all kinds of waste floating silently towards a huge concrete pipe that disappeared underground, and came out by Dickie's Boatyard, before discharging into the sea.

'Nuff ter put yer off yer grub, in't it?' Jimmie protested, nasally, still holding his nose tightly, releasing it only when they arrived in Glynne Road.

'Hope you're not late for your dinner, or I'll be in hot water,' fretted Gwen, as she knocked and walked into her aunt's house, calling out, 'Are we late, Auntie?'

'Yes you are Gwen,' snapped Beth. Her stormy black look said it all!

Gwen apologised profusely.

'Yes, twenty minutes late!' added Beth, 'good thing there's nothing cooked!'

Gwen bid the boys a hasty 'da bo chi.'

'See you again soon, ta-ra. See you, Auntie Beth.'

There was no response from her offended aunt.

However Jimmie replied, 'Thanks fer takin' us ter the pier,' then promptly removed a piece of cinder from the sole of his sandal.

Beth, who missed nothing, noticed immediately, called out, 'No need to guess where you've been? Heavens, just look at your feet, and your new sandals, my goodness! That girl will never learn!'

Jimmie and Edward thought it best not to comment and sat down at the table, as inconspicuously as possible, after washing their hands of course. Lunch consisted of leftovers from Sunday; cold sliced potatoes, lamb, bread and butter and tea. Jimmie was famished, and could have eaten more, but wouldn't have dared to ask for anything else.

The morning air had given them both an appetite, and even Edward quickly and silently cleared his plate, not leaving any of his usual crusts. He turned to his mate, emitted a half silent burp and grinned, patting his belly with satisfaction. 'Dat was good.'

'What? The grub or the burp? There yer are, Eddie lad, I told yer, yer'd be okay. Yer'll see, things'll get better fer yer.'

'What are you up to now, lads?' Beth asked, as she entered the kitchen, 'Go and sit in the front room while I tidy away. Won't be long now. Good! I see you've eaten up, not even a crust for the birds Edward, good boy!'

Edward smirked, and put out his tongue at Jimmie, then puffed out his little chest and shoved past his pal to get into the other room before him.

'Aye 'e's comin' to now, cheeky little sod!' Jimmie muttered under his breath.

They sat together on the small leather settee in Beth's front parlour, gazing at the variety of brass ornaments. There was a pot-bellied buddha, three wise monkeys, a small donkey and other paraphernalia of interest to small boys. A pair of hand-painted Dutch clogs hung on one side of the recently-installed tiled fireplace. Heavy lace curtains were draped across the bay window, shutting out most of the sunlight, and probably serving a two-fold purpose; to stop people from peering in, but also so that Beth could see out, without being seen herself. In fact all the houses had their windows heavily-draped, hiding the inside and its contents, from the prying eyes of the passers-by.

Suddenly, Jimmie blurted out, 'Look at that feller wid 'is shirt 'angin' out. Hurry up, come an' see!'

Edward jumped up and looked out, and sure enough, there was a strange-looking man outside. The lads burst out laughing at the strange fellow. He had no shoes on, one sleeve of his shirt was rolled up, and his braces hung loosely down below his waist. His appearance was unkempt, as if he hadn't shaved for weeks.

Just then Beth appeared, rubbing cream into her hands, 'I heard you laughing lads, what's so funny?'

Before they could answer, she pulled them away from the window. 'Gosh! My heavens! Don't ever bother with Mr Watkins; he lives at the bottom house with his mother, poor dear. I feel sorry for her having to look after that lunatic, so keep away from him, don't even look at him. He does some very strange things and he's not nice to look at.' Beth was quite breathless with anxiety by the time she'd finished explaining about Mr Watkins.

So Jimmie was able to get a word in, 'Yer mean 'e lives at the bottom 'ouse, with those dirty curtains? An' flippin' 'eck, just look at 'is kecks, yer can nearly see 'is er, 'is bum, that's it 'is bum.' He couldn't think of a better word.

After a long gaze, the man went off, none the wiser, but maybe curious about his new little neighbours.

CHAPTER SIX
Introductions All Round

Mr Williams, the butcher, held out his hand to Jimmie. It was meat-stained and cold, his fingers were like raw pork sausages. Jimmie was quick to release his grasp, and push his hand deeply into his pocket, after it had been vigorously shaken. The stocky man, small in stature, had bushy black hair and heavy eyebrows, which curtained his horn-rimmed spectacles. His dark eyes sparkled with laughter and he mouthed a wide grin.

'Yes I'll look after him, Mrs Hughes, when you send him up to the shop,' he promised, wiping his hands on a piece of wet muslin. 'Going to come very quickly, this rationing, you know, goodness knows what we'll be eating before it's all over? Although you'll be alright now Mrs Hughes, what with having the evacuees, that will help you now won't it?'

Both Beth and the butcher turned the conversation into Welsh, which Jimmie soon learned was for private conversation, and not for young ears. Finally, the boys were ushered from the small, dismal shop.

'Now, that's the butcher's, Jimmie, you'll remember where to come when I send you?'

'Yes, Auntie, I'll remember.'

The Co-op was just a few doors higher up the High Street, and Beth and her new lodgers were greeted by Wyn Jones, the shop manager, who seemed friendly enough, then there was a repetition of the same hand-shaking ceremony.

This time it was a warm, clammy hand that did the arm-jerking, and Jimmie heaved a sigh of relief when he was released from the muggy grip.

Edward, who was standing nearby, nudged Jimmie with his elbow, beckoning his mate to look at Mr Jones, but Jimmie, ever observant, had already noticed what Edward was indicating. The man's left eye twitched and flickered, then closed completely, only to open wide again just as suddenly. His left shoulder drooped slightly, and he wouldn't look at Beth when speaking, probably because of his affliction.

Beth purchased several items of food, and as the manager busied himself at the weighing scales, she whispered to the boys, 'Don't stare, as this might cause embarrassment, and I don't want that to happen.' She was afraid that there might not be the usual perks, especially when rationing began.

'So you both now know where I get my groceries from boys, don't you? Don't go anywhere else when I send you. It's much cheaper here, and besides there's always the divi.'

Jimmie just nodded in agreement. He was persuaded to buy a post office moneybox, which cost him sixpence, but his own choice of treat was a bright red cricket ball, whose cost had to be supplemented with tuppence from Auntie Beth, as Jimmie was now quite broke!

Edward was more thrifty, and only bought a small note-book and pencil, leaving him with eightpence, which much to Jimmie's annoyance, he jingled tantalisingly in his trouser pocket, grinning and smirking at the same time.

However the smirk soon disappeared, when Beth announced that any money left, or given to them in the future, was to go into their newly-acquired moneybox, and saved for special occasions, or outings.

The rest of the afternoon was taken up by Beth showing the boys the various shops to which she would be sending them on errands in the future. She had put their purchases into her shopping basket, and it was to this fact that Jimmie referred on their way home.

'Yer'd 'ave thought I could carry me own corky 'ome,' he whispered to his friend, 'an besides, arf of that money you got is mine, as I paid for the moneybox!'

Edward was really peeved, 'I should 'ave bought summat else, shouldn't I?'

'Serves yer right, yer greedy little bleeder,' blurted out Jimmie, only to be interrupted by a slap on the back which sent him reeling forward.

The three of them turned in amazement.

'Ello, Jimmie! Gosh! Look at you, all poshed up an' dat!'

'Is this your little sister Jimmie?' asked Beth, smiling.

'Y'eah, this is our Lily. She's two years younger than me.'

'I saw yer from up the street, an' ran down ter yer. An' this is Mrs Flynn, the lady I'm stayin' with, an' there's two more girls as well, Julie an' Margaret Kenyon.

They're nice, an' Mrs Flynn bought me a new frock, an' shoes an' dat, an' I've 'ad me 'air trimmed, an' you 'ave too, our Jimmie, yer've 'ad yer 'air cut, first wet, ha ha!' and she promptly spit on her hand and slapped her brother's head. She cackled hilariously at seeing the two baldy heads.

Jimmie and Lily and her two new room-mates chattered away together, and Edward tagged along behind.

Beth never paused for breath. Her mouth went fifty to the dozen, to poor Mrs Flynn, who was a meek little woman, who just nodded and shook her head in harmony with Beth's voice, unable to get a word in of her own.

Suddenly, Beth's voice stopped in mid-sentence, on seeing all the soldiers parading outside the barracks at the top of Glynne Road.

They lined both sides of the road, heavily-packed and standing to attention, their rifles rigid at their sides. A sergeant major walked briskly up and down the lines, muttering sternly, slapping his thigh now and again with his polished stick, then tucking it smartly under his arm. The battalion stretched all the way down Glynne Road to Garth Road, at the bottom of the hill.

The young lads were bewitched; they had never seen anything like this before, and they scrutinised the soldiers from head to toe as they walked behind them on the pavement. All at once there was a loud shout that echoed along the rows of soldiers.

'Pa - rade, slo - pe arms!' came the thunderous command.

Every movement was as precise as clockwork, culminating with their weapons being firmly placed on their left shoulders.

'Stea - dy, stea - dy.' This time the sergeant major's voice continued in a lower, softer, tone, then it boomed like a loud thunderclap, 'Pre - sent arms!'

Rifles were raised as one, then positioned squarely in front of each soldier, followed by the mighty crash of polished boots, smacking the road surface, then absolute silence.

'If anyone moves an eyelash, I'll 'ave 'em,' came the menacing whisper.

Even the civilians felt obligated to silence, each of them mesmerised by the spectacle. Then the sound of an army truck, a 15cwt Bedford with its canvas top rolled back, slowly travelled up Glynne Road. Its driver looked fixedly straight ahead, a corporal next to him sat stiffly to attention. Two officers were standing in the back, both had red bands around their hats and the same coloured stripes on their lapels. The elder of the two saluted smartly, and the truck continued on to the barracks, turning right into a large forecourt.

On the command of 'Slope arms,' the soldiers quickly marched away, and the military display was over.

Beth's face had coloured up at the sight of all the soldiers, and she had bid a hasty goodbye to Mrs Flynn and raced off down the road towards her house. Her eyes were firmly fixed on the pavement, and she didn't dare look up, but ignored the catcalls, whistles and witty remarks of the soldiers, as they marched past in the opposite direction.

She fumbled in the lock with her door key, and banged the door behind her, perspiration glistening on her forehead, as she quickly drank a full glass of water. She would like to have chatted longer with Mrs Flynn, as she was sure she would have found out lots of bits of gossip, but never mind she would see her again.

Then she remembered her evacuees. 'Gosh! Heavens! I hope they find their way home!' she exclaimed, as she inspected herself in the mirror, dabbing her forehead with the back of her hand. Her cheeks were flushed and looked ready to ignite, as was often the case whenever she came near, or into contact with the opposite sex, especially younger men! That was Beth's dilemma, that and her fiery temper, which fortunately for the boys, they didn't see very often.

Jimmie and Edward raced eagerly round to the back door, anxious to tell Auntie Beth all that went on up at the barracks, and said they were looking forward to seeing the soldiers again, especially on guard duty.

'Don't talk about it lads,' Beth said nervously, 'just go and play now near the house, tea will be ready shortly. Go on now, there's good boys.'

'Are yer alright Auntie?' asked Jimmie, with a puzzled look.

'Yes, I'm fine. Now, please go and play.'

Beth left the back door open and closed the inner door, telling the boys that if they wished to use the toilet, to wash their hands outside, and she pointed to a brass tap on the wall.

When she had gone inside, leaving the lads to their own devices, Jimmie piped out, 'Gosh I'm ready fer me tea, me belly thinks me throat's cut.'

'Yeah me too! D'yer think they'll miss one of them apples on the tree?'

'Ell don't even think of it!' Jimmie warned his pal. 'Do yer wanna gerrus in trouble the first day 'ere? 'ave yer fergot already, yer daft little sod, d'yer wanna gerrus deported. I mean reported, an' finish up somewhere else?'

Edward suddenly remembered the headmistress's last words to them, 'That they would be accountable to her for any misconduct.'

'Anyway, please yerself, Eddie lad, I'm pullin' up me ladder an' gerrin' in me own boat, an' besides that, if yer eat any of them apples, yer'll start feelin' the strain.'

Both lads ran round to the front gate, rollicking and punching each other playfully as lads do, but their high spirits sparked off the barking of Bob Jones' terriers next door.

'Shut up yer little bleeders,' came a harsh voice.

The boys wondered if this remark was intended for them, or the dogs? They both sniggered, and with raised shoulders and hands cupped to their mouths, they tiptoed out of the gate and wandered down to the putting green.

By the time they came back to the house, Beth had tea ready, and the ravenous adventurers ate their beef paste sandwiches with relish, finishing off with a piece of parkin and tea. They then washed, brushed their teeth and expected to go out to make more explorations of the area.

Instead they were ordered by Beth, in no uncertain terms, 'Get ready for bed, as Uncle Hywel will be home very soon.'

'Heck! It's blinkin' daylight yet! Bit mingy in't she? Fancy! Not lerrin us play out. It's only early, look at the sun! It's still out, an' we're in!'

Jimmie had pulled the bedroom blind aside to look out into the garden. 'Look,' he continued, 'yer can see the boatyard from 'ere, an' look, the tide's still in.'

He fell back onto his pillow, wondering if this early to bed stuff was going to fit in with his past lifestyle? He chattered on, 'Nice 'ouse an' all dat, the pier an' shops. There's the army barracks, they're the gear, but the people are a bit odd, s'pose we'll get used to 'em.'

He didn't realise that Edward was already fast asleep.

'Ah! Well! Better than last night when 'e was moanin'. Might see our Lil termorrer, yeah we'll go an' find out where she's stoppin', dat'll be a good idea.'

He prattled on until he too, was fast asleep and dreaming of the gang and Hambone, Snotty, Thomo and Willie, and why shouldn't young Eddie be in the gang too, racing along the Cast Iron Shore, paddling and splashing, with the warm sun on their legs?

But then he felt the chill of something cold and wet which startled him. He moved away quickly from his bed-mate. Though half asleep, he pushed Edward in his back, 'Hey! Yer daft little sod, yer've peed the bed!'

Edward slumbered on without even flinching.

''Ell e'd drown in 'is own pee an' not even know it!' Jimmie retreated halfway up the wall, to avoid the wet patch.

The following morning, with breakfast over, Beth made an announcement, in a very curt voice.

'I've put a rubber sheet on the bed, boys. No more drinks at night for you, Edward! No more drinks after you leave the tea-table. Now remember that, and there's a chamber-pot under the bed. Use it if you have to now, won't you? Don't want any more bedwetting in this house. I'm very annoyed, indeed I am!'

Edward blushed and looked away, as Beth, her face red with anger, addressed her new little lodger.

'And you too, Jimmie, I'm surprised at you. You should have called me to say he'd wet the bed. Heavens above, the mattress is absolutely soaking. I'll have to put it in front of the fire when I've sponged it, and fancy, me having to wash the sheets today. Monday is washing day. What will the neighbours think?' Beth couldn't contain her anger, and was really cross with the boys, as she rattled on. 'Vexed I am indeed, yes, I'm really angry with you both. Whatever will Uncle Hywel say when he gets home and I have to tell him?' She finally left the kitchen, muttering away in Welsh.

'What am I getting it in the neck for?'moaned Jimmie. 'She does yak on a bit too much, it's not fair! Bloomin' 'eck, don't look at me lar, I didn't snitch. Yer'll 'ave ter get the plumber an' gerra new washer on it Eddie lad.' With that, he gave his mate a sharp tug on the ear and retreated into the back garden, reflecting on all that had been said.

'Hell! Am I his keeper? It was bad enough thinking about school and the prospect of Corky Green, and now the bedwetting! Cor!' he thought, 'should've stayed in Everton!'

September gave them nice sunny days, and they eventually found new places around Bangor to interest them. They climbed the mountain overlooking the High Street. Really it was only a hill, but everyone called it a mountain, and to the two boys it certainly seemed as if it was!

From the top they revelled in the uninterrupted views of the University, Upper Bangor, the Roman Camp, the pier, the Straits and Puffin Island. Edward was always tired on their long treks, and complained that his legs hurt, or his feet, or he was too hot, or he had a headache!

'Yer backside'll ache, Eddie lad, if yer pee the bed again, yer Auntie Beth'll tan yer, she might even put yer a nappy on. So use the lavvie before we go up ter bed in future, or the chamber-pot. Glad we only wear vests in bed, our blinkin' 'jamas would be wringin'. Come on now, let's get back.'

Jimmie's stomach was telling him that it must be almost tea-time. His legs were tired, and scratched from the bracken and the prickly yellow gorse, which grew everywhere, and that they had waded through that day. Jimmie soon forgot his discomfort, on catching sight of his young sister, Lily.

'Ell! Nearly walked past yer! Which 'ouse do you live in down there?' he asked, pointing to Orme Road. 'Gosh! You look smart in yer new dress an' shoes!'

He was pleased to see Lily looking so happy. She explained that the house she was living in was the one with the big, brown, polished door, the one with a brass handle and door-knocker.

'Oh! Yes!' she added, 'an' the beautiful lace curtains, so you can't miss it. Mind you, I don't know if Mrs Flynn would like you to call just yet, 'cos there's two other girls stayin' there as well as me.'

Lily then handed Jimmie and Edward a wrapped caramel toffee. 'Ere shove them in yer gob. I gorra bag full off Mrs Edwards, fer runnin' errands fer her. She's a friend of Mrs Flynn. She gave me a tanner as well, she can't walk very well, an' she 'as to 'ave a walkin' stick.'

'Oh!' commented Jimmie, feeling rather peeved, but at the same time glad for his sister's good fortune. 'On the pig's back - eh?'

Lily laughed at her brother and the expression which was used in Liverpool to describe anyone who was lucky or doing well. Brother and sister gabbled on fifty to the dozen about their new digs, new clothes, new friends and neighbours and the places they'd visited.

'Me mam wouldn't know us, Jimmie, would she?' said Lily.

She then remarked how smart Edward looked, and used his full name as he preferred.

'It's alright, yer can call me Eddie, everyone else does now.' He bent down to scratch his leg, then gave Jimmie a dig with his elbow.

'My! What's got inter 'im?' teased Lily. 'Wouldn't speak ter us on the train, would 'e? Was all shy an' that. Oh! Yer just reminded me, Miss Crosby came to our 'ouse this mornin.' She loosened the caramel from her bottom teeth, with her finger before continuing. 'Y'eah, we got new schools to go to on Monday mornin'. I'm goin' ter one called Lon Popi, or summat. At least that's what it sounded like. She said she 'oped we 'ad a nice time 'an all that.'

Jimmie wondered when she was going to give him a chance to say something, as she rattled on with all her news.

'We'll 'ave new teachers as well!' she claimed, excitedly, 'so there. What do yer think of that, our Jimmie? Anyway, I'll 'ave ter go now, me auntie will be lookin' fer me, an' it'll be tea-time as well. Ta-ra, see yer later!' With that she skipped off down Orme Road, turning at intervals and waving to the boys, nearly tripping over the uneven pavement.

'Ta-ra Lil, see yer again!' Jimmie called after her, and waved continuously until his sister disappeared inside the house.

The lads wended their way down Glynne Road to their new home, merrily sucking away at their long-lasting toffees. Chums, comrades-in-arms and chuffed at seeing Lily again, and not least, their expedition up the mountain.

CHAPTER SEVEN
Dydd Sul - Holy Day

Jimmie was looking forward to having a full day with Lily, to take her to some of the places that he and Eddie had explored all week, but alas this wasn't to be! It was just when he was finishing his jam butty breakfast, that Beth broke the silence, dropping a bombshell which shattered his plans.

'Mr Ingham will be taking you along with him to St Mary's this morning. You'll enjoy it I'm sure, and there will be other evacuees there no doubt.'

Beth placed one plate on top of the other, and waited for a reply, which came from Jimmie.

'But I've never been ter church Miss, I mean Auntie. I wouldn't know what to do or owt. 'Sides, if it's dat big un, wid dat big ting stickin' up, wha' der yer call 'em?'

'Steeples,' Beth chipped in.

'Yeah steeples. It looks like a Cat'lic church,' Jimmie went on.

'Well you're not Catholics, I checked on your religion, you're Church of England, so you must have been christened as such!' Beth asserted, sinking her hands into the hot, suddy, washing-up water.

'Yeah, s'pose so, burra can't remember owt!' Jimmie was struggling with the buckles on his sandals, or desert wellies, as he called them.

Beth said, 'Well, there you are then! You have been to church after all! Just think of all the times you missed going though, backsliding, lean of soul you are my lad. We'll soon alter your sinful ways. Yes, indeed we will, Dydd Sul,

Sunday, is a holy day in Wales, and I'm sure where you come from, there are some who observe the Sabbath.'

Jimmie couldn't think of anyone at that moment, certainly not any of the gang, or the family, maybe Auntie Molly? Yes, his dad's sister, she might go. Come to think of it, he could remember them going quite often to some little place or other up near Mills Road.

'Then there was me Auntie Jo, she went to dat place on Neddy Road, what did we call it? The 'en 'ut, no that wasn't it, or was it? It was dat little place near Bucky Street where she lived with Uncle Billy and me cousins Mary, Eddie, Peter, David and Grace. Yeah, that's right, they all went to Sunday School, an' come to think of it, they all 'ad nice clothes, an' a clean 'ouse, even if it was in a poor part of Everton.'

Must be summat different about 'em? Yeah, Uncle Billy did 'ave a pint, and Auntie Jo a milk stout, but they didn't wallow in it; not like me dad, 'ell.

'e was so sozzled at times, he'd say, 'Throw it over me, an' 'e'd start to sing *Down Among the Dead Men.'*

This recollection frightened Jimmie, and his thoughts jolted back to the present. He'd managed to fasten the stiff leather strap into each buckle of his sandals, and he jumped up and raced into the hallway for his coat and cap. 'Ready Auntie Beth!' he shouted. 'Cor! Look at 'im,' referring to Edward, 'not ready yet. Come on slow coach!'

Beth straightened Edward's tie and tilted his cap forward over his forehead.

'My! Smart lads you are, yes indeed.' She was quite proud of the job she and Hywel had done in rigging them out in new clothing, thanks again to Mr Mayor! She walked with them to the gate.

'Bora da, Mr Ingham, sut dach chi?' (Good morning, how are you?) Beth greeted him pleasantly as she opened the gate.

'Da iawn, diolch, Mrs Hughes,' (Very well, thank you), replied the old gentleman, raising his trilby hat, 'the boys will be alright now with me. Hwy,' (cheerio).

'Ta-ra Auntie,' the boys piped up.

'Da bo chi.' (good-bye) Beth said, as she watched the trio depart, 'be good boys now, ta-ra.'

The three sauntered up towards St Mary's Avenue, the boys glancing up at their new companion now and again. Mr Ingham was a giant of a man, at least he appeared so to Jimmie and Edward, as they viewed him from their lowly position. He had long, grey dishevelled hair, which stuck out here and there from beneath his trilby, and over the collar of his white shirt, and the knot of his plain black tie hung loosely from his neck. His dark green tweed suit bore little brown scorch marks, caused by the hot tobacco ash that accidentally flew out of his tightly-packed briar pipe, which he sucked on constantly, at the same time bellowing clouds of blue smoke from his thin lips. His heavy moustache was stained in places, also due to his use of tobacco.

He strode happily along, his large feet encased in brown brogues, which hit the pavement heavily with each step. For all his appearance, Mr Ingham was a clever man; he had studied at Bangor University and had degrees in English and Welsh History, and was well-versed in local history as well. Suddenly he stopped and leaned against the grey granite wall, as if trying to ease some discomfort in his spine.

'This is part of ancient Bangor lads. These walls surrounded the old city. They were built to keep the invading English armies out. There were lots of battles around here,' he said, as he tapped his pipe against the heel of his shoe.

'D'yer mean real battles? Wid swords an' all dat? Cor wid bows an' arrers an' all dat as well. Cor an' warra bout us Mister, will dey fight us 'cos we're English? Gosh, don't feel safe 'ere now. Are dey all hidden in some o' dem castles we've seen?'

Edward was quite agitated at the thought of hundreds of wild 'Gogs' (North Walians) descending on them, to carve them up with swords and daggers, but he was reassured by their elderly guardian that North Wales was a safe haven, and that everyone was quite friendly and not at all barbaric, and in fact, especially hospitable to Liverpudlians, probably because hundreds of years ago, the land of Wales stretched further north, to the area where Liverpool was situated.

Jimmie thought that he might enjoy going to church after all. Mr Ingham was such an interesting, knowledgeable man, who told them of so many fascinating events, that it was a pleasure to be in his company.

'My goodness, lads!' Mr Ingham, had closed the cover of his gold watch and hurriedly placed it back into his waistcoat pocket. 'We're going to be late with all this talking. Quick march now, Mrs Hughes will never forgive me. It's not a very good start now is it? Fancy, being late for church!'

Sure enough, the service was already fifteen minutes into its proceedings, and ladies in their Sunday hats looked scornfully at the trio who had dared to be late! Others glanced slightly from the corners of their eyes. Being late for church was a sin in itself, and frowned upon by the devout and pious.

'Just do what I do lads,' Mr Ingham whispered. 'Stand up, sit down, bow your heads, that's right, the same as I am doing.'

Jimmie didn't pay much attention to what was being said by the preacher who delivered the sermon, his eyes wandered around, first gazing at the tall, stained-glass, window; then at the altar, eyeing the gold receptacles and gazing up into the arches which spanned the high ceiling, his eyes travelling down the high pillars, which disappeared through the red-tiled floors and into the foundations. None too soon, the service ended, and because they had seated themselves at the back, they were the first to leave. Mr Ingham made sure that they all had their story straight before they arrived back home.

'Wasn't too bad now, was it, lads?' and he gave a sly wink. 'We weren't late were we? Only just started so to speak!' and he chuckled as the boys agreed with him.

The old gentleman accompanied them to their garden gate, having really enjoyed their company, and was glad that they were to be his new neighbours. He loved their inquisitiveness, and he knew instinctively that they were interested in his answers. Yes, this was a new friendship, but one that was to blossom and grow over the next three years.

Naturally Beth bombarded the boys with all kinds of questions over their light lunch, but Jimmie and Edward said nothing of their sin and misdemeanor in being late for church, as that was their secret with Mr Ingham!

Hywel sat unconcerned, tapping his fingers on the window, trying to shut out Beth's continual drone. Edward folded the little bib that Beth had made for him that morning and also wished that she would stop gum-bashing.

'I'll wash up!' volunteered Hywel abruptly, 'you go and sit down, del bach. Go and talk to the boys.'

Edward and Jimmie could have cheerfully murdered him! But of course they had just been to church, so that wouldn't do at all! They retired into the front room and knew immediately what they were in for.

The bombardment continued until Mr Ingham rescued them, by calling for them for Sunday School, and though Jimmie considered that once a day was enough for religious instruction, anything would be better than having to endure Beth's nattering voice, perpetually irritating his eardrums.

Mr Ingham and the boys waited for Mrs Evans, the caretaker. She was accompanied by Megan and Sian, her daughters. She opened the door of Fron Deg, the little chapel in Union Street, tucked away behind the County Theatre. It was a small, friendly congregation, and there were three classes in the Sunday School. Little Sian Evans, a petite, doll-faced girl, sat with Edward, whose cheeks would colour up whenever she spoke in Welsh, which was the only language she knew, whereas Megan, the eldest, was bi-lingual, like her mother.

Mrs Evans was a caring mother, whose husband, Dafydd, was away at sea. So among other things, she prayed for the day when he would come safely home again, and they could be a complete family once more.

Mr Burrows the lay-preacher, welcomed the lads into the little flock, and they felt pleased that they were considered important enough to be mentioned and smiled shyly. Mr Burrows was a fat little man, with a bald head, his dark brown eyes smiled at everyone through heavy, horn-rimmed glasses, which seemed too large for his round face. He was a jolly man, with what seemed like a permanent grin on his face, and he rocked on his heels whenever he said something he considered amusing.

There were times though, when he was serious, like when he was delivering one of his sermons. With a stern look when necessary, he would pound the Bible with his clenched fist, and his moustache and eyebrows twitched, especially when he was talking about the problems of the demon drink, and deadly sins, his favourite subjects. Some in the congregation were highly amused to see the bushy moustache twitch from side to side, which unintentionally detracted from the gravity of his sermon!

New red hymn books were handed round, and all present sang harmoniously and from the heart, or so it seemed, though some of the smaller ones like Edward, were unable to read. He and Jimmie were fascinated by the Welsh tongue, and loved to listen to the others.

Whenever the weather was stormy, and the winds blew off the mountains and down the straits, and the clouds were heavy and grey, one of the chosen hymns would be one which was to become a life-long favourite with Jimmie; *Eternal Father* or *For Those in Peril on the Sea.*

Whenever this was sung, a lump would come up into his throat, and he would think of his dad and the dangers faced by all those at sea, especially so now, with a war on. He wondered where he was and what he was doing? He hoped that he had time to think of him sometimes? Then there was Tim, Gwenda's boyfriend, who was also in the Merchant Navy and she worried about him and missed him.

Beth had given the boys a ha'penny each for the collection, and they dropped the coins obediently onto the collection plate, but at the same time, hungrily eyeing the silver coins that were already lying there. Alas! They wouldn't dare take any of them, because too many eyes were scanning the holy offerings, and of course, someone far greater had His eyes on them as well. He was always watching!

After Sunday School was over, there were the usual conversations, but Mrs Evans busied herself pushing the long polished wooden benches to each side of the chapel, ready for the floor to be mopped. Edward did his best to help, but they were too heavy for such a small boy. Nevertheless his efforts were smiled upon by Mrs Evans, though Sian giggled and made childish remarks in Welsh. Her mother chastised her and told her that it was very sad for a little boy to be away from his mum and dad. So she gave him a little smile and a wave, as they all left the chapel for their various homes.

As they ate their tea, the silence didn't last for long. It was shattered as usual by a barrage of questions from Beth. 'What have you learned today, boys? How did you get on with your new friends? What hymns did you sing? Did you behave yourselves? How many people were there?'

She blew into the hot tea and paused for breath. 'You did put your money into the collection plate, didn't you? Eat now, tell me everything on the way to chapel tonight. That will be nice now, won't it, del bach?'

The last question was aimed at Hywel, and she looked him straight in the eye, as he replied.

'Oh! Of course, Beth del.'

Jimmie almost choked on his meat-paste sandwich, his mind working frantically to think of how he was going to wangle his way out of going to chapel yet again. Edward hadn't cottoned on yet to what was in store, as he was concentrating on his food, it was only when Beth retreated to the pantry to get their dishes of jelly, and Hywel was loading the crockery noisily into the sink, that Jimmie whispered to Edward.

'Did yer 'ear that?'

'Hear what?' Edward asked, innocently.

'Chapel again tonight ...' Jimmie stopped abruptly, as Beth arrived with the small green dishes of raspberry jelly and placed them in front of each boy.

'There we are lads, not quite set, dash it, and they've been on the cold slab too. Never mind, eat now.'

Hywel left the dishes in the sink and returned to his chair, only to resume his finger-tapping on the window whilst swallowing his slithery red jelly.

'Not bad though, is it, del bach?' Beth said to her husband as she sipped her jelly, Hywel agreed, as was usual. He would never dare to criticise his wife's cooking, or the way she prepared her meals, as she always thought of herself as a good cook.

Inwardly he thought, 'Hell! How can anyone get so enthusiastic about a dish of damn jelly?'

Beth always liked to be complimented, even on the simplest of meals, and Hywel always tried to comply, and the newcomers were rapidly learning to do the same.

With another meal over, the boys washed and got ready for evening chapel. Beth straightened all their ties, then eyed them up and down to see that they were all immaculate. No one ever managed to leave the house without first being carefully scrutinised. She was equally particular about herself, and many times would leave the boys standing in the hall, while she slipped upstairs to take a last look at herself in the full length wardrobe mirror. Yes, she had three boys to look after now, and she liked them all to do as she said, though Hywel had developed a slight deafness, which was very convenient at times.

It was when she slipped upstairs that Jimmie whispered to Edward, 'Yer could 'ave said summat, said yer felt sick, or yer 'ad a bellyache. Yeah, that would 'ave done it,' and he gave the small lad a dig with his elbow.

'Tell 'er yerself,' retorted Edward, rebelliously, 'I'm 'avin' nowt ter do wi' it. It's you that's doin' the moanin', sides, I don't want any o' that oil again, it's 'orrible!'

'Aw, shurrup, yer little nit, proper little sunbeams we're gonna be,' replied Jimmie angrily.

Before he could say anything else, they were being ushered out of the door and were on their way to chapel. They didn't have far to go to the Tabernacle, on Garth Road, near the gasworks, and as they entered, Beth removed the boys' caps. She made her way to the balcony, and the rest of them followed her. It was a place she had occupied since her childhood, and the seats were of red plush upholstery and quite comfortable. Perhaps a little too comfortable for small bottoms, and very different from the hard wooden seats at Sunday School. Edward grinned as he settled himself into a comfy position.

Jimmie shot him a withering look, 'Yer a little twerp, yer must be enjoyin' this Sunday lark.'

Beth smiled and nodded to her many friends in the congregation, and at the same time, pointed to the lads, then to herself, like a mother hen who had successfully hatched a couple of fine chicks.

Hywel was unconcerned, cleaning his reading glasses repeatedly, and Jimmie wondered if he felt like they did about being cooped up in an overcrowded chapel?

Hywel was a sun worshipper, as his bronzed appearance showed, and he wished he was sitting in the back garden at this minute, instead of where he was, but he had to please Beth, and after all, it wasn't for long, he could always nod off for a minute or two.

Without any warning, a thunderous blast from the huge organ pipes burst forth, almost frightening Edward out of his skin. A rousing introduction to a traditional hymn was played, at which point all the congregation stood erect, hymn books held high, and heads thrown back, as they rendered *Cwm Rhondda - Guide Me O Thou Great Jehovah.*

The harmonious Welsh voices raised the rafters, but Jimmie and Edward, not knowing the hymn, even if it had been in English, were fed up to the back teeth!

Jimmie muttered something to Edward, but before he could utter another word, he was cracked on his bald head with Hywel's hymn book, an accurate and deadly weapon. Needless to say, that quietened him down.

A fifteen minute sermon was delivered by a tall, lean, bespectacled man, in a navy pin-striped suit. His monotonous voice had a soporific effect on Edward, who was tired after a hard day. His little head flopped forward onto his chest and he started to dribble, only to be quickly aroused when a droplet of saliva landed on his bare leg. The sermon ended unexpectedly. At least, Jimmie thought so, and he was delighted to think that they would soon be outside in the fresh air, as it was so hot.

Once again the hymn books were opened, and the joyful throng burst forth once more. The two boys never seemed to be able to find the page number.

'Sian would have found it for me,' thought Edward.

Beth loved her singing, and had a well-trained, beautiful, contralto voice; once having had the pleasure of performing on radio for the BBC. Whereas Hywel, although he made every effort to stay in tune, was tone deaf, so he might just as well have remained silent. In his opinion he deserved full marks for trying, and of course, it pleased Beth.

As previously mentioned, the gasworks was close by, and there was always the smell from the coke and coal after it had been processed into gas, and this foul smell penetrated the Tabernacle. Some of the congregation became agitated when the awful pong drifted in, and when on this occasion it rose to the balcony, Jimmie and Edward started to snigger.

Beth's face coloured up, she knew why they were guffawing, and was unable to restrain her blushes. She was mortified, but relieved her embarrassment by clouting each boy on the head, followed by one from Uncle Hywel for good measure! This all happened during the last hymn.

At last a closing blessing was read by the tall preacher, during which Jimmie half-opened his eyes, and noticed a stout little woman, hurrying herself along the crowded pew, eager to get outside for some reason! Jimmie's shoulders shook as he chuckled silently.

'Owd stinky drawers, old Polly the Pong, must have been her makin' the stink,' he thought, 'else why is she leavin' in such a hurry?'

Finally, with the prayer over, people chatted together noisily. Edward, still seated, rubbed the fuzz from his eyes.

'Ready for bed now, are we?' laughed Beth, patting his head, as he rose from his warm seat.

They made their way from their seats, chatting to acquaintances and bidding them 'nos da' and emerged into the warm, September, sunlight.

On their walk back, Jimmie was thinking that the idea of bed on such an evening and so early, was unjust, and that back home he would be out with the gang, enjoying their escapades together. However he knew that there was no use arguing about the subject; he wouldn't even dare to broach the matter.

So at last they reached the house, and as soon as they were inside, Beth said, as she hung her coat on the hall-stand, 'Put your sandals under the stairs lads. Hurry now, it's way past eight o'clock!'

They did as they were told, and Jimmie's thoughts again raced back to the gang, and how he missed them all. Even though he was billeted in a nice home, for which he was truly thankful, he still missed the old way of life, which could not be easily forgotten, but he realised he couldn't have both and had to make the best of things. He pulled off his sandals and put them away.

'Me mam calls dese, Jesus boots,' Edward remarked seriously, as he placed his sandals neatly together next to Jimmie's. 'I tink Jesus'll be pleased with us terday Jim, yer know, goin' ter church an' all dat?'

Jimmie didn't respond, he had his own ideas about attending church and chapel three times in one day, especially when he never had to go at all in Liverpool.

Beth and Hywel chuckled quietly at their natural, childish remarks.

Beth suddenly clapped her hands and announced, 'Come on, now, up the dancers,' fondly recalling times when her father would come out with the same phrase.

They obediently climbed up the stairs and started to brush their teeth, 'Don't know what yer brushin' dem for, Eddie lad, they're arf 'angin' out o' yer tunnel,' Jimmie said, spitting out.

'Shurrup,' he gurgled in reply, 'nowt ter do wi' yer.'

The pink Gibb's toothpaste ran down Edward's chin.

'Cor,' he thought as he wiped his frothy mouth, 'e's always moanin.'

At last they were in bed, Edward settling down, his head buried away as usual under the sheets, curled up like a little hamster.

'Hey, lar! Yer not asleep, 'aven't yer fergotten somethin', yer thunder-mug. 'ave yerself a pee. Blinkin' 'eck, gorra remind 'im now to 'ave a wee. Cor! It's takin' yer a long time, must 'ave a bladder like a casey (football),' Jimmie yawned. 'Crikey, all dis chapel stuff 'as made me all worn out.'

Edward had just got back into bed when Beth came in, 'Nos da, lads, Clothes neatly folded? Good!' She leaned across the bed to adjust the roller blind, then drew the heavy dark brown curtains that her husband had fitted that morning.

'Blackout now lads, don't want any light showing, do we? Nos da now, sweet dreams.' She closed the door.

'Nos da!' called out the two boys, thinking how clever they were to pick up on the Welsh so soon.

'I wonder if she meant not to let the light shine in 'cos it's still daylight, or is it to bamboozle us into thinkin' it's later than it really is?' said Jimmie when she'd gone. He smiled as he remembered the blackout that his sister had tried to pin up, or nail up. 'Ell, she 'ammered a rusty old nail into the gaspipe. Cor! Coulda blown us all up an' dat.'

It had been an eventful day, and he was ready for sleep, 'Nos da,' he chuckled, 'nos da, Eddie lad.'

There was no reply from Eddie lad. He had already dropped off, exhausted by the day's events.

'Good old Mr Ingham, 'e's the gear,' muttered Jimmie, as he turned to face the dark, blacked-out, window, drew the clean cool sheet up to his chin and was soon in dreamland.

CHAPTER EIGHT
That Damn Cart

'You know where St Mary's school is, don't you, Jimmie bach? Opposite the Tabernacle, in Garth Road? Well, you'll probably go there to get assessed for your regular school, and you too, Edward, lucky boy you are. I can see your school from my bedroom window, it's the church house on the opposite side. I'll be able to watch you come and go, so no dawdling, you'll have plenty of time to get there.'

As Beth spoke to the boys, she was not impressed by their return glances, as they digested the unwelcome news about their going to school. They had assumed that school was a thing of the past; this was bad news indeed! They had so enjoyed the mornings paddling and skimming smooth pieces of slate over the still sea. To think that Corky Green and Miss Crosby, had been making arrangements for their schooling! They had also enquired of their foster parents if the children had heard from their parents in Liverpool, as was evident in Beth's next remarks.

'Your mothers must be anxious about you and where you are staying? Perhaps it would be a good idea if you wrote little notes to them. Jimmie will help you, Edward. You've got money for stamps in your moneybox now. Do you know, some evacuees have had letters and postal orders already from home, so you must write straight away, the pair of you.'

'Yes, Missus, er Auntie, I'll help Eddie with his first,' Jimmie said, and true to his word, he sat down at the kitchen table with Edward alongside him, pencil in hand and notepad in front of him.

'What's yer ma's name, Eddie? I'd better call 'er mam shall I?' He started to write.

'Dear Mam,' he spoke as he wrote, 'dat's a good start isn't it? *It's nice 'ere in Wales. Yer should see me now, an' me mate; his name is Jimmie Mac. He's nice an' he lives wid me.'*

Jimmie wrote on as if he was writing to his own family before closing the letter with *'love from,'* then turning to Edward he said, 'Just put yer name on 'ere, Eddie lad, an' put some crosses on as well, dem's kisses.' He pointed to the place, then said, 'dat'll do now. Let Auntie Beth do the envelope as I don't know where yer live, an' 'sides, I might make a mess of it.'

Jimmie was glad that was over and hoped the lad would soon learn to write for himself, or he could see it being a regular job!

Beth read the short letter that Jimmie had written and congratulated him, 'Good for you, lad. Well done indeed, fair play now, yes you've done very well. Auntie is pleased.'

Both lads raced up to Orme Road Post Office.

'Tuppence isn't goin' to go far, is it, Eddie? Not when a stamp costs three ha'pence. Anyway if yer gets mugged from yer ma, yer can split it wid me fer writin' yer letters, okay?'

Eddie agreed.

'There it goes, off ter the Pool,' Jimmie said, as he lifted Edward up so he could drop the letter into the red pillar box. 'Yer very first letter ter yer ma!' As they walked slowly back down Glynne Road, Jimmie said to Edward, 'Is der any other kids in yer 'ouse, Eddie? Yer know, brudders an' sisters?'

'No, only me,' Edward replied, 'an' me mam's on 'er own, me dad went ter join up in the army,' he said proudly but sadly.

'Cor! Yer didn't tell me dat Eddie, no brudders an' sisters, an' yer dad a blinkin' 'ero!'

As they continued their walk, they spotted some council workmen felling a huge tree. The top and overhanging branches had to be lopped off first, so that all that remained was the enormous tree trunk. Sand had been thickly-spread over the pavement, ready to take the impact, and to prevent the paving stones from being cracked when the tree fell. The lads watched excitedly from a distance.

'Wonder if they'll shout 'timber' when it drops, like they do in the pictures? It could be in Welsh. Dunno what that'd be though; it'd be summat.'

Jimmie was explaining to Edward about trees being chopped down in forests, and how the lumberjacks shouted 'timber', when he noticed the man from the bottom house, who had the torn trousers, standing near by.

'Don't look now,' he said quietly, 'but look who's der. It's dat queer feller. No, don't look! Remember what Auntie said, just move away slowly Eddie, maybe 'e won't notice us.'

'Hello Einian!' called one of the workmen to the strange-looking man, 'and how's mam?'

'Hello, Mr Jones, we are both very well you know, diolch,' replied the shabby fellow.

By this time Jimmie and Edward were almost back at the house, though they looked round a few times to check if the man was following them. He wasn't, he was deep in conversation with the workmen, so Jimmie was very relieved.

'My you've got red faces,' said Beth. 'Have you been running? Did you manage to post your letter? Tea's almost ready now, come along.'

'We saw dat funny feller Auntie,' said Edward, dat feller called Onion.'

'Do you mean the man from the bottom house?' Beth couldn't hold back her laughter, and was in hysterics bent over the back of a kitchen chair. 'My goodness, Edward, it's Einian, not Onion,' and she burst into laughter again. 'Sorry lads, can't help it, you're so funny.'

The boys looked puzzled, and couldn't really see the funny side of Beth's behaviour as she giggled like an overgrown schoolgirl.

'Have your tea, boys,' she laughed, as she left them in the kitchen.

'Not gonna tell us what's so funny, is she?' said Edward, as he ate his sandwiches.

'Musta been summat you said, Eddie, 'cos that's when she started laughin,' Jimmie said. 'Eat now. Yes indeed, eat now,' he mocked, patting Edward on the head, 'an' don't ferget ter put yer meg in yer moneybox lads.'

Saturday morning was always bustling with activity. Shoppers and merchants alike were busy. Throngs of people crowded the High Street, many of them stocking up with tins and other items that they could store away when things started to get scarce, which wouldn't be long, apparently. Two young boys were among the shoppers. One of them, the older of the two, was pushing a home-made cart.

'Here!' he shouted, 'you push it fer a change, yer'll 'ave ter earn yer keep, like me, just look at me 'ands, they're all red, an' they 'urt summat rotten!'

Jimmie dropped the shafts of the little cart that Hywel had spent all Friday evening making. He was very proud of his handiwork, as his usual limit of woodworking was chopping firewood. To a large wooden box, he had added two old pram wheels that Bob, his neighbour, had brought from the tip where he worked. It was a good job, because he could make a tidy bit of extra money from the odds and ends he found there, the pram wheels being a good example. The shafts were two lengths of rough wood, nailed one on either side, making the cart complete.

'Don't start runnin' wid it, or yer'll finish up inside it,' Jimmie warned, as he spit on his sore hands, 'damn stupid ting.'

Edward pushed the rickety contraption up the High Street. Pedestrians who saw them coming, dodged quickly out of the way, for fear of being run down, or at the very least, having their ankles smashed by the learner driver.

Jimmie walked along behind his mate, feeling stupid because the cart wheels were squeaking loudly; Hywel having forgotten to oil them. As he was going along the street, he reflected that it was a wonder Uncle Hywel hadn't stencilled his name on the side of the cart. He could just see it, H Hughes & Sons.

'Flippin' 'eck, just listen to it. It'll be singin' in Welsh in a bit. Yer'd think 'e coulda purra drop of oil on the damn ting,' he moaned to Edward.

People within earshot smiled or laughed at the funny duo with their cart, but the boys were past caring. They had their orders to do the shopping! Polfreman's, the fruit and veg shop, was their first port of call.

'Steady, Eddie! Yer goin' past; reverse back a bit! Back, back, giz the shafts 'ere!'

Jimmie took command of the cart and steered it expertly into the shop. Potatoes, carrots, one large cabbage, dark green it had to be, were loaded into the conveyance. The items were carefully crossed from Beth's list by the shopkeeper, then handed back to Jimmie, along with the change. The shopkeeper was very tall and thin, and Jimmie thought to himself, that a good pan of scouse would fatten him up.

'No fiffees?' he asked.

'Fiffees? What's Fiffees? Never heard of them,' Mr Polfreman replied, with a perplexed look on his face.

'Well den, what's dat picture on yer winder? F-y-f-f-e-s b-a-n-a-n-a-s, see der, look fer yerself.'

Jimmie was determined to get his point across, 'Those curved yeller tings dat yer unzip.'

By this time several customers were inside the shop, patiently listening to this strange dialogue. Mr Polfreman's eyes glanced across to the display posters on the shop windows and he let out a roar of laughter. He said something in Welsh, slapped his knee, then pulled out a spotted handkerchief from the pocket of his brown smock, to wipe his streaming eyes. He pointed to the sign, and in between pointing, he laughed heartily at the boy.

'Fyffes, lad, Fyffes! that's how you say it!' chuckled the greengrocer.

By now a large crowd had gathered to see what was going on. Jimmie waited patiently for the rollicking laughter to cease, while the shopkeeper was telling the crowd of people that he had never, in all his years, experienced anything like this before, and retold the tale of Jimmie and the 'Fiffees'.

There was a pause and the shop grew quieter, so Jimmie ventured, 'Right, well, giz a bunch o' dem Fyffes.' He was eager to get the purchase that his Auntie Beth had asked for to please her.

'Sorry lad, we haven't any!' came Mr Polfreman's light-hearted reply.

'Well den, why didn't ya say so?' Jimmie sighed, picking up the shafts of the cart.

They steered it out of the shop, whilst the shopkeeper again related to all his customers, the funny incident that had just occurred. The cart gave an occasional bounce on the cobbled High Street, sometimes ejecting a spud or two, Edward retrieved them and casually threw them back, oblivious to the onlookers. The rattling and ear-piercing squeaking continued, the noise getting louder and louder.

Inside the Co-op, Wyn Jones carefully placed the items that Beth had listed into a cardboard box: one jar of jam, one jar of marmalade, half a pound of cheese - Cheddar, half a pound of butter - Welsh, four jars of Sutherland's meat paste, no other would do, beef paste or beef and ham only!

With the box loaded, Wyn placed it inside the cart, all the provisions neatly-packed and orderly arranged, and of course, the two large crusty cobs, wrapped in tissue paper, were carefully placed on top. Beth insisted that the cobs had to be really crusty, she would accept no substitute, as Jimmie was soon to learn after his many return trips to take back unwanted, 'not so crusty', cobs, On these occasions he cursed the inventor of the crusty cob!

'Why de 'ell can't she be like any other woman? Or like me mam, an' gerra big soft loaf of bread, an' cut us some real door-knockers, summat yer can get yer gob into,' he would moan. 'She'd win 'ands down fer carvin' the thinnest slices in the world. Like flies' wings dey are, course, it makes the bread go further!'

On their way past the barracks, they paused to watch the soldiers change their posts, and got a smile and a wink from one of them. A cheerful smile went a long way in those dark days of wartime, and no doubt the soldier was thinking of his own kids back home, or wherever they happened to be?

On arriving back at the house and Beth being pleased with them for executing the errands so quickly and efficiently, the boys thought it a good time to report back to Uncle Hywel about the squeaky wheels and the shafts of the cart, and how they hurt their hands.

Hywel immediately squirted some oil on the wheels and sanded down the rough handles, so they would be easier for the boys to hold. He even suggested that he make a cover for the cart, so that on rainy days the contents would stay dry, at which Jimmie and Edward both nodded in agreement.

A footnote about foodstuffs and rationing.
In January 1940 rationing began. Bacon, sugar, butter and meat were rationed in March of that year, and soon cooking fats, sweets, cheese, conserves, eggs (one each per week), clothes and other things were supply-controlled. From 8 January 1940, a week's supply of groceries was limited to 4oz bacon, 12oz sugar and 4oz butter, but these allowances fluctuated according to availability throughout the war. Jam was in short supply, and

tinned items and biscuits were issued on a points system. Those who had evacuees billeted on them were paid 10/6 for the first child, then 8/6 for any additional child.

CHAPTER NINE
Old 'Tide'

Old Taid Jones had spent most of his working life at sea. He was second mate on the small coaster that operated from Penrhyn Quay up the west coast to the Caledonian Canal, delivering slate quarried by hard-working Welshmen.

Conditions at Bethesda were no doubt similar to those in any other slate quarry. Whatever the weather; rain, shine, snow, ice, cold, wet or dry, the quarrymen carried on their arduous and dangerous tasks, cutting and preparing the blue/grey stone into smooth, flat slabs. Their pay was a pittance, and their families found it hard to make a living on what their menfolk earned, even though they stayed up at the work site throughout the week, working long hours and only coming home at weekend.

Old Taid was familiar with many of these men, because of the cargo the coaster carried to various places along the British Coast. Taid was now in his mid-sixties but looked older. He had a bronchial condition, which prevented him from venturing too far outside, as his breathing was laboured and difficult. His thick grey moustache drooped over his mouth, and his light blue eyes were sunk deep into their sockets, but twinkled slyly when he slapped Auntie Megan's bottom, and he laughed heartily at his eldest daughter's annoyance. Taid often suffered coughing spells, and a spittoon was kept by the side of his high-backed basket chair. His face would quiver, and poor Meg would attend to his needs, wiping his face with a warm, damp cloth, then making him as comfortable as she could.

After all, he was her father, and for all his peculiar ways, she loved him.

Taid very rarely ventured out, but when he did he would make his pilgrimage to the Vault, a pub at the bottom of the High Street. He would amble along slowly, stopping and starting at regular intervals, whenever he needed to rest to get his breath. Shuffling along, a few steps at a time, stopping, looking around, and now and again, taking a clean white hankie from his pocket to wipe his brow, and also the inside of his bowler hat. It was pitiful to watch him as he clung to the iron railings with one hand, whilst leaning heavily on his much-needed walking stick, with the other.

Passers-by would wave or bid him good day, but never stopped for a discussion, as old Taid was noted for being argumentative and grumpy.

On reaching the pub, he always sat in the same chair near the window, and despite the condition of his lungs, proceeded to pollute the air with tobacco smoke, much to the annoyance of other patrons. He knew that smoking wasn't good for his chest, but he stubbornly refused to give up one of his few remaining pleasures, continuing to smoke black twist in his little clay pipe. His two pints of mild lasted him for two hours, then he made his exit without speaking, and began his wearisome journey back home.

On entering the house after one of these outings, his first words were always the same: 'Where's Gwen? (his grand-daughter) Is she with that rogue, that Tim, whatever his name is? Is she?'

Megan always got the rough end of his tongue, or the proverbial stick, sometimes even literally, and had threatened to leave her father to fend for himself, but she had a soft heart and he knew it, and she always relented. She cried silently in her bed at night at her father's bad moods, and wished that her husband Idris, was alive.

It saddened her deeply when she remembered how she had lost him, at such an early age, with the dreaded TB. Gwenda barely knew her father, only remembering his thick, navy-blue jersey, which she tried to pull over his neck when he'd had a pint or two. But he had been a loving husband and father during his short life.

Gwenda was sick of the harsh, threatening, conduct of her grandfather, who objected so strongly to her friendship with Tim. She would often go out to get away from his arguments, but at the same time, she was uneasy whenever she left her mother alone with old Taid Jones!

Auntie Beth was fully aware of the situation, and went across to the house frequently to appease the old man. On one of these occasions, she took the boys across to meet her father, and introduced them to him.

'This is Jimmie MacLean from Everton, Taid bach, and this is Edward Jones.'

'Speak up, lads, I can't hear you now! Speak up.'

The old basket chair squeaked, as the old man fidgeted in his seat.

'Nice ter see yer, Mister,' Jimmie said boldly, in his broad Everton twang.

'Me too, Mister,' Edward added loudly.

Old Taid laughed heartily. 'Put the kettle on, Meg. Let's have some tea, and make some for my mates here!'

Meg and Beth couldn't believe their ears, Taid was actually being hospitable, she hadn't heard him so cheery for years. They both went into the kitchen chattering about this rare event, and wondering if these two small boys could be the start of a new side to their father?

The two sisters were very close, Megan being the elder of the two, and had enjoyed a warm relationship all their lives. Their mother had been a very kind and loving person, and it had rubbed off on the girls, though Megan's capacity for affection was deeper than Beth's.

Whilst they were busy in the kitchen, Jimmie and Edward chatted to Taid.

'You say your father is at sea?' asked Taid. 'How long has he been in the Navy?'

He turned aside to spit into the receptacle, and a puff of ash flew from it onto the newspaper on which it stood. The boys looked at it and then at each other.

'Oh! He's been in over twenty years now, never see 'im much though,' answered Jimmie, 'an' when 'e is 'ome, 'e's on the ale with 'is mates. 'E's been all over the place. Argy (Argentina), India, America, places all along the Med, an' others too!'

Jimmie felt quite at ease with the old chap. Edward just sat and listened to what he considered to be boring talk, and gazed around, his mind wandering, as well as his eyes. He noticed some strange-looking pottery along the mantleshelf; dogs with chains around their necks, and white horses rearing up on their hind legs.

Meanwhile, Jimmie was deep in conversation with old Taid, not even noticing that tea and Bara Brith had been brought in on a tray, and that the two sisters were listening, enthralled by their father's interest in the boys.

'Course,' Jimmie went on, 'e's in the Royal Navy now,' and he went on to explain to Taid, that his dad, along with many of his mates, had volunteered for active duty with the Royal Navy just before the outbreak of war, and was accepted immediately.

Jimmie was proud to be talking about his dad and his achievements, and so the whole conversation was centred around the sea, the Navy, ships and the port of Liverpool.

'Aye, I know Lime Street and all the docks,' Taid reminisced, proving that he was familiar with many parts of Liverpool, by reeling off a few pub names along the Dock

Road, which he had frequented on his many trips to the port. 'Aye, lad, it's not a bad old place. I've had some good times there, and good mates as well. Come on now lads, eat and enjoy it.'

The old man invited them to eat as his hand trembled, taking a piece of the fruit cake. The sisters stared at each other in amazement. Their father's change of attitude was unprecedented, but they weren't going to grumble!

Meg smiled at Jimmie approvingly, 'Bechod! Indeed, out of the mouths of babes, yes, indeed!' she quoted, happily.

It was good to see Taid so amused, so talkative, so much at ease.

'I'm going now,' said Beth, after the tea had been drunk and the cake eaten. 'See you later now, Taid, and thank you, Meg, for the tea and cake. Da bo chi, ta-ra now.'

Jimmie and Edward also thanked Auntie Megan, and Edward said to Taid, 'Ta-ra Tite, see yer again.'

Jimmie whispered to him that it was 'Tide' and not 'Tite' and explained that it was like the tide that came in. 'Yer know, like the sea, T-I-D-E.'

At this, Beth, Megan and their father, roared with laughter, and Beth explained to the boys that the word 'taid or 'tide', as Jimmie had called him, was the Welsh word for grandfather.

'Da bo chi, lads,' Taid called as they were leaving. 'You sure are a tonic to an old sick man, ha ha!' and he exploded into laughter again.

Megan returned to her father after seeing Beth and the boys to the door, saying to him. 'Now Taid, what about a nice tail-end of haddock with bara menyn, for supper?' and she plumped up a cushion and placed it behind her father's head.

'That will do very nicely, Meg bach, very nicely indeed, thank you. I'm looking forward to those lads coming again, I am. What a nice afternoon!' and he eased himself into a more comfortable position. 'I'll just have forty winks now until supper-time,' then he promptly fell fast asleep.

Meanwhile, as Megan was busy in the kitchen, preparing supper, she was happier than she had been for a long, long, time, and thought how nice it was that Taid had called her Meg.

'The grumpy old sod hasn't called me that for years,' she said, and smiled to herself. 'Those dear little boys, bechod, God bless them!'

She sincerely believed, in her simple way, that these little Scousers had been sent to bring joy and happiness to a little Welsh lady and Gwenda, her daughter, and to an ill-tempered old taid. Yes, they were going to fit in very well these two boys, and become a bit of 'Welsh Scouse' in the heart of Wales.

Gwenda had spent most of the day with Tim, her boy-friend, from Garston. She had met him the previous summer whilst he was on holiday with his parents, visiting his aunt in Portmadoc.

Tim Price was a slimly-built young man, of medium height, with dark, crinkly, wavy hair. He was clean-shaven, and had a friendly grin, revealing even white teeth. When he laughed, his head shook, so that a curl of his hair would drop over his eye-brow. Gwenda had grown to love the young man and his courteous ways, and would finger the curl of his hair back into place, at the same time gazing into his blue-grey eyes. He was conscious of a very slight limp, though it didn't hinder him, and often joked to Gwenda about his 'wooden leg', and that if he was ever shipwrecked, he could float for days on his 'peg-leg' until he was rescued.

'You mustn't joke about it, Tim del,' Gwenda said, as she drew close to him, 'don't ever say such things, even in jest, I couldn't bear it if anything happened to you.'

Tim took her in his strong, young arms, and kissed her tenderly and she responded, kissing him back.

'You must take great care and come back to me safely,' and she buried her face into his shoulder, shedding a few tears. 'I'm sorry, dear, look what I've done to your clean white shirt,' she laughed then, and kissed him lightly on the cheek.

'Don't be upset, Gwen, dear, it will all be over soon, they say it will only last till Christmas,' he assured her, and caressed her soft light brown hair, which curled gently on her shoulders. 'We can write to each other as often as possible. I know it's not the same as being here, but it'll be something to look forward to.'

Gwen was smiling now, trying to be brave, as those precious moments together ticked away. The train was overdue but they didn't care; it meant extra time with each other, in fact, they didn't care if the train never came! Then the sound they dreaded, the thundering of the engine, could be heard not far away. Tim kissed Gwen, and they clung together, not wanting ever to part, but knowing that they must. The rest was a blur, as Tim climbed aboard, then was waving to her and she to him, as he disappeared from her view.

Gwenda gently lifted the latch on the back door, closing it quietly behind her, so as not to disturb her grandfather. She certainly didn't want a confrontation with him just now. Imagine her surprise, on entering the living room, on finding her mother and Taid eating supper together, both seemingly in a good humour.

'Come now Gwen, sit with us and have your supper. You don't want it to be cold, do you?' her grandfather said, picking a fishbone from his teeth.

Megan brought her daughter's supper to the table, a nice fish salad.

'I don't really feel hungry Mam,' said Gwen. 'It looks so nice too, but I don't think I can manage it.'

'Come now Gwen, bach,' coaxed Taid, placing his weathered old hand gently over Gwen's, 'I know what it's all about, done it too many times myself. No good these farewells and partings. What ship is he on your Tim?'

Gwenda was astounded by these remarks and stared at him disbelievingly. 'Whatever had happened to make Taid change his attitude so drastically towards her and her mam?' She replied quietly, 'He couldn't say, Taid. Only knows that he sails from Liverpool next week. He didn't know the name of the ship, or its destination, or even how long he'll be away for, so I've simply got to expect him when I see him, I suppose.'

Megan stirred her tea, as she watched and listened to her father taking an interest in his grandchild at last, and prayed that the peace would last indefinitely. It was a miracle!

After supper they sat together and listened to the nine o'clock news. Things were critical in Europe. Young men were being called up into the armed services, they were all going to be needed very badly before this war was over, and the whole of Britain was holding itself in readiness for what was to come, and may God help those in places like Liverpool, the home of the little visitors, who had suddenly helped to make Meg's home more peaceful and bearable. 'God bless them indeed!'

CHAPTER TEN
Corky and Staff

It was Monday 18th September. There were sixty-five or more boys assembled in St Mary's School Hall, in Deiniol Road.

'Mr England, a strange name for a man living in Wales,' Jimmie thought, was a slim, spritely, middle-aged man, with rosy cheeks and bright blue eyes. His rough-sounding voice seemed out of place with his character. He was very pleasant though, as he shepherded the boys into two large rooms, which extended into one when he pushed back the folding, floor-to-ceiling partition, smiling and joking with them. He positioned himself in front of a long blackboard and on it he chalked, in bold block letters:-

CROESO I GYMRU - WELCOME TO WALES

After registering, each boy was assigned to his respective school, and introduced to the staff who would be teaching him. Much to Jimmie's relief, he was to go to Garth School, just as Gwenda had predicted. Altogether there were forty boys destined to go to Garth, beginning on the 20th September.

The craft teacher, Mr England, looked like a little boy standing next to Mrs Barge, nicknamed Maggie. She was very broad in the backside, stocky, and looked as if she was ready for a scrum down. A stern look enveloped her face, and her hair was shingled. Jimmie tried to avoid her strange, piercing gaze. She didn't look quite right in her tweed skirt and white satin blouse. Her feet were gigantic, and on them she wore black brogues, which looked more like men's shoes than women's.

Never had Jimmie seen such feet attached to something so small in stature; she seemed as wide as she was tall, and he seriously wondered if she shaved?

Mr Roberts, responsible for history and geography, stood next to Maggie. He was tall and lean, and the two together gave the impression of a long mop and squat bucket. He looked rather untidy for a teacher. He had wispy, mousy hair, which he wore long and swept back. He had a long, hooked, nose and brown eyes, which narrowed as he scanned the boys over his half-moon, rimless, spectacles. His sports jacket and dark grey flannel trousers had the appearance of having been slept in, and looked shabby.

Mr Land, the sports and arts master, was next in line, and his appearance was just the opposite of his colleague. Jimmie thought he looked very smart indeed, as if he was dressed for a night out on the town. His black hair was heavily Brylcreamed and brushed into a neat parting. His eyes were very dark, like pieces of coal, and he looked more like a foreigner than an Englishman. His nose turned up a little, though without spoiling his good looks. In fact, he was a very handsome man, young too, compared to the other members of staff. Also, as Jimmie was to learn later, Mr Land was very athletic, and an excellent art teacher.

Last, but certainly by no means least, the boys were introduced to the headmaster, George 'Corky' Green, who was notorious for his harsh caning. Willie had told Jimmie all about Corky, back home in Liverpool, so he had an in-built dread of the man.

Corky Green was not very tall but he was slim, and his grey suit hung loosely on him. His thin, tight, lips opened narrowly into what Jimmie thought was a threatening grin, barely showing his teeth; more like a snarl. His thinning hair was combed straight back, and the only good feature about him were his bright blue eyes, though they were set beneath a rather large, protruding forehead. His ever-constant companion, a thin but flexible bamboo cane, nestled under his right armpit.

He leaned awkwardly, resting his left hand on the nearby desk, which was later to be used as a caning buttress, when administering punishment. Though his position and manner demanded respect, he earned only hatred and enmity from both boys and staff alike.

Corky's face was as hard as granite, and sometimes even the colour matched. Jimmie wondered how someone could become so aggressive, simply because of an injury to his foot in the Great War? Maybe he felt self-conscious about the unsightly heavy boot he had to wear to balance his height, who knows? When he vented his anger so heavy-handedly, was it perhaps in retaliation for the injury he had suffered?

He was to be admired in some ways, striding briskly, despite his disability, from his temporary home near the railway station, to school every morning, leaving many a man standing, only using his green Rover car when the weather was inclement. In fact, when petrol rationing began, he garaged his vehicle for the duration of the war.

September days seemed never-ending, and it was pleasant to run down the winding cinder path, alongside the Afon, or gingerly cross the little unfenced bridge spanning the murky water, to then race through the long grass to school, where Beach Road merged with Garth Road.

The school itself was built of granite and had a blue slate roof. There was a low wall which sheltered various kinds of shrubs. The front entrance was used only by the staff, as pupils entered via a narrow lane, which ran up the side of the school and into a rear playground.

Jimmie soon made friends with many of the lads, who were a good lot or, as Jimmie said, 'the gear'. One pal, to whom he became quite close, was named Arthur Ross, and reminded Jimmie of his best pal back home in the Pool.

Poor Arthur suffered eye problems, and also to his embarrassment, had little bald patches on his head, and always wore a soft, black, shiny helmet, like the one that Amy Johnson wore in her plane.

Chubby Arthur carried home-made drumsticks down the inside of his stocking, and often beat out an accompaniment to *Sons of the Sea, All British Boys* and *Maggie May*. All the lads would join in the songs, or clap, stamp and whistle, much to the annoyance of the neighbours, whose gardens ran close to the boundary of the playground.

Sadly, Arthur's drumsticks were confiscated, so the whistling and warbling ceased. Arthur had a grin that spanned almost the whole of his face, and he confided to Jimmie with a wink, that he was going to whittle another pair.

Alas! These were also taken away from him, and he received two strokes of Corky's cane across each hand into the bargain. Undaunted he grinned, licked the palms of his hands, blew into them, and tucked them under his arms and returned to his desk, smiling from ear to ear. Arthur did make another pair, but wisely kept them out of sight of Corky Green.

The teachers in general, were very good to the boys, often overlooking the childish pranks they got up to, and thus earning the respect of their pupils.

On one occasion, when Mr Roberts had made a joke in class, and the boys laughed rather loudly, he warned them with a grin, 'Don't laugh too loudly, boys, or you'll turn Corky, green!'

The class was in uproar, and Corky gave strict instructions to the form teachers that any hilarity in class had to cease, except of course, when the headmaster himself, made a witty remark in assembly, then everyone was *expected* to laugh. Almost every boy had tasted his bamboo weapon, and Jimmie tried his best to keep out of trouble, dreading the time when he too, might feel its sting, after first hearing it whistle through the air before it fell onto soft young hands, causing indescribable, and sometimes, undeserved pain. Maybe Corky had an obsession, a secret mission, to cane as many boys as he could.

'Yeah,' said Jimmie to Arthur, 'I'll bet he's gorra soddin' great book recordin' all the whippin's that he's done.'

Time passed by and, in early December, Jimmie was racing across the field on his way home from school, when he was stopped by a boy from Friars School, a noted bully, older and stronger than himself. He barred Jimmie's way and grabbed him by the coat collar, restraining him.

Jimmie was not afraid of him but was worried that Corky Green would be passing along the road on his way home and he didn't want to be seen fighting, 'Let me go!'

'Don't give me any of that bloody Scouse talk, you sodding little ginger Mochyn.'

The Welsh lad had spoken in English, except for the last word, so Jimmie responded, as he tried to wriggle free, 'What was that you said in Welsh, lar?'

'Don't lar me, you Mochyn, dirty Scouse pig. Everything was peaceful here before you lot arrived.'

Before the Welsh lad could say another word, Jimmie twisted himself around, broke free from his clutches, and in true Scouse fashion, swung a mighty blow to the side of his face. He then shot off like a buck rabbit, down to the bridge, only to be caught up along the cinder path. Both boys rolled about, punching each other several times around the head and face.

Jimmie's thumps seemed to be having little effect on the college lad, then he remembered someone describing how he'd been 'nutmegged', and as he seemed to be coming off worse, he caught hold of the lad's collar, lunged forward, at the same time butting him with his head. Immediately his opponent was bent double, blood dripping through his fingers from his mouth, much to Jimmie's surprise, as he didn't think he had really hit him that hard.

He stood his ground, fists raised, 'Come on den, yer Welsh bugger, come on, let's see what yer can do now. Yer won't cross me path again, will yer? 'Cos next time I'll put yer bleedin' eye in a sling.'

The Friars lad retreated without a word, tears streaming into his bloodied mouth, his white shirt stained red.

Jimmie patted the dust from his jacket and trousers. Bits of cinder were embedded in his hands and knees. He limped along to Auntie Meg's house, where Gwen bathed the cinders and dirt from them with warm water, Dettol and pink lint.

'So, you gave him a pasting did you, Jimmie, bach?' old Taid asked approvingly.

'Well,' said Jimmie, 'it was either me or him, an' I were sure it weren't gonna be me. Yer see, I 'ad ter give 'im a nutmeg, 'e'd 'ave killed me udderwise.'

Taid laughed all the more. 'Did you hear that, Gwen? He gave him the Glasgow kiss,' and he chuckled as he lit his pipe, 'bet he won't do that again!'

'Ouch! Ouch!' Jimmie winced, as Gwen rubbed his hands.

'They're going to be sore, but I'll have to get them clean or they'll fester. There you are now, we'll just put some Germolene on them then that's a good job done.'

Old Taid looked on approvingly, 'Aye you've done a good job there Gwen, got enough cinders out of him to keep the fire going for a week,' and he winked at her, as she returned to the kitchen carrying the bowl of dirty water.

She was pleased that Taid was taking more interest in her and making life more tolerable for her mother.

Jimmie was a bit worried when he got back to Glynne Road, and wondered what Auntie Beth would say when she saw that he had been fighting, but much to his surprise, neither she nor Hywel said a word about it. Jimmie wondered if that was due to the fact that he now had a 'grandfather' keeping an eye on him, and they dare not risk a confrontation with him.

It was another early night for the two boys, 7pm on the dot. But it was no use protesting as early to bed was their fate, as long as they were at Auntie Beth's house.

'Into bed now, both of you, want you both fresh and bright for school now, don't we?' Beth coaxed. 'Early to bed, early to rise, makes boys healthy, wealthy and wise.'

'She's always quoting that,' thought Jimmie, but he couldn't figure out where the wealthy part came in. He hardly ever had any money, and if he did, it went straight into the moneybox!

'Ad yer well an' truly on the ropes, didn't 'e Jimmie that Welsh lad?' Edward said.

'Aah! Get yer peein' done, if yer don't, yer'll be a real early-riser,' Jimmie laughed, as he turned over to the window, his usual position.

'Nos da, goodnight, lads,' called Beth as she went downstairs.

'Goodnight, Auntie, nos da!' both lads responded together.

'Like His Master's Voice!' Jimmie commented.

'What's 'is master's voice?' Edward wanted to know.

'A bleedin' record, if yer wanna know!' replied Jimmie, impatiently.

'Good soldiers of the Lord,
Now the battle has been won.'

Corky Green beat time to the singing, his glasses perched on his forehead,

'Take shield and mighty arm.'

Without warning, there was a mighty crash. He had hurled a wooden blackboard duster at one of the lads who was not singing. Missing his head by inches, the missile landing noisily against one of the desks. Prayers were said for the men at war, the families at home and for the school.

'Abbott.'

'Sir.'

'Arrowsmith.'

'Sir.'

'Beecham.'

'Powders.'

'Who said that? Who said that?' Corky's cane crashed against the partition, almost shattering the glass panels.

The staff immediately saw the funny side and turned away from the angry master.

'I'll give you powders. I'll powder your hands for you!' he snarled in temper.

He continued to take the register.

'Lawton.'

'Sir.'

'Lewtas.'

'Sir.'

'MacLean.'

'Sir.'

Corky stared threateningly at Jimmie when he answered, 'Get out here boy. Stand over there.' He pointed to his desk.

'Magee.'

'Sir.'

'Newton.'

'Sir.'

It seemed like an eternity to Jimmie.

'Tye.'

'Sir.'

'Ross.'

'Sir.'

Jimmie looked at Arthur and shrugged, his mate winked and gave him that special grin. All were present. Corky signed the register, then slammed the book shut. He strode quickly towards Jimmie, and without saying a word, grabbed hold of his left wrist and gave him two stinging lashes on the palm of his hand, and then did the same with his other hand, ignoring the fact that his hands were already sore from the day before with the cinders.

'Go and run your hands under the cold tap,' Corky told Jimmie, 'and no more fighting.'

Mr Roberts accompanied Jimmie to the cloakroom. He didn't say anything, but the sight of Jimmie's swollen and bleeding hands was enough. He kept his thoughts to himself but said kindly, 'Take your time, MacLean, there's no rush.'

Jimmie felt as if he had no hands at all, but when the numbness wore off, he was in extreme pain. That evening, Hywel commented on the state of Jimmie's hands and told Beth that he was going to see Green, but the threat never materialised.

Jimmie complained to Edward, 'Uncle Hywel, for all his keep fit and PE in the evenings with the kids at Friars, and showing off his biceps and hairy chest and pretending to box, is a big soft bleeder. He hasn't the stomach to face Corky, even though he is much bigger, and could easily eat him for breakfast. If me old feller had been 'ere, 'e'd a knocked 'im back to Liverpool. Anyway 'e isn't 'ere, so I'll 'ave ter make the best of it!' sighed Jimmie, putting on a brave face.

Christmas came and went. The expected parcels from Liverpool never came. Edward had saved his pennies and so had Jimmie, the latter buying himself a pair of 'footy' boots and an old 'casey' (football), probably one that Hywel had scrounged from one of his evening classes. Edward bought a searchlight, which he played with continually, but was surprised and upset when the battery ran out. However, he enjoyed playing with his khaki-clad lead soldiers, and made funny noises and fought battles in his own little world.

The winter snows arrived, and the High Street was blocked. Hywel realised that it was impossible for the lads to do the shopping in the cart, so he had a brainwave. He would make a sledge! Heavy boards were nailed across two thick pieces of wood, and that was it, except for a piece of rope to pull it with, looped through two large staples on the front.

There were no steel runners which would have made it easier for the lads to pull it, and when it got wet they had to use all their combined strength to shift the loaded sledge, which often got stuck in the snow, the boxes sometimes becoming dislodged and sliding off. Their hands hurt more than when they were pulling the cart, but it was something they just got used to, coming to hate the snow rather than enjoying it, as most children do. They didn't even want to bother making snowmen or snowballs. They would certainly be glad when summer came!

After doing the shopping on Saturday mornings, they had to play out, even on the coldest days, and so Woolworth's became one of their regular haunts. The sledge, stupid contraption that it was, was left outside on the pavement, and they hoped that it would disappear, but there was no such luck! Anyway, Uncle Hywel would only make them another one. They stamped the snow off their feet and clapped their arms around their bodies before going into the store.

Jimmie said humourously, 'Blinkin' freezin', it's enough ter mek yer put another pair of bootlaces on, gerrin' us out of de 'ouse so's dey can 'ave a quiet day in on their own.'

They wandered into Woolworth's, and the tall, blonde supervisor smiled at the perished, rosy-faced, pair. She was used to seeing the two of them, and allowed them to remain in the store to stand by the iron radiators to dry off, or to get warm. Miss Davies, her second-in-command, also got to know the boys and let them stay, knowing they were not up to mischief. She felt sorry for the poor kids, they only wanted to thaw out.

Sweet rationing had not yet started, but the lads were always penniless anyway, and unable to buy any of the goodies on display. The tall brunette, with the big brown cow-eyes and thick lips which were painted bright red, always moved her jaws slowly, as if she was chewing or sucking on something that she'd secretly popped into her mouth. Sometimes she'd wink at the lads with one of her big, brown, eyes and beckon them over to the counter, whenever the supervisors were out of sight. She would look slyly around, then when the coast was clear, she would hurriedly put a few caramels, or other sweets, into their chapped hands, and at the same time, put her finger to her lips as if to say, 'Don't tell.'

The winter seemed endless, and Jimmie often lay awake at night, thinking of the gang and what they were doing? He also thought about his dad and where he was, was he in danger? He hoped he would see him soon. And what about his mam and the baby? He didn't even know the baby! Mary, Nellie and Art, what were they getting up to these days?

'Good bunch o' geezers they are!' Jimmie grumbled, 'not even droppin' me a line. Ah! Well!' he thought, 'gorra get that sheet o' corrugated iron termorrer, wonder warr 'e's gonna do wid dat?'

Bob, the 'demon barber', as Jimmie called him, had come across two pieces on the tip, and had already brought one back and put it in the garden for Hywel, but the other had still to be collected.

After their usual Saturday morning errands, they set off to Bangor tip, at the top end of the town, near to Caernarfon Road. On collecting the metal sheet, which was hidden under some bushes, so that no one else would take it, Jimmie realised what Hywel had let them in for when he saw the size of it.

The weight alone, never mind the size, made him wonder how he and Edward were ever going to get it down to Glynne Road. Between them, they slid it from beneath the foliage and struggled to get hold of each end.

'He (meaning Hywel), wasn't gonna carry it all that way. Suppose we get stopped an' somebody says we've nicked it?' he complained to Edward.

In fact they did get stopped, by a little fat man, as they were leaving the site, but when Jimmie mentioned Hywel and Bob, they were allowed to go on their way unhindered.

'Should 'ave brought the cart,' Edward panted, struggling at the rear.

Jimmie, walking in front, hands behind him and banging his bottom on the corrugated sheet with every step, shouted, 'That'd be no bloody good!'

They looked a sorry sight as they proceeded, with difficulty, down the High Street, and bore the brunt of many rude remarks and laughter from shoppers on the way.

Jimmie thought the awful journey would never end, but on reaching Glynne Road, he saw Hywel standing at the gate, waiting for them to arrive.

'Could 'ave come if he'd wanted to, the lazy bugger,' he muttered to Edward, just before they got to the house.

'Good lads,' said Hywel, lifting the metal sheet effortlessly up and over his head, 'have any problems?'

Without waiting for an answer, he carried it round the side of the house and into the back garden, leaving the boys behind and giving Jimmie the opportunity to grumble aloud.

'No, no problems, only carryin' the ruddy ting. Blinkin' 'eavy an' all. Blinkin' comin' all dis way ter fetch an' carry, shoulda gorra couple o' Irish Micks ter stop wi' 'em, dat's what dey shoulda done.'

The expedition had taken the boys most of the afternoon, so they had missed their dinner, and it was only tea that day, an early bath for their aching limbs and then bed! Neither of them had the energy to play around in bed or even to talk, as they were so exhausted, and they both fell asleep immediately.

Meanwhile, in the front room, Hywel sat in his easy chair, legs outstretched before the fire, wriggling his toes, well contented with his booty. He was planning the job that he would undertake, now that he had the equipment.

'Yes, just a few fine days and I'll redesign the garden,' he thought, 'get some early potatoes in. Yes, I'll try some marrow this time.'

Bob had been successful with marrows.

'I'll take some of the flowers out, and replace them with more vegetables. After all, we've been asked to dig for victory. I reckon there'll be less in the shops, so we can supplement with our own veggies.'

He was deep in thought, planning his new project, when Beth brought in his steaming cocoa, switched the radio on and listened eagerly to the nine o'clock news.

'No blinking good news, del bach,' she said, twiddling the control knob to another station. 'There you are now, much better that, isn't it?'

She moved her chair a little closer to Hywel, as the strains of dance music drifted out of the speaker, she put her arm over his shoulder, and they gazed into the red glow of the coals and sipped their nightly beverage.

'At least we're doing something for the war effort, del,' Hywel said, taking hold of her hand. 'You know,' he continued, 'I'm thinking of joining.'

The word 'joining' sent a shiver through Beth and immediately she let go of her husband's hand crying out, 'Joining? Joining? Joining what indeed?'

'It's alright, dear, don't get all agitated, it's only the local defence! There's about twenty of the lads from the council yard already in, and another fifty or so are swelling the ranks next week, maybe more. So I think we're going to have a good fighting force here in Bangor. So don't worry, I won't be going away.'

Beth settled herself again, and stroked his almost bald head. She stared into the fire, imagining her Hywel marching in front of a parade wearing his smart uniform. 'Yes indeed, she could just see him. How proud she would be, just as long as he didn't have to go away. She would have to see that he didn't.'

CHAPTER ELEVEN
Dig For Victory

The staff at Garth School gladly accepted the gardening equipment from Bangor Council. Some neglected land across the road from the school had been assigned to them, and their first job was to clear it of the grey chunks of stone. This the boys did, under supervision, by piling the stone into walls, which would give some sort of shelter for the plants they were to put in, as the east winds were so treacherous in this part of the country.

The boys enjoyed being outdoors and accomplished their tasks willingly, eager to show what they could contribute to the war effort. Everyone was doing his bit and joining in with relish. Besides, they had to show their appreciation to Bangor Council for the use of the land.

After their classroom instruction for the day, they went across to their plot and set to with gusto, first clearing the rough turf with new mattocks, again donated by Bangor Council. Now they were really digging for victory! Yes digging, and plenty of it was needed, before anything could be planted. So with lots of blood, sweat and tears, they unitedly cleared the huge plot of land, and were then ready to plan out their victory garden.

Rows of potatoes were sown first, as they were regarded as a priority. Their work was painstakingly undertaken, but they found it rewarding. Seaweed was used as a good manure, which they hoped would result in them growing a bumper crop. Blisters were the only pay the boys received, but they cheerfully bore their battle scars, except when Corky meted out his punishments, and didn't seem to care that the boys' hands were blistered. If anything, the canings seemed to be getting more frequent, much to the disgust of the staff, especially Mr Roberts.

John Lee, a scruffy-headed lad from Upper Bangor, received more than his fair share of strokes. He was a plain-looking lad, except when he pulled funny faces, much to the amusement of the others. Corky didn't appreciate his talents, and he would lay into him without pity.

Jimmie often wondered, 'Why members of the staff didn't intervene? Maybe they too, were afraid of Corky.'

The same boy was given ten strokes on each hand for being late, and the following day his hands resembled boxing gloves, they were so swollen and he couldn't even turn the pages of his exercise books, let alone hold a pen or pencil.

Just as another unfortunate was about to get the same punishment for a minor offence, Mr Roberts, in a flash, leapt over to Corky, and snatched the cane from his hand and snapped it across his knee. 'Enough!' he shouted, 'we've seen enough!'

Corky angrily pushed Mr Roberts, saying, 'You shouldn't interfere. It's none of your business.'

Mr Roberts retaliated sending him reeling backwards. The class was in uproar, desk lids slammed up and down, and rulers slapped noisily.

'Give it to 'im, Robbo,' the lads cheered. 'Give it 'im!'

The pushing and shoving continued, then both men locked their arms around each other, at which stage, Mrs Barge and Mr Land ordered the boys out into the playground, and dismissed them for the morning.

Mr Land told them all not to discuss this episode with anyone, certainly not their foster parents, so as not to discredit the previous good name of the school.

Five of the boys decided they were not going back to their foster homes but were returning to Liverpool; they had had enough! So they made their way to Maesgeirchen, got onto the railway track and headed for Aber, then to Llanfairfechan, only to be brought back late in the evening, by the local police. This procedure of trying to walk back to Liverpool, became known as 'the Aber run'.

The following day these boys were paraded in front of the classroom execution block, expecting at least ten of the best, but there wasn't even a cane in sight! When the morning service ended, all too soon for the runaways, a brief but informative talk was given by Corky, his forehead visibly perspiring, causing his glasses to slip down continually. He warned of the dangers of the railway lines, fast-moving trains, and other unforseen perils. After that he turned his attention to the enormous success of the Victory allotments and the expected bumper harvest.

Upon which he announced, 'We will dispense with the usual rule of class today, and go and do some weeding and hoeing.'

At this signal, the assembled children were dismissed and dispersed into small groups, chattering happily and wondering what had happened to bring about this turn of events?

However, once outside in the playground, they were handed hoes, forks and hand trowels, then marched across to the allotments. Obviously the two burning topics of the morning were the five runaways and Corky's comedown.

They never learned the outcome of the tussle between the head and Mr Roberts, and the lads were disappointed at not being able to detect any physical evidence of the previous day's fight. There were no crown jewels visible on either combatant!

In Bangor Library there were some excellent exhibits from various schools. 'Dig for Victory' was the slogan, and sketches painted, crayoned or pencilled, were on display. The drawings could be funny, serious or otherwise, as long as the theme 'Dig for Victory' was conveyed.

Garth school had taken both first and second prizes, which did not go down very well with Friars College at all. Especially so as Mr Land, the art teacher, had spent many hours giving the more proficient pupils extra tuition after school.

CHAPTER TWELVE
Hywel The Artful Dodger

The Summer of 1940 was glorious, and on one of these balmy days, with Saturday chores over, Beth made some beef paste sandwiches for them, and a piece of parkin each, then sent them off to meet Lily, to spend the day at the open-air swimming pool. It was a sea water pool, which filled up regularly with the tide. The children loved it, and spent the rest of the day in and out of the clean sea water, not noticing that their hands had become wrinkled, like prunes!

They sat on the sand together, chattering like monkeys, with Lily making fun of their swimsuits. Jimmie's was a Captain Webb style, with shoulder straps, which he would slip down and tuck under, so that it would look like regular trunks.

Edward wore an old pair of underpants that Beth had dug up from somewhere, but that didn't stop them from enjoying themselves. Sometimes the man at the turnstile let them in free of charge, so they bought an apple with the money, then returned home by way of the Roman Camp, swinging their wet 'cossies' as they went.

On arriving back home, and after waving goodbye to Lily at the gate, they were just in time to see Hywel placing long planks of timber over a deep, oblong hole. It had three steps going down into it, and was shored up on all sides. A well had been dug in the bottom to allow water that had gathered to be ladled out. This was yet another job for Jimmie to do several times a week, much to his dismay.

'Yeah, trust muggins as usual,' he thought to himself.

He went indoors, while Edward stayed to watch, as Uncle Hywel placed the corrugated sheet over the planks, then piled the earth that he'd dug out, on top of the metal sheet, patting it firmly, then standing back to admire his handiwork. He was feeling very well pleased with himself at accomplishing his mission.

Jimmie observed it all from the bathroom window, and decided that perhaps Uncle Hywel had done a good job for once?

Several of the neighbours called in to inspect Hywel's air-raid shelter, and praised his efforts, but no one else bothered to follow his example. After all, they weren't expecting any air-raids were they?

Hywel was also well pleased with his first attempt at growing marrows. Day after day he returned home from work and went into the garden to monitor their progress. The buds appeared first, then blossomed, then the shape of the marrow developed, and grew into an 'airship', as Jimmie described them.

'Yes being a gardener was very satisfying,' Hywel felt quite patriotic, to think that he was doing all this for the war effort. Actually he was doing even more for the war effort.

He had told Beth, that he intended to join something. So without further delay, he joined the local LDV (Local Defence Volunteers), known by the nickname of 'Look, Duck and Vanish'. So on certain evenings, he donned his brown boiler suit, heavy work shoes, green shirt and military raincoat, tied in front, rather gangster-style.

'I'll be late tonight, del bach. We've got manoeuvres over in Maesgeirchen. Got to hurry now, as there's a parade and briefing. So tara, rwan,' and he kissed his wife on the cheek and rushed off in the direction of the post office where they all assembled.

Beth peered through the net curtains at her Hywel, dashing off to do his duty for King and country.

The Bangor company of LDV assembled, and the three rows stood to attention to be inspected by Captain Hatch, an Englishman, who had served in the Great War. He was accompanied by Sergeant Lewis, a Welshman. The captain side-stepped along the lines of men, making comments, and tapping certain items of dress, and questioning appearances that he disapproved of. Then the men were given their orders.

The whole company, less two privates, were marched up Bangor Mountain. Once there they rubbed soil into their faces, shoved bits of twigs into their hats, then organised themselves into two smaller groups, and trotted off in opposite directions. It was still quite light, as Double British Summer Time was in force, and they were to rendezvous at 23.00 hours, so it would not be completely dark.

The Captain ordered them, 'Get as close as you can to each other without being seen, then attack each other with your makeshift weapons.' He then positioned himself overlooking the 'battle' area, and congratulated himself on the men under his command.

After all, the majority were middle-aged, even elderly, and yet they were to be commended. They did their best, and given the right weapons, would have been more than a match for the enemy.

The two privates who had stayed behind, were positioned on the roof of the post office, scanning the skies for anything unusual; though they didn't have any clear idea of what they would do if they encountered anything unusual! Indeed, they were very glad on this occasion that they had been left behind, as it was the early hours of the morning when the 'fighting force' returned; tired and bedraggled, all reeking of cow-pats and manure.

Captain Hatch thanked the men, apologised for the late hour, and hoped that their wives would be in a good frame of mind and understand that it was a necessary duty. He dismissed them in a whisper, and they exchanged salutes, then each went his separate way home, feeling stiff, sore and a little worse for wear.

They followed the little white line painted on the kerb edges, as this was their only visible guide in the blackout, and Hywel, feeling rather pleased with himself all the way home, mentally rehearsed the news he would have to tell Beth.

Captain Hatch had taken him aside saying, 'I am going to recommend you for a stripe.'

Yes, he would then be Lance Corporal Hughes of the Bangor LDV. The recommendation was for outstanding achievement, together with his youth and physical ability, both of which, the Captain reassured him, would stand him in good stead, when he was eventually called up for active duty. This spoiled it a bit really, as he hadn't planned on joining the armed forces.

'Beth wouldn't like that at all,' Hewel thought. His confidence waned as he got to the garden gate, and he wondered what his wife would have to say about the late hour, and especially about the awful smell of his clothes?

'Ah! Well! Here goes,' he thought, and knocked on the front door, not daring to enter in his condition!

Beth opened the door, peering cautiously into the darkness, 'Is it you, Hywel? Is it you?'

'Yes, del bach, sorry for being so ...'

He got no further with his explanations, as Beth interrupted him by saying, 'Good heavens! What's that awful, obnoxious smell? My heavens! You can go around the back way. I can't have you trailing through the house smelling like that.' She held her nose, 'and you can throw all your clothes over the clothes line to sweeten them!' she added curtly, as she closed the front door and went upstairs to bed, abandoning her husband in total darkness.

Hywel did just as he was commanded; he fumbled around, sliding on the polished lino in his stockinged feet. 'Does she expect me to take those off as well?' he thought.

He eventually made it to the bathroom to soak his weary body, in the few inches of warm bathwater that was allowed during wartime. 'Damn this bloody war!' he cursed.

Sad to say, there was no hot beverage for the man of the house that night!

The Bangor Company of the LDV paraded several times a week. Later on they became known as the Home Guard, and were kitted out with uniforms and half a dozen rifles. Captain Hatch was proud of his detachment, they were shaping up very nicely, and were now much more of a fighting force. The only problem was, who would get the rifles? Of course it didn't matter too much, as there was no ammunition anyway!

Beth was delighted when Hywel marched down the path in his new uniform, the rifle, that was his for a week, was slung over his shoulder, and he boasted a stripe too! My goodness! How proud she was, and never hesitated to tell him so. He looked so handsome that she fell in love with him all over again! However, she also never refrained from telling him how annoyed she was when he arrived home late, after his field exercises. Yes she was upset at this, as it interfered with her routine. Also being left to sit alone, was making her think that being in the Home Guard wasn't such a good idea after all!

'Yes! Hywel should be thinking of alternative ways to serve his country, which didn't interfere with their way of life; something non-military. The possibility that this Home Guard business could lead to him serving in the armed forces, sent cold shivers down her spine. Maybe he should consider something on the home front, like farming or munitions? No! Not suitable, that wouldn't do at all!'

She'd recently read in the Chronicle about the Auxiliary Fire Service. Good fit men were being recruited locally, to alleviate the burden on the regular firemen, and to leave them free to attend to more serious problems in other areas. The more that Beth considered this alternative, the more she was convinced it would prove to be much better all round. After all, the military training that he had undergone in the Home Guard, would naturally make him a prime candidate to be called up.

'Right,' she said to herself, 'that's it!' and she rummaged through a pile of newspapers to find the item in the Chronicle.

She eventually found it, then said, 'Ah! Here we are!' and she read the following:

'Fit men wanted, part-time, as auxiliary firemen. Urgently needed to carry on their own profession and report for night duty on a 72 hour cycle. One night at fire station, one night at home on call, and the third night off. Apply at local fire station.'

'Well now, that's marvellous isn't it? A uniform too, goodness me, and he won't be coming home smelling of all sorts of unsavoury things.'

She realised, of course, that the job would be unpaid, but it would still work out much better in the long run. Yes, she'd show it to Hywel when he came home. He didn't really need much persuading to abandon the Home Guard.

Although to save face, he told Captain Hatch, 'I want to change over, because I feel that there is more of a chance that I will see real active duty with the fire service.'

'Well I'll be sorry to see you go Lance Corporal, our loss will be someone else's gain.' After which comment, the captain thanked him for his contribution to the unit, saluted and dismissed him.

The following week, Hywel volunteered his services at the local fire station. He was to be trained for fire-fighting and anti-gas work. It wouldn't be long before he was fitted with his navy-blue uniform, and of course his black axe.

Again Beth was impressed, 'There's something special about a man in uniform, and her Hywel looked wonderful! She also congratulated herself, for thinking of it in the first place. She would now know exactly when he would be home at night, and their free evenings could still be spent in the Anglesey Arms or the Black Bull at Bethesda; there was always some good Welsh singing from the men up there.'

This became the routine of their lives, almost for the duration of the war. Much to Beth's satisfaction, Hywel never had to face the dangers of serving in the armed forces.

CHAPTER THIRTEEN
A Visit to Liverpool

Jimmie sported a huge grin, from ear to ear, as he jumped off the Crosville bus in Liverpool, to be met by his mother.

She took hold of his small case, borrowed from Auntie Beth, at the same time, commenting, 'My, you've grown lad. Yer lookin' well, and who is this? Is it yer pal, Eddie?'

'Yeah this is Eddie. Is 'is ma 'ere?'

'Wait with us lad, 'ere yer are. Is this yer mam?'

Without another word, Edward was whisked off by a young woman, whom Kate and Jimmie presumed to be his mother.

'So long!' Jimmie called out after him.

Edward turned round hastily, 'Ta-ra, see yer next week, don't miss the bus!' And with that, he was gone.

Jimmie and his mother made their way home by tram to India Street. He stared in disbelief at the devastation of the places that he knew. Rows of houses, shops and other public buildings had been razed to the ground, leaving only empty spaces and smouldering ruins. Rubble was piled high along their route. Jimmie had never imagined that this could happen to a city like Liverpool. In the twenty or so months that he had been away, all this had happened!

On eventually arriving home, there was no one in, but he found the house surprisingly clean. The old, cast-iron fireplace had actually been cleaned with black lead, and it was shining. Because it was May and the weather warm, the fire was out, but laid with paper and chips of firewood, sticking through the bars of the grate, like teeth ready to be pulled. A large piece of coconut matting had been laid in the centre of the floor, and a bold red and white check tablecloth draped the old wooden table. The overall impression was very homely, and not at all what Jimmie had expected to see.

Before long, his thoughts turned to Art, and he wondered how long it would be before he, or Nellie, or their mother would be popping in to see him?

As if Kate had read Jimmie's thoughts, she said, 'Oh! By the way, Art doesn't live over the street any more. They all moved away to the outskirts, just before the bombing started, and I've never had sight nor sound of them since. Shame really, not even our Mary has heard from Nellie, and you know what good mates they were. Hope they're all alright. Knowing them, they'll turn up one of these days, like bad pennies! Ha ha!'

Kate filled the old cast-iron kettle; blue flames spread around its base as she lit the gas. The little black stove didn't look out of place next to the old sandstone sink. They were both looking the worse for wear, but at least they were clean and that's what mattered to Jimmie.

He said, 'Looks nice, the 'ouse, Mam. It's different, wouldn't 'ave known it if I'da come on me own. No, I wouldn't.'

'Oh! Aye yer would, yer'll never get lost lad,' Kate answered, as she placed cups and saucers and plates on her new tablecloth. 'I've managed ter collect a few extra things tergether,' she added, indicating the crockery.

'There, we'll 'ave a nice cake too, ter put us on till tea-time,' and she fumbled two large, square, 'pudding cakes' from a paper bag. They almost overlapped the sides of the plates. 'Shoulda dropped these buggers on Berlin, the war'd be over in no time,' she laughed.

Jimmie happily joined in. It was nice to be home.

Kate poured the tea and sweetened it with 'connie-onnie'. 'How's our Lily, is she alright? Nice couple those Flynns, I believe. Course it's a good old Irish name (Kate was proud of her Irish connections), I'm sure she'll be looked after, and what about you, lar? Do you like it where you are? Are you well fed? Yer a nice smart lad now, not like some of these scruffy buggers around 'ere. Mind yer, there's norra lot left now, all evacuated like you, now that all this bombin' is on. Every night it's been, for over a week, no let up at all.

Well! do yer like it where yer are?' Kate paused and lit a Woodbine, then took a sip of her tea, 'Cor! I'm ready fer that!' She blew out the smoke and it permeated the air.

Jimmie had forgotten what that was like, as he hadn't been used to it for twenty months. He fingered his huge heavy pudding cake, 'This is nice Mam,' he commented, trying to avoid her many questions.

'Why hadn't someone dropped him a line, he wondered, maybe with a tanner postal order in it? Other kids got letters nearly every week with pocket money in, so why hadn't anyone bothered about him?' He gazed over the rim of his cup containing the sweet tea, and thought, 'Ell, did I used ter drink this stuff?'

'Yer can fill me up,' Kate said, handing her cup to Jimmie, 'been waiting fer this all day. That blinkin' bus was late comin' in. I was talkin' ter that young lad's mam, what's 'is name?'

'Eddie.'

'Yeah Eddie. Shame 'is dad is missin' in France. Went to 'elp those poor buggers on the beaches, an' didn't come back.'

Jimmie felt sick at the idea of little Eddie not having a dad. 'Eck, it's gonna be tough fer 'im if 'e finds out, an' 'avin' ter go back ter Bangor an' leave 'is mam,' he thought to himself. Aloud, he said, 'I shouldn't lerron Mam, about Eddie's dad. Don't say owt will yer, if yer see 'im next week? 'e gets upset easy, an' this is 'ard.'

The blockbuster of a cake was only half-eaten. He pushed the plate away and drank his tea, now more to his liking and thought about Eddie, 'Poor kid,' he sighed, 'poor kid!'

It was Irish stew for tea, and Jimmie's older brother, Willie, ate two large platefuls, and mopped up the thick, brown gravy with a chunk of bread.

'Come on, Jim, not eatin'? Come on lad,' he coaxed, 'I've been famished all day 'umpin' heavy canvas about, won't be doin' it much longer though, thinkin' of gerrin' a milk-round.'

The pay wasn't much at Langdon's tarpaulin factory, but it would suffice for the time being. With many of the menfolk away in the forces, there were lots of vacancies to be filled, so Willie was on the lookout for a better job.

'Gerra move on, Jim,' said his brother, 'if yer want ter go ter the pictures. It'll 'ave ter be the first 'ouse, if we can gerrin.' He pushed his chair back and swilled his face at the sink, 'Don't see much of the gang now,' he spluttered. 'Hambone's still around, Jackie Gilbert an' Greevie; some in the Merchant Navy, only seventeen as well, silly buggers, sittin' ducks they are.'

Willie combed his mousy hair, then smoothed his shirt collar over his jacket, 'There, ready. Come on, Jim. Let's go.'

Jimmie half-expected his brother to go racing off, but instead he strode along with him to the 'Tivvie' in Roscommon Street. Mr Legget, the old commissioner, still sat there on the side with his raw potatoes, cutting them into thin slivers with his penknife, and placing them slowly and deliberately into his mouth.

'Be sprouting out of his ears one of these days,' Willie laughed. 'Two threepennies please,' he said, throwing a tanner onto the sloping brass tray.

'Tar lar,' replied the girl with the peroxide hair behind the glass partition. She winked at Willie, and chewed on her chewing gum, deliberately showing the contents of her mouth. 'Ow's your Bobby? Never see 'im these days. Tell 'im I was askin' about 'im.'

Willie rudely picked up the tickets, and headed into the semi-darkness of the cinema without answering her. 'Sit 'ere,' he said to Jimmie. 'Can yer see alright, Jim?' he enquired, putting a bar of Caramello into his brother's hand.

'Yeah, I can see fine,' answered Jimmie, thinking, 'what a treat! Chocolate! Something he had hardly tasted all the time he'd been away.'

'Take some chocolate back wi' yer Jim, I've plenty. It's alright, they're not knocked off. A favour fer a favour, yer know!' he winked.

The brothers were enjoying the George Formby film which was at its climax, with motorcycles racing around the Isle of Man, when the film was suddenly interrupted, and the screen went blank. There was a warning that everyone had to make for the exits immediately, and get to their shelters as quickly as possible. The sirens sounded their ominous wailing. Willie grabbed Jimmie's arm and they both dashed back home to India Street, where Kate had already collected blankets and a Thermos flask.

'Hurry up, now! I've got the baby. Just been to our Joanna's, good job we got back in time. Come on!' They quickly entered the brick shelter with the reinforced concrete roof.

'These bleedin' things'll be no damn good, if we get a bullseye,' one old nag complained, sitting near the entrance.

'No good sitting there an' hopin' ter be the first one out!' laughed Kate. 'There y'are,' she turned to Jimmie, 'take yer little brother fer a minute,' and before he knew it, a bundle of blankets was thrust into his arms.

'Eck,' he thought, 'I'd fergotten all about you,' and he gave the bundle a friendly shake. The only thing he could see was a rosy complexion and a mop of straw-coloured hair;

'this was his little brother Eric, not quite two-years old, and he didn't even know him!'

'Here lad, I'll take him now. Sit 'ere,' said Kate, having settled herself down.

'Where's our Willie?' asked Jimmie.

'Aw! Don't worry lad,' his mother reassured him, 'he'll have gone off ter help the wardens, ARP, or anybody who might need 'im, or anything else 'e can gerris 'ands into!'

The night seemed endless. Bombs screamed down in various locations, causing utter devastation wherever they fell. Fire engine bells could be heard clanging, and the thud of buildings crashing to the ground. Jimmie worried about the sight that would confront them when they emerged into the street again. At least this made him appreciate the reason for his evacuation from Liverpool.

'Ah! Well! Dat's anudder one over wid,' announced the old nag, and before the all clear sounded, she was up and out of the shelter before anyone had realised the raid was indeed over.

The MacLeans wended their way up the dusty street to their house. 'Still there I see,' said Kate, who had half-hoped that her house had been hit, so that she could be rehoused to a safe area. She closed the door behind them, and making sure all the curtains were well-shut, she lit a candle.

'This'll suffice,' she said and showed Jimmie up the familiar, winding, narrow stairs and into the bedroom. The old iron bed had been replaced with two single beds side by side, and another in the corner. Clean, multi-coloured, quilts had been turned down in readiness for tired souls. It all smelled clean and fresh.

'Ah! A bed to myself at last,' sighed Jimmie.

'Night, God bless lad, nice ter 'ave yer 'ome,' Kate said, smiling. She pulled the bedroom curtains back.

'You'll be alright now, they won't be back. Our Willie'll get in 'is own bed when 'e gets in. Goodnight sleep well, yer've 'ad a long day, really don't know what they sent yer 'ome for, with all this danger. Said she wanted a 'oliday, said everything 'ad got too much fer 'er.'

'Who yer talkin' about Mam? Who wanted a rest?'

'That Mrs Hughes, who you stay with in Bangor. She wrote to the authorities in Liverpool asking if you and young Eddie could come 'ome fer a week, so's she could 'ave a break wi' 'er 'ubby,' she told him with disgust.

'Arf a dozen kids is what she wants Mam, short o' summat ter do,' growled the lad. 'Anyway, goodnight Mam, nice ter be 'ome again.'

Jimmie turned over in bed, his thoughts returning to the raid, the first he had ever experienced, and he hadn't liked it. 'Gosh,' he remembered, 'the baby slept right through it. Wish I had. Scared stiff I was,' then he dropped off to sleep, exhausted.

He half-awoke later that night to hear someone singing,

'When the red, red, robin,
Comes bob, bob, bobbin' along.'

'Must be 'appy,' thought Jimmie, 'silly old codger! Tanked, too, no doubt! Who could blame him?'

Willie turned in at 5am, and was up and away by 7.30. He'd been busy assisting at the first aid centre, down Great Nelson Street. He'd learned some of his skills at work, and now assisted the St John's Ambulance men and women. They were grateful for all the help they could get, like many of the other volunteer services. It had been a busy night for them all, the raid hadn't ended until 2am, as on many another night, and they too, were tired out, but glad to be alive.

Kate listened intently to the little relay set she had rented, another luxury she had managed to acquire, although she told herself it wasn't a luxury at all, but a necessity. She wondered about her husband, as many wives and mothers did.

As she listened, she spoke out loud, 'Thought they would. Thought they'd go fer the docks, what the U-boats missed in the Atlantic, the bombers try ter get, the buggers. An' the freight goin' out up to Edge Hill and other outlying areas by rail. Our Bobby's worked the clock round twice, poor devil. Don't know what time 'e'll be up, never even bothered ter take the clothes off 'is back! He was just too tired; it's a damn shame.'

'Ello lad,' she added, on seeing Jimmie making an appearance, 'ave some toast. Put yer own jam on, an' put yer own milk in, yer know 'ow yer like it,' she said, pouring the tea. 'Glad I didn't make a noise gettin' outa bed, didn't want ter wake Bobby.'

'What does 'e do now Mam, 'e used to work fer Bout's Haulage before I left.'

'Oh! 'e drives cranes down at the docks, never stops, even when there's a raid on. They get the ships unloaded as fast as they can for fear of them getting sunk in the dock by the bombin'. 'e earns good money an' all that, but is it worth it? I s'pose someone's gotta do it, Never gorrin the Navy like 'e wanted, 'cause of 'is 'earin' perforated eardrums or sump'in' like that, then 'e 'ad that accident with the swingin' plank in the park, when 'e was young, nearly gettin' 'is eye knocked out, an' finishin' up at St Paul's Eye 'ospital. Lucky to be able to see at all. Never mind now, 'e's doin' 'is bit fer the country as best 'e can, an' good fer 'im! There's more tea in the pot if yer want some, 'ad enough to eat 'ave yer?'

'No thanks, Mam,' said Jimmie, who had been listening to his mam with interest. 'Nice to spend time with her,' he reflected, 'I'm gonna 'ave a wash an' brush me teeth, then I'll 'ave a walk round ter me nin's.'

'Yer nin's in 'ospital, Jimmie, 'asn't been too well. Old age I think. She plays 'ell at night with the nurses, tellin' 'em ter stop all the bangin', when the bombs are droppin' - poor queen!'

Bobby slept till late afternoon. 'Yer shoulda called me Mam, I was gonna take Jimmie out, now I 'ave ter get ready fer work. Will yer put me some 'ot water in the sink fer a shave? 'Ave ter gerra move on.' Bobby bent down to fasten the laces on his steel-capped boots. 'Tell our Willie ter gerra tin 'at, if 'e's doin' volunteer work. They've all gorrem.'

He swished his shaving brush in the hot water, then lathered the ginger stubble on his face. 'Ah! Yer 'ere, our Jimmie, nice ter see yer. How are yer? 'Eck you've grown!'

Jimmie was glad to see his eldest brother, he'd missed seeing him the day he was evacuated, and as he entered the room, he knew instantly, just by his look, that a fondness yearned to erupt, and he wanted to hug him, but that wasn't the way things were done in the MacLean household. Affection wasn't shown in that way. So Jimmie just grinned at Bobby, and that was enough for the two brothers.

After Bobby had washed and shaved, he donned his blue boiler suit, tied a white silk scarf around his neck, checked his tuckbox and flask and said, 'Everything's okay Mam. Don't know when I'll be 'ome.'

Then he turned to Jimmie, 'Oh! By the way this is fer you,' and he handed him a long package, 'should be able ter play that, been savin' it fer yer!'

He watched as his young brother unwrapped the gift. Jimmie's eyes lit up when he saw the long mouth organ, 'Brand new, isn't it? It's smashin', Bob, ta, Echo Deluxe! 'Ell! Bet that set yer back a bob or two! Ha ha! a bob or two,' and they both laughed at Jimmie's unintentional pun.

'Well?' Bobby smiled, 'aren't yer gonna try it? Give us *Springtime in the Rockies,* or what's that one yer play fer me mam, when she's turnin' the mangle? Yeah - *Let the Rest of the World Go By.'*

Jimmie was choked. 'They did care after all!'

'Ere's a quid fer yerself as well. Gorra get goin' now.' Bobby pushed his bicycle from the yard, and lifted it up the two steps into the street. 'So long, lar, look after yerself, an' giz a shout if yer need me. Don't ferget!' With that, he was away, pedalling like mad.

Kate stood at Jimmie's side, and they both waved until Bobby turned into Roscommon Street.

Jimmie stared into the shiny chrome plate of his new harmonica. The light dazzled his eyes and made them water, or was it tears?

'Come on, lad,' said Kate, 'let's 'ave an early tea, then get the flask an' blankets ready for another raid ternight!'

The week at home soon passed, much of the time spent in the shelter, but it had been good to be home again, even for such a short while, but sadly Mary didn't get an opportunity to come to see him. Maybe next time?

Willie gave Jimmie a ten shilling note and a box of Caramello bars.

'Thanks Will, take care, see yer.'

Kate kissed Jimmie on the cheek, 'Ere yer are, lad,' she said, 'ten shillin' fer yer. Don't bother ter write, we'll all be okay. Look! Eddie's waitin' fer yer on the bus,' and she handed the small case up to Jimmie. 'Tell Lily we're alright. Ta-ra, lad.'

'We're runnin' late Missus,' the bus driver said, 'got ter get goin,' and with that, the green bus pulled away.

Willie waved continuously. Kate smiled, just as she had at Lime Street that Sunday, 3rd September 1939.

Jimmie read her lips, 'Love you, Jimmie. Love you, son.'

The two boys didn't speak for a while, both of them had their feet on their cases, and both stared wistfully out across the Wirral peninsular, as the bus trundled its way along the twisting coast road.

They were both tired; the dark rings under their eyes were evidence of their lack of sleep whilst visiting home. The fatherly driver monitored them in his driving mirror, and thought it strange that two young lads should be so quiet, and not larking about as young lads usually do. Edward dropped off to sleep, his head lolling from side to side with the motion of the bus as it swayed round the bends in the road. The driver seemed almost out of control of the huge machine, as the enormous steering wheel spun and turned through his hands, but his professional composure was unshakeable. It was only when the bus came to a grinding halt, and people chattered to each other in their native Welsh, that Edward finally awoke and looked around.

'We'll stop here for ten minutes,' the driver announced.

Edward opened his pack of sandwiches, 'Here yer are, Jim,' he said, handing Jimmie a corned beef one. He dared not look at his pal, as he felt tearful and emotional, at leaving his mam yet again, and he didn't want Jimmie to think he was a soft lad.

'Gosh! Ta, Eddie! They look good. Yer ma's even cut the crusts off. Come on lad, yer gotta eat summat, 'specially as yer ma 'as taken the trouble ter purrem up fer yer. Mmm, smashin' these!'

He snapped the metal top off the bottle of Edmondson's pop, that Willie had also given him for the journey. 'Ere, 'ave a swig o' that!' and he thrust the bottle in front of Eddie, 'Yer won't want ter pee will yer, before we get there, will yer?'

'No, I'll be alright.'

Jimmie broke a bar of Caramello in half, and handed one piece to his pal. 'Got some more o' these, our Willie gorrem fer us,' he boasted, opening his case. 'Look, an' our Bob gorrus this. I'm not gonna play it though. I might clog the reeds up,' he said, clasping the lid on the box containing his mouth organ. This was his most treasured possession, and he wrapped it up very carefully in his hand towel and fastened up his case.

Edward seemed to recover somewhat, and became more himself. The two chatted about the bombing and the previous week's activity. There was no mention of Eddie's dad.

'Maybe he hasn't been told,' Jimmie thought, 'an' I'm certainly not gonna tell 'im.'

The small boy was fretful enough, without any more bad news. Meanwhile the bus journeyed through the Welsh countryside, taking them ever nearer to Bangor.

CHAPTER FOURTEEN
Back in Bangor

The green bus came to a halt and the boys were first to alight, as they'd occupied the front seats. They made their all-too-familiar way up to Glynne Road and knocked on the door.

'My goodness me! Just look at you both. You do look tired! I'll run the bath for you, then you can have your tea and an early night. Come on now, take your things off and I'll shake your clothes at the back door!'

Beth took the boys' suits and shook them vigorously into the garden, her motives blatantly obvious, 'Just in case,' she said to herself, 'you never know.'

The lads made their way to the bathroom in vests and underpants, and soaked in the warm water, liberally doused with Dettol.

After a sandwich tea, Beth informed them, 'Your money will go into your moneybox. You have done well, both of you, indeed you have. I'll look after the chocolate, and whenever you want some, it's in the drawer. And Jimmie, you mustn't play your mouth organ in or near the house, that's a good lad.'

Needless to say, that was the last they saw of the Caramello bars and the Echo Deluxe mouth organ, Jimmie's pride and joy, also suddenly and mysteriously disappeared. Jimmie searched high and low, everywhere that he was permitted to venture; his bedroom, the kitchen, the garden shed, anywhere that wasn't out of bounds.

Beth asked, with a sly smile, 'How on earth did you manage to misplace your musical instrument?'

It was only when Gwenda took them to see the new attraction anchored in the Straits, that Jimmie stopped brooding, and temporarily forgot his harmonica. The old wooden battleship, the Conway, had been brought from Liverpool for safety, and to escape the ferocity of the blitz. She was anchored close to the Anglesey shore, west of Bangor Pier.

Naval cadets from the Conway would come ashore in launches, to buy provisions, and both lads came to recognise many of them who would stop for a chat, as they carried their trays of bread and fresh foods along the pier.

Taid told the boys that he could remember when the ship was anchored in the Mersey, and had sailed past it on numerous occasions, and described her to them in detail; her three towering masts, her rows of guns - 96 in all, her white lines running along the sides. He was just as excited as the boys, when discussing ships, especially one as beautiful as the Conway.

Old Taid had missed Jimmie and Edward, and was glad to see them back. The boys, too, had a wonderful time seeing the old ship and their old friend.

Gwenda was also happy, as she'd heard that Tim's ship was docked in Liverpool, and that he would soon be home. Jimmie worried about Edward; he was not always himself, and he reckoned that the little lad was fretting inwardly. So he took it upon himself to be his big brother and watch out for him.

One of the sights they enjoyed seeing together, was a Spitfire flying low down the Straits, over the old warship. Hywel was kept busy on his 72 hour stints, both at the fire station and at home, on call. The AFS had been renamed in August 1941 and was now the NFS. Fires were deliberately started on Bangor Mountain, on a regular basis, and had to be extinguished before nightfall, as German planes passed over that area, flying up the coast from the south, through mid-Wales and over the mountains, towards Liverpool.

Several bombs were dropped on Maesgeirchen one night, but little damage was done and luckily no lives were lost. If the bomb aimer was directing his sights on Liverpool, he was more than a little off his target.

Hywel looked more like a chimney sweep than a fireman. He, along with other members of the NFS, had been beating down the burning bracken with wet sacks, and returned home later as black as the ace of spades, wondering what Beth would have to say?

As usual, she had plenty to say! She was white with rage, but not with Hywel or the NFS, but with poor Edward. 'Just look at these, del bach!' and she thrust Edward's underpants in front of him. 'The dirty boy! My goodness, dirty boy you are indeed, Edward!'

Both boys were standing in the hallway, Edward minus his underpants and trembling with fear.

'Good gracious me!' roared Hywel, as he grabbed Edward by the collar and hoisted him halfway up the stairs, at the same time slapping his bare bottom and legs, 'dirty little bugger! Don't want any of that in this house! Get upstairs!'

The little boy was terrified, and Jimmie immediately saw red. He ran up behind Hywel, grabbing hold of his canvas belt and hung on, screaming, 'Leave 'im alone! Leave 'im alone, can't yer? 'e's only a little kid!'

With that, Hywel turned round angrily and roughly pushed Jimmie away, 'Get out of my sight,' he roared and continued to smack Edward, ordering him to get into the bath, and then go straight to bed.

Jimmie could hear Edward screaming, and was powerless to help, so he left the house that night and headed out over the smouldering mountain to the golf course, and towards Maesgeirchen, making his way to Liverpool, in his mind.

As he trudged through the burnt bracken, he muttered, 'Soddin' mad he is. I suppose it's 'cos he's had to do a bit of work, puttin' the fires out! Then hittin' poor Eddie like that! I hate him!' It was late by the time he managed to get to the railway line near Aber, only to be met by Mr Roberts, his teacher.

'And where do you think you're going, young Mac? Just look at your face!'

Jimmie didn't realise that his face was as black as Hywel's had been. It was of course, from the smoke from the fires and his clothes also had a sooty smell.

'Come on then, let's get back. You won't be the last to do the Aber run. Don't worry though, you'll be alright.'

Apparently, Mr Roberts and Miss Davies, the WVS lady, had been contacted by Hywel when he realised that Jimmie had gone missing. On their arrival back at Glynne Road, neither Hywel nor Beth spoke, except to thank the searchers for bringing back the runaway, and apologising for the inconvenience.

By the time Jimmie had bathed and gone to bed, Edward was 'driving the pigs', so Jimmie just climbed over and got in beside him, up to the window, and he too, was soon fast asleep.

The following day, Auntie Meg invited Jimmie and Edward to tea, Beth having gone to visit another sister in Llanfair, PG.

Taid had learnt about Jimmie running off, and also about Edward's smacking episode, and he was upset, his heavy eyelids half-closed over his sad eyes. He and Gwenda made all their exchanges in Welsh, as she related to him all the events of the night before. His fists banging on the arms of his chair, expressed his feelings about the matter, and even though the boys didn't understand a word, the tone of his voice clearly demonstrated his inner anger.

Later that day, Hywel came to pick up the boys to take them back home, and Taid's anger finally exploded. His hand shook as he lit his pipe with the home-made paper spill. Then he blew out a gust of smoke into Hywel's face, and launched into him in a mixture of Welsh and English.

Jimmie couldn't make a lot of sense out of the one-sided conversation, he only gleaned, by the few words that were spoken in English, that Taid was looking after their interests. This man loved them, he actually cared!

While Taid was telling Hywel what he thought of him, Hywel was standing by the door, white and shame-faced, and looking as if he was about to make a run for it. Taid kept on pointing first at Edward, then at Jimmie. He was very agitated, and it was obvious that Hywel was getting a real telling off. He nodded feebly now and again, but did not manage to utter a single word.

CHAPTER FIFTEEN
Grub

The lads admitted to each other that they never had liked Beth's dinners. She tried to make scouse, but her version was an insult to whoever invented it! She usually reserved whatever meat was put into the dish for Hywel, and what was ladled out for the boys was more like potato soup.

Jimmie used to complain to Edward, when they were alone, that it was too weak to pour out of the pan, and Edward appreciated the joke. Once Jimmie found a large lump of gristle in his dish, which almost made him heave.

Beth was unperturbed by his reaction, and trotted out her usual response, 'Can't waste good food now, can we?' and threaded the gristle onto a piece of string, and put it out for the birds.

Jimmie glanced over at Edward, winked and whispered softly to him, 'Even the poor little tits will be turnin' their noses up at it.'

Both lads would like to have objected more forcefully to Beth's lack of culinary ability, but were obviously in no position to do so. She could have tried a little harder, they argued to themselves. Even they knew that recipes based on the restricted wartime rations were given out on the radio food programmes, dried egg being a popular ingredient. Lots of economical meals could be concocted; that's of course if people could be bothered.

Jimmie couldn't remember the last time he had had a real egg, but there was always the smell of eggs and bacon cooking on Sunday mornings! On such days, after washing and dressing, the two lads would go to their places at the kitchen table, only to be confronted by a plate of rendered, melted, dripping, with a dollop of brown sauce for flavour, and bread to dip in with.

It didn't take long for the fat to solidify and become, as Jimmie would say, 'thick enough to skate on.'

Food certainly was in short supply though, and quite a number of kids complained about not having enough to eat. Lads from Garth School even started raiding the allotments for turnips, swedes and new potatoes. Jimmie and Edward often went to Tyroden, to collect 'kewins' (periwinkles) and boil them in an old tin can they found on the beach. They helped to fill a little space, but they made them very thirsty, resulting in Edward wetting the bed more often, so they had to be removed from the menu!

A popular song of the time with the boys was the following:

'Bless 'em all, bless 'em all,
The long and the short and the tall,
We're all blinkin' starvin',
And live in Caernarvon,
So cheer up my lads, bless us all!'

This was most appropriate, as Bangor was in the county of Caernarvonshire at that time.

The mountain continued to be set on fire. Friars lads blamed the Scousers, and the Scousers blamed the Friars. Hywel was no doubt, between the devil and the deep blue sea, as he still had his PE evening classes at Friars, and Jimmie was at Garth! No, he wouldn't dare show favour to Friars, in case Taid got to hear of it. He'd got the message from the old salt and so, under his guardianship, life became a little more tolerable for the lads.

The Sunday evening chapel going ceased, giving them an extra two hour's leisure time to enjoy regular visits to the pier with Gwenda. They'd skim small pieces of slate on the water, inside the wreck of the old wooden ship, the Fortuna, her ribs sticking up out of the mud.

Jimmie thought of the time when she was a live, working ship, delivering slate and cement to various locations. He also sat and gazed at the splendour of HMS Conway, and tried to observe the activity on board and all the comings and goings of the crew. These were times that he loved.

His Saturday morning shopping expeditions became even more of a chore, as the High Street grew busier and busier; good for the shopkeepers but not for the boys, as they tried to manoeuvre the awful cart around the shops. The busier times were due mostly to the stars who broadcast regularly from the BBC in Bangor, and many of these people could be seen around the city. People like Tommy Handley, Arthur Askey, Lucan and McShane (Old Mother Riley and Kitty), Billy Ternent, the band leader, Jack Train, Bebe Daniels and many more, some of whom were in uniform. They entertained millions in the British Isles and abroad during the war years. The evacuees, as well as the Welsh children, were often invited to live programmes of Itma. It's That Man Again; Tommy Handley was always a favourite of Jimmie's.

'Well! If it isn't Poppy Poopah!
'Can 1 do yer now, Sir?'
'Don't forget the diver.'
'I've brought this for you, Sir'
That's nice - what is it?'

And so it went on. Their entertainment brought happiness into people's lives, and helped them to forget, for a while at least, that Britain was at war.

Charlie Chester was another favourite entertainer, and put on a grand panto - Cinderella - in St Mary's Church Hall. His Army Concert Party, The Crazyliers, and the girls from

Liverpool Victoria Approved Society, gave up their time to bring happiness to the kids. Some of whom had lost their parents in the blitz.

At that time also, Billy Ternent led the resident band at the County Theatre, and all the stars did their famous variety broadcasts from the County, in Dean Street. The lads from Friars were beginning to integrate with the Scousers, and only on odd occasions would there be a bit of a scrap, or a few ill-chosen words, spoken in haste.

The worst episode was when Garth School had the honour of carrying the Welsh Flag on St David's Day; an honour previously carried out exclusively by the Welsh people. So it was indeed an privilege for Garth!

Jimmie had been allowed to join the cubs, and was at that time, marching with the scouts and cubs, wearing his blue and yellow neckerchief which he had bought, of course, with his own money. He heard the rumpus that erupted, and witnessed the various flags jolting from side to side, but the brass band came to the rescue by striking up a stirring march, *Men of Harlech,* and continued playing until the cathedral was reached, and that was the end of the furore!

CHAPTER SIXTEEN
Gorilla

It was autumn, 1942, the bombing in all the major towns and cities seemed never-ending. This worried Jimmie, especially as he hadn't heard anything from home. Letters were always few and far between, but it had been a very long time since he had received one.

The two sisters who were staying with Lily in Orme Road, suddenly returned to Liverpool, as some close member of their family had been seriously hurt, and they never returned to Bangor. Jimmie envied them, and felt very homesick and longed to see someone from home.

Then one day he came home from school for his dinner, and who should be sitting in the front room, but his dad! He couldn't believe his eyes! Then he suddenly felt sick, wondering if anything was wrong?

'Hi, Dad!' was all he could manage, and he kissed him on the cheek.

His father patted him on the back, 'Alright, son?'

'Yeah, I'm okay Dad. How long yer been 'ere? When yer goin' back? It's good ter see yer. 'ow's me mam an' everyone? Where's yer ship? Where've yer been?' Jimmie couldn't control the stream of questions that he wanted to ask his dad.

'Too many questions now, Jimmie bach,' Beth said. 'Come and have your dinner. Your father has had some ... Come and enjoy your ham and tomatoes.'

Jimmie was staggered, 'Ell! where the 'ell did she get the 'am?' Aloud he said, 'Can't eat anything Auntie, really I can't. I'm too excited.'

'Well, just have a piece of cake then until later.'

Beth didn't argue about the ham. She covered it with another plate, and decided that she or Hywel would be able to make a nice sandwich with it later.

Jimmie would have loved to have taken his dad around Bangor, to show him off to all the people he knew, but they only had a few hours together.

Rob's face was pale, but when he smiled, his grey-blue eyes sparkled. His voice was gentle and quiet as the two conversed. In all too short a time, Jimmie was accompanying him to the railway station.

'Tell Lily that I'm sorry I missed her.'

He gave Jimmie two ten shilling notes, 'Here y'are, one fer each for you. On second thoughts, here's another one for that little feller who's staying with you,' and he handed another note over to Jimmie for Edward.

Yes, Jimmie was proud to be seen with his dad. He looked so smart. Although he was a little bent, he was sprightly enough, and as he walked, his bell-bottom trousers flapped around in the slight breeze. The stripes and badges on his jacket were evidence of his long service and aptitude within the Navy.

Jimmie thanked him for the money, then added, 'You didn't say where you'd been on your voyages, Dad.'

'Oh! a place called Murmansk,' Rob said, as he took a packet of Capstan cigarettes from inside his jacket and lit up.

Jimmie didn't probe any further. His dad must have good reasons for not wanting to talk about his travels, and besides, he only wanted to be with him, and time was short.

'I'm gonna leave you now Jim, got to leg it, otherwise I'll miss my train.'

'We're not quite at the station yet. Look it's over there,' protested Jimmie, pointing a short distance away.

'Yes I know,' replied Rob, 'but you know how it is, these goodbyes. Anyway, ta-ra son, look after yourself, won't you now?' and with that he kissed Jimmie on his cheek, turned on his heel and quickly paced up to the station.

As he walked, he swayed from side to side as all seafarers do, a walk which was very familiar to his son. Jimmie watched until he was out of sight, and wondered if he would see him again, and when? He trudged slowly down Deiniol Road, painfully aware that each step was taking him further away from his dad. How he wished he had been travelling back with him, to be able to share a whole journey with him. How good it would have been to kick a ball around on the beach, or have time to climb the mountain together, or show him the Roman Camp, but time and circumstances beyond their control, would not allow any of these things.

Jimmie reflected how great it would have been to take his dad up to Woollies, and show him off to the supervisors and the lady with the big brown eyes, behind the sweet counter. Yes, he would have been proud to have had his dad there with him. He heard the train pull into Bangor Station and then depart. He couldn't understand why his dad had come all that way just for a couple of hours?

'Blinkin' war,' he cursed, as he realised that his dad had actually come because he cared about him.

He thought bitterly of Uncle Hywel, and how he had his day job and duty with the NFS.

'A doddle of a time he's having, and look at me old feller, going away to fight in the war, and havin' to leave his wife an' kids!' He couldn't understand the sense of it all.

'No good goin' back to the house just yet,' Jimmie reasoned. 'She'll only have me runnin' up to town for somethin' or other,' so he sat in the tall grass near the river. 'Stinks a bit, but it's better than bein' nagged at, 'sides, they'd have me goin' back to school, an' I don't feel like going to school just yet.'

He reflected on his recent past. He had a clean home in Bangor, and evacuation had shown him a different way of life, but he felt claustrophobic. He had no freedom like in Liverpool, he felt trapped, he needed to run with the gang again, to jump, laugh and lark about like in the old days; but the old days had gone, things were never going to be the same; only boundaries, limits and restrictions. Now Beth had also put a stop to his cub night.

'She said it was too late coming home at half past eight!' he muttered to himself in disgust.

Jimmie and Edward had to be in bed by the allotted time, so that Beth and her husband could go out. Often the two boys would hear them come home, laughing and giggling, and Hywel sometimes whistling a selection of the hit tunes of the day: *Who's Taking You Home Tonight?*, *Goodnight Sweetheart*, *Silver Wings in the Moonlight* and, to cap it all:

Hey Little Hen,
When, when, when,
Will you lay me an egg for my tea?

Eggs were something they certainly didn't get, well only the whiff of them on a Sunday morning!

'That's it! Damn it!' Beth exclaimed. 'The damn griller is broken and I was going to do Welsh rarebit for tea.'

Jimmie wondered what on earth 'Welsh rabbit' could be, as he made his way to the gas office with a note from Beth.

The attendant read Beth's request to have the griller on her cooker fixed, and he told Jimmie that a maintenance man would call in a few days to fix it.

During that week, the only thing on Jimmie's mind was the circus that was coming to the Beach Road playing fields. The posters around Bangor showed lions and tigers, and also featured a large pig that could jump over a high fence, as well as clowns, acrobats, monkeys, horses and numerous other animals.

It was very exciting, and Beth had agreed to let the boys go, but the money would come out of their moneybox of course. The two boys were highly-delighted that she had agreed to let them go, and eagerly counted the days up to the Saturday of the circus.

Jimmie had washed and dressed and Beth was upstairs, changing, when there was a loud knock at the door. She shouted down for Jimmie to answer the door, which was a rare privilege in itself.

Jimmie looked up at the tall man in the brown smock, his nose was red, and he grinned, saying, 'I've come about the griller.'

Jimmie could hardly contain his excitement, and ran to the foot of the stairs shouting up to Beth, 'Auntie! Auntie! It's a man from the circus, he's come about the gorilla.'

'Good heavens! What gorilla?' thought Beth to herself, thinking that maybe one had escaped?

She quickly galloped down the stairs, then caught sight of the man, whom she recognised immediately, and she roared with laughter.

'Come in, Mr Thomas, come in!' her laughter echoed all over the house. 'Good heavens, my goodness!' She was doubled up, slapping her knees.

'What is it, Mrs Hughes? I know I've got a red nose because of my cold,' the man apologised with a puzzled look, wiping his nose, 'but why all the hilarity. Surely I don't look that funny?'

Jimmie couldn't see the joke either, but just stood and watched the man select a spanner from his tool box, in readiness to start removing the broken griller from the cooker.

Eventually Beth was able to compose herself sufficiently, to explain to Mr Thomas what had occurred, and that her evacuee had thought he had come from the circus, about a real live gorilla!'

He too, could then see the funny side, and Beth and he joked about it in their native tongue, punctuating their conversation with outbursts of laughter.

Jimmie was disgruntled and didn't laugh at all. All he could think about was the circus, and how odd these Welsh people were! Anyway, he was glad that something had made her split her sides.

Aloud he said to Edward, 'Come on, Eddie! Gerra move on it's Saturday, an' yer know what that means! It's shopping first before we can go to the blinkin' circus!'

CHAPTER SEVENTEEN
Miss Crosby OBE

It was winter 1943, and Hywel had changed his job once again. He was now working for Saunders Rowe. He wouldn't say what kind of work he was involved in, only relating to Beth that it was confidential. He was away most weekends, and worked on varying shifts, so obviously his voluntary work with the NFS came to an end and his services with them were terminated.

The old sledge was converted into a type of cart, this time with four wheels. The front axle was firmly fixed to a batten underneath, so it didn't turn, and the driver had no hope of steering the contraption, but there was a rope fastened to the front, so the boys had to do what they could and make the best out of a bad job.

Modifications were made to the cart but were never successful, so that eventually, the two front wheels became buckled, due to the continual running into the kerb. Jimmie blessed the day when he was asked to chop the firewood on a regular basis, and naturally Hywel's brainwave was the first to get the chop.

Another regular job that Jimmie inherited, was emptying the water from the well in the shelter, several times a week. He had visions of being buried alive in the blinking thing. It was never used as a shelter, but enterprising moggies, were able to get their intimate pleasures in the seclusion of the bunker.

Jimmie was amused by the thought of himself and Edward lugging the large sheet of corrugated iron all the way through Bangor on a Saturday afternoon, just to give the cats a bit of pleasure! Another of Uncle Hywel's unsuccessful projects! Jimmie often wondered what the neighbours really thought of it!

With Hywel working away most of the time, Beth would occasionally allow the boys to stay up until eight o'clock. She would never venture out in the daytime, only at night, when she would visit Megan. Now and again, she actually took the boys to her youngest sister's home in Upper Bangor, but it was so boring for them, having to sit and listen to the sisters nattering in their own language, and it was a relief when it was time to go, and they certainly knew what nos da meant!

Walking home in the blackout, Beth put her arms around the boys, and followed the beam of faint light on the white lines at the edge of the pavements from her torch, which Jimmie held for her. It was good to be outside, even if it was dark.

'You'll have to learn Welsh properly, then you'll understand when we speak in our native tongue,' she said to the boys, 'yes indeed. Let's start now as we're walking home, we'll start with Llanfair PG. Now repeat after me say Llan, no Ll, and push your tongue up, Llan. Oh! Never mind,' sighed Beth, getting frustrated, 'just say it as you think.'

'Lan-fur-pu, what's next?' asked Jimmie.

Beth managed to get through five syllables, by the time they got back to Glynne Road.

'Keep repeating it over and over again,' she advised, 'then you'll be a proper little Welshman. A Welsh Scouser.'

On his way up to bed, Jimmie kept on repeating the long word, 'Clan-vur-puk-wing-gik, gorrit!' he beamed, 'now fer some more!'

In the days that followed, he finally mastered, in his broad Liverpudlian accent, the longest name he had ever heard of. It was a place in Wales. It didn't have the slightest resemblance to the authentic version, but he was proud of himself, and impressed many people with his knowledge of the Welsh language.

He learned how to count up to ten,

'In-dye-tree-padwak-pimp-kwirk-site-who-id-now-dirg.'

At least, that's how it sounded to him.

'Sorry I didn't learn earlier, it's the gear this Welsh,' Jimmie said to Edward, delighted with his progress.

However, Edward wasn't at all impressed, and paid no attention to his pal's enthusiasm, 'Huh! Welsh, yer'll not 'ave ter talk like that when yer get back ter Liverpool, or yer ma won't understand yer.'

It was good to have Sunday afternoon free from attending Fron Deg Chapel and Sunday School, even though it was raining.

Mr Ingham had told Beth, 'An evening service has been planned instead, and a very distinguished person will be giving the sermon.' He knew who it was but didn't divulge that information. All he was prepared to say was that the boys would enjoy it. 'Come to think of it,' he added, 'so will everyone else, I'll be ready and waiting for the boys at six o'clock.'

Usually, there was a lot of activity from the army exercises and drilling at the barracks. Bren-gun carriers raced up and down Glynne Road, and soldiers marching off in platoons to do manoeuvres in the mountains. These activities were always missed by the boys because of Sunday School, but on this particular day, they were able to watch it all.

They lost track of the time and were late getting home, resulting in a scolding from Beth, and tea having to be hastily gulped down, with Edward almost choking himself in the process.

Mrs Evans opened up early, and hymn books were being handed out by her two daughters, to the queue already formed by eager parishioners. It wasn't long before the small chapel was tightly-packed. There was just one vacant seat at the right-hand side of the body of the hall, apparently for the mystery guest speaker. Everyone was silent in anticipation of this VIP, who was going to deliver the special sermon.

It was almost time to start, when a bustling noise was heard by the congregation, and the chubby figure of Miss Crosby emerged. Mr Burrows, the lay preacher, stood and shook her hand, smiled and showed her to her seat. He then took up his position in front of the rostrum and introduced the first hymn.

The congregation rose, and sang with gusto in melodious union, whilst Miss Crosby knelt humbly on the bare wooden floor, her hands tightly-clasped, motionless in prayer, with a strong air of calm about her. On rising to her feet with some difficulty, she smiled, then joined the rest of the singers in the last verse of the hymn.

After being introduced, she stepped onto the rostrum, then greeted her audience in a husky voice, displaying that all-too-familiar gap in her front teeth.

'How are you people getting on with us Scousers? Are we behaving ourselves? I hope so, you've all been ever so generous and kind, and on behalf of all the people in Liverpool, I would like to thank you sincerely. All of you, for the way you've accepted us, and the hospitality that's been shown to both children and teachers. I'm not going to give the usual kind of sermon, instead I'm going to talk about myself, well I'm allowed to aren't I?' she asked, as everyone smiled.

'Now then,' she continued, 'make yourselves comfortable, shuffle if you have to, cough, sneeze, laugh, but don't throw anything, especially tomatoes. I hate them.'

This triggered a roar of laughter, and some of the ladies in the congregation were still tittering when Miss Crosby tried to continue.

'Go on, girls, let it all out!'

There was more laughter.

'Right, I can see that you're happy, so I'll begin.' She took a single piece of paper from a long white envelope.

'Do you know?' she asked, as she opened out the paper, 'When I got this a few years ago, I nearly fainted when I opened it. Would you like to know what it says?'

She looked around at the sea of faces. 'Well? Would you?'

She waved the paper around, and there came an audible 'Yes!' from everyone in attendance.

Miss Crosby then read the letter, which was an invitation for her to attend Buckingham Palace for the honour of receiving an OBE.

'Well!' she exclaimed, 'you could have knocked me down with a wet Nellie!'

She laughed along with the crowd.

'Fancy me going to Bucky Palace! Do you know, I couldn't sleep, and I couldn't eat. Mind you, I was glad to shed a few pounds, but I thought to myself; why me? Surely there must be others who are much more worthy of this honour than me?'

As she continued, she had her audience captivated by her easy manner, and you could have heard a pin drop.

'Now then, what am I going to wear for our King George? I want to look my best for him, 'tisn't every day one gets to meet the King! I wonder what his favourite colour is? And shoes? Now there's my downfall. I can't wear new shoes, not with my bunion.'

There was more laughter. They were really enjoying this sermon. Miss Crosby explained how she visited TJ Hughes in Liverpool, and other fashionable shops, trying on various dresses, suits and hats.

'I hate hats too, they don't do a thing for my looks. I decided that moderation, that was it, would be the best way. I'll dress simply and discreetly, that'll be the best for me.'

She talked about the suit she eventually decided upon, chosen for its simplicity, and the modest brooch in her lapel, and how she'd got a bit flustered when she thought about skirt lengths.

'Have to get the length just right for when I do my curtsy. I don't want to show my bloomers!'

There were more howls of laughter.

'Royal blue they were, me knickers.' Miss Crosby took a sip of water, whilst the congregation was in stitches.

Almost an hour had now gone by, though it seemed like minutes. Everyone was so enthralled with their guest speaker, and her natural wit and charm, her straightforwardness and open manner. She finally held up her OBE medal for all to see.

'Come and have a closer look afterwards, if you want to,' she invited them.

She concluded with this brief, but heartfelt message, 'Don't ever try to be something you're not, just be yourself. Help others and they will help you. Be generous and kind to all, and your reward will be great in Heaven, that's what Jesus taught, and the world will be a happier place for following his advice.'

It wasn't the usual custom to applaud in chapel, but Miss Crosby OBE, was a very special person, and she was given a standing ovation that evening.

Everyone wanted to shake her hand and inspect the medal, so it was very late indeed when the chapel finally closed its doors that night. She was the talk of Bangor for weeks to come, such a popular figure around the city, and always approachable. She was that little woman who brought so much joy and happiness to everyone she met, and who had a genuine love for her fellow creatures.

CHAPTER EIGHTEEN
Da Bo Chi

Gwenda waited anxiously at the station for Tim to arrive. She had received a telegram saying he was back on shore and was quite ill, and was going to stay with his aunt in Portmadoc, a small village near Caernarfon. He'd been on a number of trips backwards and forwards across the menacing Atlantic Ocean, and the frightening voyages had extracted their toll upon both the physical and mental health of the gentle young man. He was discharged from the Merchant Service, much to Gwenda's delight.

They hugged and kissed each other on the platform. The past didn't matter, they were together once more, and they walked arm in arm from the station, gazing into each other's eyes.

'It's all finished with now, darling,' Tim reassured her, 'we'll be together now forever.'

They stopped. Gwenda was crying, but they were tears of joy. Tim wiped her face with his big hankie and said softly, 'Come on now, smile. That's my girl.'

With open arms, Megan welcomed Tim home, and much to his surprise and astonishment, Taid was quite cordial with him, indicating that he wanted to make amends for his past stubborn behaviour.

There was much to celebrate that night. Tim and Gwenda got engaged, she had now reached the age of twenty, and her grandfather gave the couple his blessing! Megan was delighted for them both, they deserved to be happy.

On his doctor's advice, Tim eventually took a farming job, and slowly he regained his health. They saved hard for their future, and eventually married and remain so to this day.

In September 1942, the evacuees at Garth, on reaching their fourteenth birthdays, were returned to their homes to take up employment as jobs were still plentiful.

By this time, Jimmie was thirteen and a half, and had lived in Bangor for three and a half years. He loved school, and in some ways would be sorry when he left. Things were easier at school by now, there was hardly any caning, except for the persistently unruly, and though some of these harassed their tutors as much as they dared, all was forgiven, when eventually it was time for them to leave.

Then there were handshakes all round and such comments as, 'See yer in the Pool, lar!' and 'Ta-ra youse lot.'

Friday morning was a day for digging up potatoes, carrots and any other produce that had not been stolen over the weekend. Everything was washed, and anyone wanting to purchase any vegetables was charged a small sum to cover the cost of seeds, bedding plants and fertilisers for the following season.

At mid-morning, it was the practice for boys to receive a gill of fresh milk, ladled out by Maggie Barge. Jimmie had scarcely started to drink his on one particular morning, when he was called by one of the teachers and told to go home immediately.

As he dashed across the field, past the allotments, his mind raced, as if in competition with his strides, and he wondered what on earth he was being sent home for?

On arrival, he immediately noticed that brown paper carrier bags were packed and standing in the hallway, he was told that his and Edward's belongings were in the carriers. Beth had hastily made a few sandwiches and placed them on top of the bags. Miss Davies, the WVS lady, had gone to bring Lily from her school in Lion Pobty. Mrs Flynn having also been hastily notified, so that Lily's clothes were packed and ready for her departure.

Edward, with not a care in the world, and not knowing of these arrangements, meandered down to the house for his dinner, and Beth ran to the door to meet him.

'Hurry up, quick lad, come on gerra er…' she paused, 'get a move on, you're going home!'

Both lads had a quick swill and brushed their teeth, packed their toothpaste and brushes, then Beth called out, 'Quick, she's here!'

Miss Davies drew up in her little Ford, the boys jumped in the back, the front seat being already occupied by Lily. All their belongings were piled into the boot.

'We'll have to hurry Mrs Hughes, or they'll miss the train. I'll call and see you on the way back.'

'Just a moment,' Beth called out, 'here,' and quickly handed Jimmie and Edward some of the contents of their moneybox, which she had smashed open in haste. 'Ta- ra now,' she gulped and disappeared into the house, without looking back.

'Think she's upset,' commented Lily, staring ahead and enjoying the view, as the car sped up towards the railway station. Miss Davies had barely enough time to get the baggage and the children onto the platform, before the train raced in.

'The guard will look after you, and your mothers will be meeting you at the other end. So don't worry, just take care now, and God bless!'

She slammed the heavy carriage door, then they were on their way. She waved until they were out of sight.

It was unbelievable! Everything had happened so swiftly that morning, that the children had no time to think what it was all about, but were later to learn that Jimmie and Lily's mother had been re-housed after losing her home in the blitz, so her children could be returned to her, thus saving the

Government money. Mrs Hughes had only been notified at the last minute of the children's departure.

After they had left Conway, the children slowly nibbled their sandwiches, deep in thought.

Jimmie wondered, 'Would he ever see any of his school mates again? Liverpool was a big city, and many who returned would have moved to another area to begin a new life, so contact would be almost impossible.'

Many of the dirty terraced houses had been razed to the ground, and were now gone forever. Did it really take a war to get rid of them? The war had cost thousands of lives, military and civilian, not only in Liverpool, but in other cities and towns around Britain.

Not being able to eat all his sandwiches, Jimmie crammed the remains of his packed lunch down the side of his carrier bag. He felt something rigid. He drew it out, and scrutinised the odd-looking package, wrapped in newspaper. He hastily tore away the numerous layers, and as he tore, he guessed the contents of the mysterious parcel. It was his Echo De Luxe mouth organ, as new and shiny as the day it had vanished! How strange that it should suddenly reappear, but he didn't question the matter, as he was only too pleased to have it in his possession again. It was something that he treasured more than anything else.

He was then jolted back to the present situation by Edward tugging excitedly on his sleeve, 'Hey! Jim! I got ten pence off me Auntie Beth, dat's alright in't it?' and he jingled the coins in his pocket.

'A penny fer each year of yer life,' Jimmie calculated, as he counted his cash. It amounted to one shilling, twelve pennies, 'that's just as much as we landed in Bangor with,' he said.

Lily didn't comment on the amount of her money, but firmly held onto her tightly-packed purse!

310

'Cor!' shouted Edward, 'just look at dem fellers over der, stickin' big forks in the grass.'

Jimmie smiled, he seemed to remember that being said a long time ago. He wondered, as they travelled along, who it was that continually set the mountain on fire and chuckled to himself, 'Might have been that daft sod Onion. Aye, it probably was. Always supposed to 'ave a roll o' newspaper down 'is kecks, come to think of it.

I never said ta-ra to Gwenda and Tim, or to Auntie Meg and old Taid. What would they say? They'd be upset for sure, but Auntie Beth will explain it all to them,' he consoled himself.

The railway lines criss-crossed like spaghetti, and it baffled Jimmie as to how the train chose its designated direction? The engine suddenly came to a hissing halt, and the carriages were jolted slightly.

The door swung open, and a guard popped his head into the compartment and announced, 'Come on Eddie Jones, this is your stop, your mam will be waiting for you. I'll help you with your things. Warrington, that's where you've to get off.'

'Eck, Warrington? But I thought we were all goin' ter Liverpool?' Jimmie said.

'No, not to Liverpool. This is a Manchester train, you two are going up to Manchester, and this young feller is getting off here. See, that could be his mother,' the guard added, pointing to a young woman with a worried look about her.

Mrs Jones grabbed Edward, and lifted him from the train, whilst their friendly escort collected his belongings.

Jimmie was stunned for the second time that day, 'So long, Eddie. See yer, lar.'

Then Edward was gone! Someone he had lived with for over three years, and grown fond of, gone so suddenly, maybe never to see each other again!

'Eck,' gasped Lily, 'that was quick. Coulda told us 'e was gerrin' off 'ere.'

Just as the guard had told them, the train pulled into Piccadilly on time!

Kate waved frantically, as she caught sight of Jimmie peering out of the window, and raced to the nearest carriage door to greet her two children. After thanking the guard for looking after them, they made their way along the lengthy platform to catch another train, which would take them to their final destination.

As they travelled, Kate explained how she came to move to another area, safe from the bombing.

'So what about the 'ouse, Mam?' asked Jimmie.

'Oh! That's gone, lad, with the rest of 'em.'

'But where are yer livin' now, Mam? Is it where we're all gonna stay tergether?'

Kate smiled, 'Yes, that's where we're all gonna live now, in a place called Nelson in Lancashire.'

'Nelson?' puzzled Jimmie, 'the only Nelson I know about, is the feller wid one eye!'

Part Three
THE COBBLED SLOPE

CHAPTER ONE
Back Home With The Family

Kate MacLean had a glint in her eyes, as she walked down the cobbled slope and into the station yard with Jimmie and Lily on either side of her. She was more than glad to have her children back from Bangor, as they had spent almost four years away from her since the outbreak of war.

'Yer'll like Nelson,' she said. 'They're not a bad lot, but wait till yer 'ear 'em talk. Cor! They're not like us from Liverpool. Mind yer, youse two are like foreigners. Can't understand yer, 'specially you our Lily. Proper little Welsh rarebits yer are. Yer da won't know yer when he comes home; though when that will be God only knows. Still he's doing his bit fer his King and country, despite his age, God bless 'im! Goodness knows where he is, haven't had a line from him fer months! Still, no news is better than bad news so they say.'

Kate suddenly fell silent, and seemed about to give way to tears, when Jimmie, sensing his mother's concern, promptly changed the subject, by asking her, 'Are there any other families from Liverpool that have been bombed out, living here in Nelson?'

It wasn't as if he'd fallen in love with the place, far from it, for from what he'd seen earlier from the train, the ugly mill towns, with their towering mill chimneys spewing out grimy black smoke, hadn't impressed him at all. On the contrary, he was feeling rather dejected after leaving the clean sea air and surroundings of his previous home. He did take some notice however when his mam pointed to Pendle Hill, a famous local landmark dominating the horizon, and as Jimmie was to learn later, steeped in folklore and tradition.

Recovering her composure, Kate stopped for a moment to get her breath, arched her aching back, then replying to Jimmie's query she added, 'Yer, course there is lad, lots of families from Liverpool. Let's see now, there's the Kings, the Adams family, McCarthys, Evie Foster and her kids. Poor woman, her hubby got killed on the East Lancs. Road. Fell off the back of a lorry so he did, after cadging a lift. He was only coming home on a weekend pass. Evie was devastated, what with losing her home in the blitz, then her husband losing his life like that, 'ell it's a wonder she pulled through at all.

Anyway, enough of all that doom and gloom, now where was I? Ah yes! There's the Twists, and of course there's yer Auntie Mollie, yer da's sister. You remember her don't yer? You look surprised lad?'

'That's the auntie who lived on Mill Road isn't it?' Jimmie asked.

'Yer haven't forgotten her then? Miracle of miracles. What a blessin' it was that they were all in the shelter when the 'bread-basket' (land-mine) was dropped. It wiped out the whole road and part of the hospital.'

Kate was about to continue relating the ravaging attacks that the Luftwaffe had carried out, when Lily interrupted her, saying that she wanted to go to the lavatory.

'Sorry girl,' said Kate, 'I don't know when to stop when I start talkin' about home. Come to think of it, I could do with a pee meself. We'll call in at the Co-op at the centre, that's where I get all me shopping. Percy Feather, the manager, won't mind us using his lavvie; besides it will be an excuse to let him know I'll be callin' in tomorrow to get me weekly rations, an' that there'll be another two books to register with him. Yer have brought 'em with you, haven't you? Yer ration books, that is?'

'Course Mam, Mrs. Hughes put mine in with my clothes so it wouldn't get lost, and I know that our Lily has hers as well, 'cos I asked her.'

'Right then,' said Kate, 'let's get down to the Co-op then, before our Lily wets her pants, an' me as well!' she laughed.

Jimmie was relieved when he saw the Co-op coming into view, but not half as relieved as his mother and sister, who both rushed inside the shop, which thankfully was quiet at the time.

Kate walked towards the man behind the counter and whispered something to him about the toilet.

With a smile he nodded his head, whereupon Kate and Lily disappeared into the back room, leaving Jimmie to mind their cases.

Jimmie looked around him, thinking that though this shop was similar to the one in Bangor, somehow it was also quite different. Even the manager too, though he seemed friendly enough, and gave him a wink, before smiling broadly at him.

Eventually Kate and Lily emerged. Kate thanked Percy, then explained who the two children were, and said that she would be bringing the extra ration books for them by the next day.

'Are you sure you wouldn't like to take something with you now, Mrs Mac?' Percy asked. 'How about some nice lean back bacon, or a thick slice of gammon, either one would go down nicely with an egg and fried tomatoes.'

Anxiously he re-arranged the slices in the tray, as the heat of the day hadn't helped to keep his produce looking fresh. It certainly didn't look as tempting as it should, so like all capable grocery managers Percy was doing his best to get rid of the unsavoury-looking bacon. He really knew that he shouldn't have sliced so much, well not in this warm weather, and with trade a bit slow.

'Hell Percy lad! Yer not tryin' to palm me off with that stuff are yer? Just look at it. It's curlin' up at the sides. You keep it any longer and it'll be runnin' out of the door by itself. Anyway giz a pound of yer streaky, and half a pound of boiled ham. I'll have some of yer better stuff tomorrow, an' I don't want yer cuttin' me coupons, not fer this lot, 'ell they wouldn't serve this in the British restaurant!' Kate put on an indignant look, to which Percy replied in a humorous voice.

'Now would I give you anything but the best Mrs Mac? No! No one could put one over on you, never in this world, and I wouldn't like to try!' He laughed heartily!

Percy's face, distinctively colourful due to countless little blood vessels, was even redder as he laughed loudly, taking off his horn-rimmed spectacles, and wiping his eyes with the back of his hand, his shoulders dancing up and down with laughter, which reminded Jimmie of a puppet on a string.

'Can't see what's funny,' said Kate huffily. 'Anyone would think I'd cracked a joke or summat?'

'Forgive me, Mrs Mac,' said Percy, whipping a clean white handkerchief from beneath his striped apron, then blowing noisily at his pointed nose. 'It's just your sense of humour, and the way you talk in that broad Scouse accent. I wish all my customers were as cheery and friendly as you. However,' he continued, replacing his spectacles which magnified his brown eyes, 'I'll have everything ready for you tomorrow, and maybe a little bit of something special from under the counter. I only said *maybe* though,' he laughed.

'Ell, anyone would think you were up to summat, Percy Feather. Huh! Feather by name an' by nature too, tryin' ter tickle me fancy yer cheeky bugger, an' me eight months pregnant. Shame on yer! Ta-ra then.' Then chuckling to herself, and at the same time thanking Percy for the use of his lavvie, Kate ambled out of the shop with her two offspring.

'See you Mrs Mac. Leave the door open lad,' he called to Jimmie, who by the look on his face, couldn't see anything amusing at all, except for the manager all roused up and tittering at Kate's comments.

'You haven't paid for the bacon Mam. Does he, does Mr Feather let you have tick?' Jimmie called out, as he caught up to his mother and sister, with both carrier bags banging against the sides of his legs.

'Don't call it tick up here lad. Put it on t' slate, that's what they say, on t' slate. Well summat like that, anyway I'll give him his money tomorrer, that's if the bacon tastes alright. Aye eggs, bacon an' fried toms, how's that strike you?'

Jimmie's mouth watered at the very thought of the sizzling fry-up, 'Smashin' Mam. Cor! Eggs and bacon, never had it before, neither in Liverpool or in Bangor!'

'Yer mean to tell me lad, that yer never got yer rations? Why! The miserable lot of so-an'-so's. Got the money off the Government didn't they? I heard about evacuees not gerrin' their fair share of food. Still yer 'ome now lad, at yer mam's. I'll feed yer up, and by the look of it, yer could do with a few pans of good, hot scouse down yer belly. You too, our Lil.'

'It wasn't like that fer me Mam. I wasn't like our Jimmie,' said Lily, sweeping back her fringe of auburn hair, 'I got proper meals, with meat an' that. Mrs Flynne fed us well enough with whatever she could get, an' she was very good to me, that she was. She cried buckets when she came to see me off this mornin'.'

Lily gave a deep sigh and looked up, wondering to herself whether her mother had made the right decision in bringing her home from Bangor? She had been happy there with Mrs Flynne.

Kate repeated herself saying, 'Well yer 'ome now, the pair o' yer, an' yer'll get fed properly. Percy's good to me, lets me 'ave me fur shur, (fair share), what with all us lot, we won't go short of owt, not like it used to be back in Liverpool, 'ell they were cruel wicked days, don't know how we kept body and soul together. I wouldn't like to go back to that way of life. Times 'ave changed for the better, at least for the likes of us.

Fer others, well I wouldn't like to say, but even though there's a war on, I feel we've been given a new start here in Nelson.'

By this time they were wending their way down Fleet Street, and Jimmie's curious gaze took in the rows and rows of neat terraced houses, with their sandstoned steps, and cream or white net curtains to their windows.

His eyes then found a towering red chimney, 'What's that Mam?' he asked.

'It's a place where all the rubbish from the dustbins is taken. People around here call it the destructor's yard, 'cos they take cats and dogs there to be put down fer a few coppers. Poor little sods,' she explained.

Jimmie fell silent at these sad words, thinking of all the animals going to their death. 'What a horrible thought!'

On a more cheerful note she announced, 'There's a swimming baths back there, yer'll be able to go with the school, as yer've still got a few months to go lad, so I suppose it'll be Bradley where yer'll finish yer education. It'll be handy, as it's only two minutes away from our house in Dalton street.'

'Do I have to go Mam? Seems a blinkin' waste of time if you ask me!' groaned Jimmie.

'Well I'm not askin' yer lad. I'm **tellin'** yer that yer'll 'ave ter finish yer schoolin', otherwise the school bobbies will be on ter me. Besides Lily will be goin' there as well.'

'But she's got years to go yet Mam, not like me, only a matter of months. What the 'eck.' Jimmie curbed his tongue, before he regretted what he was about to say.

'Don't look so miserable!' exclaimed Kate, 'a few months aren't goin' to hurt yer, 'ell I could do that standin' on me 'ead! Make the most of it 'cos when yer've done, yer'll 'ave ter gerra job and gerrout ter work.'

Kate had a determined look about her, and for once Jimmie sensed the seriousness in her voice, so he thought it better not to argue, though he felt just as determined that he would try to talk his mother round, and persuade her to let him off having to go to school. There must be ways of doing it, for it hardly seemed worthwhile for only a few months.

It was Lily who broke the silence, by commenting that she wished it was her who only had a few months left to go to school instead of years. 'A hairdresser, that's what I'm going to be when I leave school. A ladies hairdresser!' She tossed her auburn hair about as she spoke, feeling sure that she could influence her mother into letting her do just that when the time came.

'You'll do no such thing our Lily! There is no money in shop work or the like! Mill work, now that's where the money is! As they say up here in Nelson, brass. Where there's muck, there's brass! Yer'll never be out of work as long as people need cloth fer clothes an' household stuff. So ferget all about shop work. Anyway there's a couple of years yet before you leave school. In the meantime yer'll be a good help fer me, an' you too our Jimmie. Yer can both help ter look after yer three little sisters an' yer brother, especially when I'm havin' the baby, there'll be plenty to do believe me!'

Jimmie remained silent, the very thought of working in a mill sickened him. He'd read books about children who worked in the pits and coal mines, little black children in America working in the cotton fields, little slaves, that's what the books said, and Jimmie imagined that the cotton mills wouldn't be any different.

He had heard of the unhealthy working conditions and long hours, never seeing the daylight in the long winter months, no none of that was for him, but he knew enough to keep quiet for now.

He leaned forward as they trudged along to Dalton Street, to the home he hadn't even seen yet. He felt tired, as it had been a long day. He glanced across at Lily; she looked back at him and pulled a face, she was quite obviously thinking the same thing as he was.

They were wishing that they were back in Bangor, as since their mother had mentioned working in a mill, they both instantly disliked Nelson. There was also the prospect of having to look after the other kids, those siblings that he hardly knew. They were little strangers to him, as they had been born during the time that he and Lily had been evacuated.

At last they finally reached their destination, number 58 Dalton Street. It was a large gable-end terraced house, situated opposite a group of cotton mills, that he was soon to know as Dyson's, Clegg's, and Walton's.

The gable of the house overlooked a small river, known locally as the goit, which carried filthy discharges from the mills further up the valley, as well as the water from the local wash and swimming baths. It was infested with rats and other vermin that thrived in the slimy backwash. When in flood, it was perilous to say the least, and for anyone having the misfortune to fall in it, there would be little chance of survival.

There were also obnoxious smelling fumes from Lanry's bleach works and Haworth's dye works, polluting the air and adding to the unhealthy environment

Kate struggled to turn the key in the lock, the height of the keyhole almost getting the better of her four feet, ten inches.

She laughed, saying, 'I'll have to put some horse muck in me shoes to make me grow taller.'

Jimmie didn't see the funny side of it at all, as he and his sister followed their mother along the dark lobby, past the front parlour and the bottom of the staircase, into the largest dining-room he had ever seen. There were two large sash windows in the room, one overlooked the aforementioned river, the other the backyard.

'And this,' Kate announced proudly, 'is the kitchen!' She led the children through a door from the dining-room and into her spotlessly clean kitchen, showing off her new gas stove, mangle and gleaming copper gas boiler, in which she did her weekly wash. There was also a metal kitchenette and a large dining table with chairs grouped around it.

'We always eat in here; it's big enough when the rest of 'em are comin' in, in dribs an' drabs. Come on now, get yer bags an' I'll show yer to yer rooms upstairs, then when yer've put yer things away, come down, an' I'll make yer some tea.'

Jimmie sat on the edge of his bed with the flock mattress feeling a little subdued. Any slight movement made the wire base of the bed creak and clank noisily. He was at a loss for words for once in his life. He could see out of the window from where he was sitting. There was a row of houses opposite with their brass letter-boxes and door-knockers shining in the late afternoon sunshine. The doorsteps were scrubbed clean and donkey-stoned, and everywhere looked as if it was ready for inspection.

He sniffed thinking to himself, 'At least the neighbours are clean, judging by the appearance of the houses they lived in. He could hear the muffled drone of machinery, as looms clattering their monotonous tune, drifted their sound in through the open window, that was until his mother disturbed his thoughts by slamming the window down on its sash. He hadn't heard her enter the room and the noise made him jump.

'Forgot to close it this mornin' our Bobbie, it's been open all day so it has, not as though there's anything to pinch; anyway they're decent enough folks around here, thank goodness! It's not much to look at, but a big improvement on the house we had in Liverpool.

Yer'll be bunkin' in with yer big brother, how's that suit yer? An' yer can share the built-in wardrobe, though there's all sorts of paraphernalia in it, but it should suffice.'

Kate flung open both doors of the wardrobe saying at the same time, 'he'll be lookin' fer a clean shirt this weekend.' She scooped up an armful of dirty shirts and underwear, 'Untidy bugger, I keep sayin' he'll do his own washin' if he can't remember to bring it downstairs.' Then as an afterthought, Kate reminded Jimmie to make sure that the blackout curtains were all drawn together, as she had been ticked off by the local A.R.P. warden only last week, for allowing a chink of light to penetrate the darkness outside.

'I gave him what for though,' said Kate, folding her sturdy arms, revealing the tattooed anchor on her left forearm, 'I told him I'd purris bleedin' lights out if he ever knocked on my door again. It's a good job my Robert's not here, or he'd have sent him packin'.

Mind you, to be fair, the nervous little man came back the day after with an apology,' Kate laughed heartily, 'Poor little bugger, I felt sorry fer him really, his blinkin' helmet was miles too big fer him. I could only see his nose and moustache, maybe I shouldn't 'ave spouted on at him like I did. I invited him in, only to have another good titter when he removed his tin-lid, fer he was as bald as a billiard ball. Full marks to the lad though, he was performin' his duty, an' that's the main thing. Trouble is, he's never off the doorstep now, expectin' his cuppa. Still he's 'armless enough! Anyway, come downstairs when yer ready, an I'll make some tea. There's a good lad.' She smiled at Jimmie, and he smiled back as she left the room, pulling the door to behind her.

He chuckled to himself, at last seeing the funny side of the conversation then thinking, 'His mam wasn't too bad after all, her bark was always worse than her bite. She had always been able to hold her own, despite her size. She was a real trouper.'

Jimmie's eyes scanned the room he was to share with Bobbie, his oldest brother. Dull green distemper covered the walls, not at all to his liking, but clean all the same. The dark wood built-in wardrobe dominated the room, and thick, dark brown curtains hung at the window with the blackout curtains underneath. He suddenly felt down-hearted again, remembering the bright sunny room at Mrs Hughes' house in Bangor, which he had shared with young Edward Jones.

He was startled from his reverie and gasped, 'Hell! you scared me half to death, I never heard you, our Lily, peering with your gob around the door. It's enough having to live here, the house gives me the creeps, and it's so big, let alone you putting the wind up me.'

'Think yourself lucky our Jimmie, at least youv'e got a window and daylight coming in; you can see outside, not like me, I've only got a skylight in, an' that's boarded over, so as the light doesn't shine out. An' to top it all, I've got to share with our Maisie, Cathy and Olive. Four of us! I'll feel like a blinkin' sardine, dossin' in with three of 'em. It's goin' to be like livin' in India Street all over again!'

'You don't have to remind me of that,' Jimmie replied as he followed his sister across the landing. He had felt disillusioned himself, as soon as he had set foot in the door, but his mam had tried so hard to give them a decent home; it wouldn't be right on her if they were to grumble. She was doing her best for her large family, with her husband away at sea doing his bit.

'That's our Bill's room,' said Lily, pointing to another door. In the past everyone had called Bill by the name of Willie, but now that he was older he had insisted on being called Bill, mostly due to the fact that some uncouth character had said that Willie meant something that dangled between a lad's legs.

His mother had disclosed that, 'It was a proud name William, and that he was named after William of Orange, she being a member of the Orange Order, so it wasn't fitting to have the mickey taken out of the name.'

So Bill took umbrage at anyone who addressed him in an improper or vulgar manner.

'An' this is me mam's room, it overlooks the yard, an' you can see right up the goit. I'm learning aren't I? I remember me mam calling the river that.'

'How exciting, don't remind me,' said Jimmie sarcastically, 'can't see what there is to rave about, it's a stinking river, that's all it is if you ask me. I'd much rather be looking out over the Menai Straits,' he said wistfully.

He glanced around his mother's bedroom, and had to admit that it was particularly clean. Sparkling white sheets were neatly folded over a pink Alhambra quilt on the double bed, and two large fluffy pillows, with frilled edges, rested against the polished wood headboard. A small dressing-table, with a mirror, Kate's pride and joy, stood across the corner near the window. A picture of her Robert, Jimmie's dad, in his naval uniform was placed with care and love amongst little pottery trinkets on the crocheted mats.

There was no carpet or lino covering the floor, but the floorboards were scrubbed white due to Kate's efforts. One had to give credit to her, she had become very house-proud; she had been given a second chance, and she appreciated it.

Though every stick of furniture she owned had been donated to her by the town welfare and other voluntary organisations, she had welcomed it all with open arms, as she had lost all of her meagre possessions in the blitz. She took a zealous pleasure in cleaning and polishing everything in sight until it gleamed and sparkled, and though antiquated, the furniture was good, and soon restored to its original condition.

Kate was no stranger to hard work, so it wasn't a hardship to her. As a young woman she had worked with her mother on the great liners that berthed in Liverpool, cleaning and polishing, scrubbing and mopping in preparation for the elite on their luxury cruises.

No matter what kind of work it was, Kate would turn her hand to it to feed her young family. She worked as many as fifteen hours in one day, and she even learned the art of splicing worn and frayed ropes, a job normally done by men.

Though small in stature, she was as tough as they came. She had to be!

Kate knew what poverty was, and to have a house large enough in which to keep all her family together, and in a safe area away from the bombs, was indeed a blessing.

This home, and all the things she had been given to make a fresh start, gave her hope for the future, and also joy and pleasure knowing that for the first time in her life she had a home she needn't be ashamed of. In fact she could be proud of.

'Hats off to Nelson Council, who had been responsible for giving her this fresh start in life, in a decent town where people were friendly, and for many other families like herself, from Liverpool who had been rehoused, so that seeing these ones from back home, hadn't made her feel like a stranger.'

She had laughed to herself when the sideboard had been delivered, it was such an old thing. She secretly thought it should have gone down with the *Titanic*, but it had good deep drawers with a cupboard on each side, so it was a very useful piece of furniture, and by the time she had finished with it, cleaning it with vinegar and warm water, then polishing it until the item shone and showed up the beautiful grain of its wood, it was much admired.

Lily's voice piped up, and Jimmie was startled as he was deep in thought. 'You've got to put the light on when you come through to my room,' she said, as she reached for the switch, 'though where I'm going to hang all my dresses and other things I don't know? There is a makeshift cupboard in here, in this other room, see!'

Lily led, and Jimmie followed into another spacious room. 'It's a bathroom as well as another bedroom, and also a place for airing clothes and towels,' once again Lily nosied into the contents above the large hot water tank.

'So I see,' said Jimmie, as he slid his hand along the edge of the cast iron bath, amazed at its length and depth. 'Hell!

You could bloody well drown in here!' He turned on the cold tap to demonstrate, but quickly turned it off again, as it gushed out, splashing the sides of the bath, and Jimmie's arm furiously, 'S'truth, what a force! At least it won't take long to fill.'

Lily frowned at him, adding, 'You'd better not let mam hear you swearing. She'll clonk you one for sure, she'll knock the living daylights out of you.' Then turning to the cupboard, she rattled the twisted wire coat-hangers and shoved them to one side, suggesting that perhaps she could move her things in here? She looked as if she was about to cry, 'I don't know, everything's got me thinking.'

'Well that makes a change,' said Jimmie, trying to cheer her up, 'you don't normally think, you just blurt things out.'

She stood motionless, with a confused expression on her face, the events of the day had unfolded rapidly before her. Leaving Llon Popty school that morning, the tearful goodbyes with Mrs Flynne, then she was off to the station to get the train for the journey to Manchester, where mam had met them only to tell them that she was starting yet another new life in a place called Nelson. It had all been too much for her young mind to take in. She felt as if it was all a dream; did it all really happen today?

'Well?' said Jimmie, 'are yer gonna keep me standing here until midnight?'

She turned to her brother, whom she had completely forgotten, 'Oh! I'm sorry Jimmie, do you think we'll settle down here okay?'

'What's made you ask that our Lily? You seemed happy enough when we were walking down from the station. It's no good getting yourself upset, we've just got to make the best of it. It hasn't been easy for mam either has it? You wouldn't want her to think you're not glad to be home would you? Sure it's different, but we were away a long time, and at least we're all together again aren't we? Now we are home, the only thing is it's a new home, a different home, you'll be alright when you get used to it, after all I'm in the same boat you know.'

'That doesn't make me feel any better our Jimmie,' she blurted out, 'coming out with those stupid statements. I just feel like yelling myself to sleep tonight, like I did in Bangor, the first night we were there. I didn't know where you'd gone or who with, in a strange place. Have you forgotten what it was like?'

'How could I ever forget Lil? Why that little feller who was with me cried so much that night, and peed himself, and I suppose that's what happened to thousands of other kids like us. Poor little sods, but we are with our family now, not strangers. Mam has worked very hard and done her best to make a decent home for us, at least we won't starve here, and we won't be forced to go to bed at seven o'clock every night. We'll soon get used to it. Okay it will be strange at first, like anything new, but in a few weeks you'll forget all about Bangor.'

Jimmie's voice was drowned at that moment by a clattering outside. It was the sound of many pairs of feet in Lancashire clogs, as droves of mill workers swarmed from the mills nearby. Then the weaving sheds fell silent, the two children temporarily forgot their troubles, as they both scrambled onto the window-ledge, to get a better view of the army of cotton workers emerging from the mills.

There were men with flat caps on their heads, puffing away at pipes or cigarettes, glad no doubt, to be outside in the sunshine. There were women and girls, the latter linked arm in arm with their chums, chattering merrily, and happy too that their day's work was over. Without exception they wore the black woollen stockings and clogs, which were the trademark of Lancashire mill workers; their bright floral pinafores covering their blouses and skirts. Cotton dust or dawn, as it was commonly named, had covered their hair, making them look prematurely grey.

Yes the children were now being introduced to a new set of people, as well as a new life in Nelson, Lancashire!

Jimmie and Lily were unaware of their mother's presence in the room, as they were so interested in the goings on down below in the street, until Kate stretched across them, sliding the window shut.

'I've shouted of you twice that your tea was ready. I see you've tasted a little bit of Lancashire life down there,' she pointed to the busy street. 'The noise doesn't bother me now as I've got used to it. You won't notice it either after a few days.'

'I don't know about tasting Lancashire life Mam, but I'm ready to taste my tea. It smells good, it really does!' Jimmie jumped down from the window-sill, then assisted Lily.

'Well come on then,' said Kate, 'the pair o' yer, before it gets cold. Yer can have it before our Bobbie an' Willie come in. I mean Bill. They'll be here before long; wait till yer see the look on their faces, be glad ter see yer, they will. Then I'll go an' fetch the kids from Evie Foster's, she'll think I ran off wi' another feller – ha! ha!'

'My that was good, Mam! Just what I needed! Didn't realise how hungry I was. Fit fer a king! Never had anything like it all the time I've been away.' Jimmie stabbed his last piece of sausage, dipped it in the remains of the egg yolk and bacon fat, then stuffed it into his mouth.

Kate smiled, sipping her tea as she watched her son mopping his plate with a piece of bread. 'Glad you enjoyed it lad, but leave the pattern on the plate. If you want some blackberry jam help yourself. I'll cut more bread, don't be frightened of using the butter, there's plenty, the kids don't like it, they only like maggie-ann (margarine).'

'Honest Mam, I couldn't eat another thing, I'm f'lup! It was scrumptious! Thanks very much, that'll put me on fer a week, I'm sure,' said Jimmie, patting his belly.

'Nonsense! In a few days you'll be eatin' me out of house and home, that you will. Twaddles there, (referring to Lily), doesn't seem to have much of an appetite, could be the long journey that's fagged her out. Go on, lie on the sofa if yer want to Queen,' she said softly to her daughter, 'you'll feel better when you've had a rest, you'll be pestered to death when the others come in. They'll be wantin' to know all about you and North Wales. Yer speak like proper little Blodwens. Leave the sausages if you don't want them, I'll throw them back in the pan with the rest for Bobbie's and Bill's tea. What the eye doesn't see, the heart doesn't grieve over. Sounds like them comin' now,' Kate said, hearing the back gate slam. 'Just watch our Bobbie's face, he'll have a grin like a Cheshire cat. There, what did I say?'

She scraped the remains of Lily's tea into the frying pan as the lads walked through the back door. 'Aren't yer pleased to see 'em?' asked Kate.

'Course we are Mam, been a long time hasn't it Jim?' said Bobbie shaking Jimmie's shoulder.

Bill kissed his little sister on the cheek, then patted Jimmie on the back. They all exchanged greetings with one another.

Though Jimmie thought, 'There should have been more to it than just a pat on the back after such a long time away. A hug and a squeeze wouldn't have gone amiss, though he could never remember any of the family showing the kind of love and affection that he always longed for.' The thought crossed his mind, 'Even a bloody dog would have made a fuss and licked his hand. Never mind, the feelings must be there somewhere, his was a family that just didn't show their emotions.'

For an instant Jimmie relived the evacuation, the war, the bombings when he briefly visited home, and the long years away from his family. He supposed that those were the reasons for the way he was feeling. He stood near the kitchen sink watching, as his two big brothers lathered their arms up to their elbows, then rinsed off the suds. Neither of the two elder boys spoke during this ritual.

Then Bobbie blurted out, 'It's been a right buddy day. Soddin' machine kept breakin' down. I'll 'ave a right buddy go at Powell in the mornin' – lost all me bonus. If 'e expects me to make it up tomorrer, he's another buddy think comin'. I'll tell 'im what to do wid 'is buddy job, if 'e gets narky wid me! There's plenty more jobs kickin' around.'

Kate wasn't the only one who smiled whenever Bobbie dropped the letter 'L' from the word bloody, and at first Jimmie thought, that he was referring to his pal or buddy at work, or maybe Bobbie pronounced the swear word that way, so as not to sound rude or uncouth?

'Here we go again,' moaned Bill, as he swilled his arms under the cold water tap, then turning to Bobbie, 'Yer've only been in the job three months, an' yer talkin' of leavin' just because of that! S'truth, yer comin' away with a good pay packet. Yer wanna keep yer trap shut, or else they'll sack you, never mind you packin' it in. They'll soon get somebody to replace you.'

Bobbie rounded on Bill saying, 'You'd better keep yer buddy gob shut an' mind yer own business. I was talkin' to me mam, not you!' He snatched the towel from Bill, 'you're not unloadin' wagons an' carryin' heavy planks of wood. Aye, doin' that as well as me own job. You'll never break into any sweat, carryin' pints of milk around; doddle of a job you've got lad. Jammy bugger, getting' on at the Co-op, 'ell you've finished at dinnertime!'

Whereupon Bill retaliated by saying, 'You'd never get up at four in the morning Bobbie as I have to do.' As he was saying this he produced three large tins of evaporated milk from his jacket, that he'd hung behind the kitchen door. 'These'll come in handy fer yer Mam, I'll bring some eggs tomorrer.'

'Thanks lad,' said Kate, as she took the cans from him and placed them inside the kitchen cabinet.

Jimmie was taking in the scene set before him and couldn't believe his eyes when he saw the contents of his mam's cupboard. 'Who would have thought that there was a war on? There were tins of ham, corned beef, fruit, all kinds of jam, and even tins of salmon! There was Spam and many other kinds of groceries, the like of which he had never seen before. The shelves were groaning as if about to collapse. It didn't seem possible that there was so much food,' he thought.

Kate turned and saw Jimmie's face, she laughed and told him not to look so surprised, 'Yer want to look in the other cupboard in the livin' room, this is only a quarter. I told yer Percy looks after us didn't I? Yer never know how long this war's going ter go on, so we've got to be prepared, haven't we?'

'Yer can say that again,' Bobbie chipped in, 'Snooks there, (referring to Bill) will end up doin' porridge if 'e's caught knockin' things off.'

'Just soddin' green-eyed, that's yer problem,' Bill said, stirring his spoon noisily in his pint pot of tea, 'look after number one, an' that's me!' he continued to reiterate by repeating, 'Yer'll get nowt in this world if yer don't look after number one.'

Kate by this time had heard enough of the bickering between the two lads, 'Just less of it now, yer like a couple o' damn mongrels with yer arguin', so shut it the pair o' yer! Goodness knows what our Jimmie an' Lily think of it all, so grow up, fer God's sake, an' let's 'ave some peace in the 'ouse!' She banged two large plates down on the table, laden with food, 'Now get that down yer, an' let's hear no more!'

With that Kate ushered her new arrivals from the kitchen, through the living-room and into the front parlour. Her face broke into a grin, 'Don't worry about those two, take no notice, you'll soon get used to it, they get on like a house on fire really, that's when they've both got it off their chests. Good job our Mary's away in the W.A.A.F.s, never know when she's goin' to turn up.'

Kate and the children were seated by this time, and Kate took a packet of Senior Service cigarettes out of her apron pocket, commenting at the same time, 'Bad habit this, got everybody smokin' has this blinkin' war.' The cigarette danced about between her lips as she spoke. 'Steadies the nerves though it does, aah!' She blew clouds of smoke up into the air, then continued, 'About our Mary, I never know who she's bringin' home next, it's always somebody different. I think she feels sorry for some of 'em. She makes me laugh though, I almost split me sides when she puts the talk on, like Lady Ascot, or is it Astor? Yer, Lady Astor, that's what yer dad calls 'er. She's stationed at Wilmslow.' Kate took another drag at her cigarette, 'God knows what she does there, she'd be better off at home.' She removed a stray bit of tobacco from her lips.

'Goin' across to Evie's now, I'll be home in an 'our, so do what you want, only don't go far away. Play in the yard, get some fresh air, it'll do you good. See yer now, won't be long.'

With that Kate departed leaving Jimmie and Lily to decide for themselves what to do. The very thought of going into the yard to get some fresh air made Jimmie cringe. 'Fresh air,' he thought, 'well that was really the understatement of the day!'

He prodded Lily with his elbow beckoning her to follow him, then made his way out of the front door, with her trailing behind him. Jimmie had the bright idea of trying to find the school that their mother had told them about, and mentioned this to his sister.

So off the two went, Lily skipping along behind her brother, down the street, over the river, past the cotton mill and up Crawford Street. As they tripped along, they laughed together about the episode between Bobbie and Bill.

Bobbie was sitting on the doorstep when he saw the children returning from their adventure. They hadn't realised that they had been gone for such a long time. Kate had been worried about them, thinking that perhaps they had lost their way. Bobbie told them this adding, 'I knew you'd be okay, I knew you'd find your way back.' He'd had a good wash after finishing work for the day and felt much better.

'No we were fine, we found Bradley School, then went along a street called Regent Street, then round by the swimming baths. It sounded crowded as we passed, then we remembered which way we had come with mam earlier in the day, and here we are!'

Bobbie smiled as he looked at his young brother, they were like two peas out of the same pod, though Bobbie's auburn hair was lightly Brylcreamed, and pressed into waves. In the middle of his forehead was a small red birthmark, rather like an Indian caste mark.

Kate had said that when Bobbie was born, his father was in India, and that being the case, Bobbie considered himself very lucky. Though the luck hadn't shown itself yet, well only bad luck. Like the time when he was small, and almost had his head knocked from off his shoulders with a plank swing in the park, resulting in him having to have his eye sockets stitched at the hospital, and almost losing his sight. Then there was the time when his eardrums were suspected to have been perforated due to the bombing. So Lady Luck hadn't shone favourably on Bobbie so far, though if one looked at it in another light, at least he was still alive!

Bobbie smiled again at Jimmie and winked slyly, as he took a harmonica from his pocket. 'Give us a tune Jim, yer can still play on it, can't yer?'

'I'll do better than play yours, I'll get my own, the one that you bought me, remember? Hang on a sec!'

Jimmie raced upstairs to his bedroom and returned in no time at all, 'See! Look!' he held out the harmonica in its box, then gently removed it, displaying the sparkling chrome of the instrument, in as new condition as when it was given to him, explaining at the same time about the disappearance of his precious gift from his brother, and how, because his playing annoyed his foster mother in Wales, she had confiscated it to a place unknown to Jimmie, only to see the light of day as he was travelling back home years later. How surprised he had been to discover it in his carrier bag with the sandwiches that Mrs Hughes had made for him.

After banging it across his palm, he blew and sucked and vamped like a professional! At least, **he** thought so! He began to play a wartime favourite, *Woody woodpecker*, then *Run rabbit run*, and many other popular tunes.

His elder brother joined in. In no time a small crowd had gathered to listen, and eventually starting to sing along.

Bill, who was upstairs changing, listened too, and thought, that for once his brothers sounded good together. Then seeing the opportunity to make a bit of money, suggested that they placed one of mam's pudding basins in front of them to make a collection after the performance.

Though the music sounded good to most of the neighbours, this was not so to Mrs Dyson, a quiet lady living next door, but her husband enjoyed it immensely.

'The harmonicas remind me of the time we marched along in the 'Great War' of 1914,' Mr Dyson explained. 'Ours is a quiet neighbourhood now, and the noise might give offence to some; there could be complaints.'

Kate was a bit put out and told her budding musician sons to play a bit further afield in the future, as she didn't want to upset her new neighbours! After all she thought, 'Living next door to her large family of eleven, soon to be twelve, couldn't be easy, but she would do her utmost to keep the peace and be on good terms with all those who lived around her. Yes, 58 Dalton Street was going to be her home now, and there was enough trouble in the world!'

The Maclean family, noisy though they were, were accepted into the community. Eventually Mrs Dyson too having been won over.

Little bells jingled inside the wooden handles of Lily's skipping rope as she jumped merrily, singing her skipping songs. Although she loved to skip, she was feeling a bit tired now, for after all it had been a very long and eventful day. Jimmie saw his mam coming across the street from Evie's house with her younger children.

He immediately jumped up, saying to Bobbie that he would go for a wash and get ready for bed. That had been the pattern of his life for almost four years, and so the natural instinct of bedtime at seven o' clock would be hard to break.

'Yer jokin' lar!' said Bobbie in surprise, 'Bed? It's only early yet, but yer can go an' get washed, then get yer jacket. It'll be cool comin' home.'

After a quick swill and brushing his teeth Jimmie raced downstairs, missing the bottom three steps in his eagerness to discover what his big brother had in mind?

Cathy and Olive, the younger sisters that he hadn't known until now, giggled together as little girls do when a stranger visits the house. Eric was busy examining his anti-aircraft gun, a present from Evie Foster's lad, Tommy.

Kate's face broke into a smile, 'Yer know lad, they can't remember you, but they'll soon get to know yer.'

'I feel the same, Mam,' said Jimmie, 'I hardly know them either, let's see, Olive was the one born in the blitz wasn't she?'

'That's right, got hit in her little chest with a lump of shrapnel when only a few weeks old. It's a wonder she survived, poor little mite.' Kate stroked Olive's dark hair, so much like her own, 'but she's alright now, though she gets the shivers when the siren goes off, but it was a good move comin' here, we're safe from the bombs.

An' this is our Cathy, I named her after me, three generations of Catherines, that's her proper name. Catherine the Great, a good Irish name.'

'But we're not Irish are we Mam?' asked Jimmie curiously.

'Don't you kid yerself son, you've got Irish blood in yer as well as Scottish. Will yer just look at her,' Kate said stroking Cathy's auburn hair, 'A real pixie if you ask me,' she laughed.

The little girl's eyes met the floor shyly, not daring to look at this new big brother with the strange Welsh accent.

'An' this is Maisie,' Kate tutted, 'no mistakin' this one, keep sayin' that she came from behind the dustbin, just look at her? Have you ever seen anyone as blonde as she is? Can't understand why she's so different from all the rest, still she's all mine with her lovely peaches and cream complexion. Well say summat to her our Jimmie, after all, they are all yer little sisters, and they've been lookin' forward to yer comin' home.'

Jimmie, not being used to girls, took a step forward and gave each of them a peck on their cheeks, then glanced at Bobbie, waiting to get away to the picture house. He looked at his watch anxiously, he had heard the story about Olive and Maisie so many times, and wanted to make his getaway.

'Where you off to then?' asked Kate.

'Goin' to the Majestic, just make it for the second house if we hurry Jimmie.'

'Not before you leave yer wage packet!' Kate exclaimed, obstructing Bobbie's path. She was used to marlicking around with her sons, giving them a bear hug, but her bulk and pregnant condition wouldn't allow for it at present, so she just pretended to spar up to them instead.

'Steady on, Mam,' said Bobbie, 'Yer shouldn't be exerting yerself in your condition, me wages were there on the table fer yer, that was until Joey the Jew gorris eye on it, so I stuck it back in me pocket!'

'Don't let him hear yer call him that,' Kate said, as she fingered the familiar brown envelope, quite satisfied with the contents, 'just cut it out, you're not his dad, so less of it! The name Willie was bad enough. Struth! I don't want any more fights with youse two. S'pose yer've taken yer pocket money out?' Kate asked, referring to Bobbie's wage, then handing back the long wage slip.

'Yer, that's right, Mam, nuttin' more, nuttin' less,' grumbled Bobbie, then continued in the same strain. 'Blinkin' 'eck, what with buddy pay as you earn, pensions, this an' that taken out, me buddy money seems to be less every time I get paid. Yer think yer well off after sweatin' yer guts out all week, then the buddy Government delve into what yer've slaved for. Like ter see that buddy fat lot down in Whitehall do a bit of hard graft. Sittin' on their soddin' brains, some of 'em,' Bobbie was getting quite agitated as he continued, 'What I take out fer me beer an' smokes just about lasts me the week, an' I'm back to square one, so I was wonderin' if I could give yer board money instead, as from next week?'

Bobbie crossed his fingers behind his back, he needed that good luck just now, more than ever.

'Of course yer can lad,' was Kate's reply.

Bobbie could hardly believe his ears, until Kate finished her sentence, 'course yer can board, but yer'll get ter a bleedin' boardin' 'ouse to do it, not under my roof! But I'll tell yer worrall do, I'll give yer an extra bob or two, an' we'll hear no more about boardin' an' that's that! Now off with yer. Don't keep our Jimmie waitin', an' you, our Lily, you can 'elp me get the kids up the dancers won't you? There's a good gairl. Then me an' you'll 'ave a nice custard tart an' a cuppa, then you can tell me all about your time in Wales. That'll be nice now, won't it?'

Lily shrugged unconcernedly, but the thought of the lovely custard tart appealed to her, so she jumped up and followed her mother upstairs with the younger children.

Meanwhile Bobbie was thinking, 'I should have kept my gob shut about boarding. I should have waited until a more opportune moment.' He buddied at every other word, 'but at least I'll have a bob or two extra for my trouble, and that will help me out a bit.'

Jimmie was giggling to himself as he ran alongside his brother, trying to keep up with his steps. He was certainly going to enjoy being back with Bobbie, even if it was only for the laughs.

The second house at the Majestic had already started by the time they arrived, adding to Bobbie's displeasure and annoyance, but at least it was only the Pathe news they'd missed. The big picture was yet to come.

Jimmie, on the other hand, was thrilled to bits to be out so late and going to the flicks; he couldn't thank his brother enough, and even more so when Bobbie bought him a choc-ice. He chuckled and wondered what Mrs Hughes in Wales would have thought about it all? Normally he would have been tucked up in bed long ago!

Jimmie was excited right down to his shoelaces and couldn't sit still. 'Wallace Beery was the star of the film; he was one of Jimmie's favourites, a tough guy, and there he was brawling with three rebel soldiers in a film about the American Civil War. He always came out on top!'

Bobbie took sly glances, and saw the sheer pleasure on his young brother's face, and though Bobbie never showed his true feelings, considering it to be soft, he truly thought the world of Jimmie, and was delighted to say the least, at having him home again.

Jimmie, who had never expected such a treat, was in a world of his own, though just at that moment, there was a love scene on the screen, which didn't appeal to him in the least, and again his thoughts wandered as to how Mrs Hughes would react? Still he was home now, so it didn't matter one jot!

As they walked home together that night, Jimmie thought about the events of that long, long day, and his mind was drawn to the one and only time he had gone to the cinema, the Plaza, in Bangor. 'He'd found a sixpence in the High street whilst he was doing Mrs Hughes' Saturday shopping, and promptly pocketed it!

After his lunch, the sixpence, burned a hole in his pocket, and he had wondered how he would spend it? He decided to dodge off away from his small companion, Edward Jones, who was billeted in the same house, and from whom he could never get away! He was like a flippin' shadow,' Jimmie thought, 'he followed him everywhere! So he decided to make a quick getaway up the road when Edward wasn't looking, and headed for the Plaza, leaving Eddie to his own devices.

It was only on his way home that Jimmie began to wonder what sort of a reception he'd get, as it was already half-past four, and he'd been missing since half-past one! He'd had three hours of glorious freedom!'

However he wasn't left to wonder for very long as Mrs Hughes was waiting at the garden gate, looking up, and then down, Glynne Road.

As soon as he reached the gate she grabbed him by the arm, shouting at him in the Welsh tongue, scolding him, then slapped his legs, and sent him to bed without any tea.

Jimmie wondered as he lay in bed on such a lovely summer evening with his tummy rumbling for the want of something to eat, if it had been worth it?

'No,' he thought, 'it hadn't been such a stroke of luck after all when he found that sixpence, but he really had enjoyed seeing his hero – Errol Flynn!'

From that day onwards he never let Eddy out of his sight and convoyed him everywhere, well almost everywhere!

He was under the impression that Auntie Beth as she liked to be called, had eyes in her backside, and could see his every move wherever he was, school, playing, shopping, chapel, she always saw to it that her evacuees were washed and in bed by seven on the dot!

He was suddenly aroused from his reverie by Bobbie's voice saying to him, 'What about a bag of chips from Whittakers?'

'What a treat he'd had that evening. Oh yes! He was certainly glad to be home, even if it was in Nelson!'

CHAPTER TWO
From Home to Isolation
and More Goodbyes

Whether it was his mother's good cooking, his natural growth, or a combination of the two, Jimmie quickly grew out of his clothes.

He wasn't big for his age, not by any means, but his nice grey flannel suits fitted where they touched, as well as becoming the worse for wear, and his shirts and pullovers were holier than thou, due to his climbing, fighting, jumping over walls and fences, and all the things that healthy boys usually do, but everything was more so with Jimmie, as he had been so restricted when he was in Wales, that he had gone mad when he got his freedom.

His mother took him to Wraw's, men and boy's outfitters on Leeds Road, and kitted him out with hard-wearing navy blue serge trousers and jerseys, to the extent that her clothing coupons would allow. After all her financial situation had to be carefully considered, as she had other children to clothe.

Jimmie had settled in at Bradley School after much grumbling initially, saying that, 'It was a waste of time for only a few months.'

But fate was to take a hand in Jimmie's immediate future, when Lily, Maisie, Cathy and Eric were found to be covered with a rash. After being inspected by the doctor, who arranged that they should all go to an isolation hospital in the country in case any of the other children caught it. Jimmie was outraged when told he was to go too!

'But I'm okay,' he protested loudly.

His protestations fell on deaf ears, so he had to go, like it or lump it!

Kate told them it would only be for a short time, until she'd had the baby. 'Besides,' she said, 'you'll be back before you can say Jack Robinson, and you can keep an eye on the kids.'

'Jack Robinson, my bloody foot!' blurted out Jimmie without thinking, 'how do you think I feel having to tag along with this lot, when there's nowt wrong with me!'

'We'll have less of that talk our Jimmie,' said Kate, 'you're going an' that's that.'

'This is all because of that stinkin' river, yer shouldn't have gone over the railings to get your tennis ball, our Lily. A pound to a pinch of salt that's where you got the infection from.'

Lily began to cry, 'Don't blame me, I'm sorry we came home from Wales, just look at me, I'm covered with spots! And don't say it's no use cryin' over spilt milk, you're clever with words our Jimmie, but you're not clever enough, 'cos you've got to come with us, so there!' said Lily peevishly. During this time Lily was examining her spots and trying to show them to her brother.

'Alright Lil, put yer frock down, I don't want to see yer rash, and most of all I don't want to catch it either. Struth! In Wales it was bad enough having to look after Jonesy, but now I'm stuck with four of you!'

The big green ambulance drew up outside the front door just as the mill workers were making their way back to work after dinner. They gaped as the children came out of the house one by one, accompanied by a nurse, who assisted each of them into the vehicle.

Jimmie was quick to jump in unassisted, he wasn't an invalid, and he would show her that he didn't need any help! 'Fancy!' he muttered, 'coming at this time when everybody can gape and stare, it'll be all around the mill like a dose of salts, that Mrs Mac's kids have been carted off to God knows where in an ambulance.'

The driver, a short, stout little fellow, slammed the rear doors and turned the handles, to make sure that they were locked, then climbed into the front.

Jimmie noticed the shiny seat of his black trousers, and the rolls of fat that hung over his shirt collar as he settled himself down behind the wheel. He had a small Hitler-type moustache, that made Jimmie suspicious of him.

'Never trust anyone with a moustache like that,' he thought to himself.

The engine started and the vehicle slowly moved away. Kate and her friend Evie, waved until they were out of sight; the three youngest children were excited at the thought of a ride in an ambulance, not realising that it would be some time before they were back home again, but Lily was crying, for she was fed up of moving away. She'd had enough of it in her young lifetime. Jimmie too was fighting hard to keep back the tears, but he told himself that big boys don't cry, or so Mrs Hughes in Bangor used to say.

Just at that moment Jimmie caught sight of some kids going back to school, and was very glad to say the least, that the windows of the ambulance were dark, so that although one could see outside, those outside couldn't see in! He heaved a sigh of relief at this.

His mind, ever active and calculating, turned to where they were going. No one had named a place. It had been referred to as only to the country, they had said this over and over again, so he looked out of the window to take his mind off the situation.

Eventually the cobbled streets of the town were behind them, and the ambulance headed in the direction of Wheatley Lane and Fence, which were two pretty villages, then they turned into Padiham Road and the open country, which took them further and further from Nelson and home.

For a moment Jimmie's attention was drawn to an itch on his back. 'Had he imagined it, or was it real? Was he also infected with this dreaded disease?' He tried to twist his arm up the back of his jersey to scratch, and Lily, seeing his plight, came to the rescue.

'Here I'll scratch it for you, you must have got it after all!'

She was about to claw her nails across her brother's back, but he drew away from her in a flash, horrified at the thought of Lily touching him, as she'd been fingering her spots since leaving home.

'I know you mean well, indeed you're kindness itself in giving things away, but in this instance, this is something you'd better keep to yourself. No offence, Lil,' said Jimmie, as he backed away from her.

Tears welled up in his sister's eyes, the floodgates were about to open, when the ambulance ground to a sudden halt.

Lily brushed the tears from her face as Jimmie announced that at last they had arrived at their destination, wherever that was?

'Don't be upset Lil, I didn't mean to hurt you, but it's bad enough having to come away again, especially as there's nothing wrong with me, but at least we are together this time.' He stretched out his hand to her as the rear doors were flung open, the bright afternoon sun almost blinding them as the ambulance driver helped them down onto the gravel driveway, the nurse assisting the younger ones.

A dark-haired nurse, who seemed to be in charge, ushered them through the large double doors and into a great hallway. 'There we are, children, in we go. That's the ticket. Doctor will see you shortly, just take a seat.'

Though at that time, the children didn't know, but they had arrived at a place near Clitheroe named Waddow Hall, a stately home, which had been converted to an isolation hospital for the duration of the war.

The children looked around them. Large oil paintings in ornate gold frames, hung high on the walls, and stern, stony faces looked down on them as if in disgust that such riff-raff should be allowed to invade their ancestral home!

It didn't take long for the dermatologist to appear, directing them into his examination room, where he examined each child in turn, then confirmed that they had contracted scabies, a mite living under the skin, which caused their sores and itching.

They were then manoeuvred hastily up the broad, sweeping staircase to the first floor, and were shown to their rooms. Eric and Jimmie were to share, as were the girls, in a room directly opposite.

After each of them had received a hot soak and a scrub, with liberal amounts of Dettol in the bath water, they were then smothered in a pink ointment, before being clad in pyjamas many times too big for them.

This procedure reminded Jimmie of the day when he had arrived in Bangor, and memories came flooding back of how his hair was cut and all his clothes disposed of. The bath that he and Jonesy had shared, had also held the same strong smell of Dettol.

A smile crossed Jimmie's face at seeing Eric, his little brother, swathed in the oversized blue and white striped pyjamas. 'Yer look like Dickie Downie lad, an' doesn't this pink stuff stink?'

The nurse in charge had hardly spoken all this time, and Jimmie thought she had the most long and miserable face he had ever seen. Her large, prominent teeth didn't help, and he started to snigger.

The nurse herself was forced to smile at seeing the boys in their fashionable pyjamas, and she cupped her hand over her mouth to stifle her giggles as she left the room briefly, re-appearing again, to tell them to get into their beds.

'Right boys,' she said, 'your clothes will be laundered and returned to your rooms later. Bed now, and rest.'

'Who's Dickie Whatsit?' asked Eric, jumping up and down on his bed as soon as the nurse had left the room. 'Tell me, who's Dickie Whatsisname?'

'It's Dickie Downie, but it's too long a story for your young ears, an' you'd better get back into your flea-pit before old Sourpuss comes back. You heard what she said, bed and rest. S'truth! I don't know what for, there's nothing wrong with me!'

'I want to know, I want to know, tell me who is Dickie...' Eric shouted.

'Well get into bed then, okay, Jimmie interrupted him? He was a little feller on a jar of Bovril,' Jimmie explained, as the small lad settled down at last.

'Me mam always gives us OXO, not Bovril,' Eric said.

'Never mind,' said Jimmie, getting rather frustrated, 'Just settle in, we're going to be here for quite a while, so we might as well get used to it. I'm just going to see what the girls are up to, so hang on a bit, Be quiet, there's a good lad, play blind man's buff or summat, just to occupy your mind until I get back.'

Jimmie eased open the large door quietly, and peeped out to check that the coast was clear, turning and telling Eric once again, to be quiet as a mouse, then adding, 'Be back in a sec, won't be long. If anyone comes, tell 'em I've gone to the lavvie.'

Jimmie winked at Eric with *both* eyes, he hadn't yet mastered the art of blinking with just one eye, 'an' don't scratch, yer'll get better quicker if yer don't scratch.' He emphasised once more what a good lad he was, as he was really quite fond of the lad, with his strawberry blond hair and the bluest of blue eyes, shining out from his pink and white complexion.

Everyone always said he was too pretty to be a boy. He was a calm child and would play for hours with a piece of string, or play at burning holes in a newspaper, with the thick glass from an old flashlight, though that little caper didn't last long once he'd set fire to the racing page, causing Kate to miss her daily flutter on the nags.

Maisie was distinctly blonde. The MacLeans had the unique Irish Celtic eyes, inherited from their maternal grandmother, and though Maisie had the Irish paddy to go with them, she had the look of an angel, just as if butter wouldn't melt in her mouth! Her temper though, outshone any in the family, and all hell broke loose when she threw a tantrum!

However, Jimmie thought the world of the young ones in the family, and they in turn worshipped him, and though they had their moments, he took on the role of chief protector, especially now in their present situation, and that was the reason he was sneaking off to discover how his sisters were faring?

'I sneaked out to see how you are getting on. Are you alright?' Jimmie asked, closing the door gingerly behind him.

'If we were alright we wouldn't be here, would we?' snapped Lily, 'I hate it! I don't like this place, I want to go home!'

'Sorry,' apologised Jimmie, 'it was a stupid thing for me to say. Anyway I just came to let you know we are in the room opposite, so we aren't far away from you. How do you like my jamjars, smart eh?' He gave a twirl, showing off the oversized pyjamas. 'I could get two more people in here,' he laughed and held out the waistband. He then made the girls laugh by strutting up and down the room doing an imitation of

Charlie Chaplin, swinging an imaginary cane, and breaking into a song, *If you were the only girl in the world.*'

Jimmie's little act made Lily and Cathy laugh even more, though Maisie didn't seem impressed and shouted, 'Popeye! Do your Popeye thing and Olive Oyle!' Then she buried her head beneath the sheets.

'What's up with blondie?' asked Jimmie, 'my act isn't that bad is it?'

He turned to Lily who was also leaping into bed.

'And what is the meaning of this?' shouted a loud voice behind him, making him jump three feet into the air.

'When you've finished your dramatics, and variety show young man, you can go to your own room. There's cocoa and biscuits waiting for you, and by the way, the toilet isn't in here, so off with you and no more fooling around.'

Jimmie squeezed past Sister O'Brien, as she stood square in the doorway, not even daring to raise his eyes to her, that was until he was well behind her. Then he gave a cheeky grin and a thumbs up sign to Lily, before hightailing it back to his room.

Sister O'Brien turned to the girls, 'Hello you three, I didn't know that you had such a talented performer in the family,' then she smiled, wrinkling her nose. 'I'll get him to do, *Mother Kelly's Doorstep* sometime, but not in here, you've got to stay in your own rooms for the time being. Though why Jimmie is here at all I can't understand, he hasn't a spot on him, he's as clean as a whistle. He'd be better off at home poor lad!' Sister O'Brien's voice was gentle, and she felt sorry for the children, 'Never mind,' she said, 'and don't be afraid of me girls, me tongue's not as bad as me looks. In a couple o' weeks you'll all be as right as rain an' back home with yer mammie.'

She lifted the silver watch pinned to her uniform. 'Goodness! Is that the time? I'm going to have to be on my way home, I've almost five miles to go by bicycle. At least it's not raining. Nurse Wilson will be popping in to see you before lights out, and if you want anything, just ring the bell. I'll dash off now, see you in the morning. Bye-bye!' and with that she was gone.

She didn't go into the boys' room, but made her way down the stairs smiling to herself. 'That Jimmie was a real comic.' She thought of his earlier performance and chuckled. 'It was only mischief, after all they are only children.'

Jimmie was still awake when nurse Wilson made her rounds.

'What, still awake? You must be Jimmie, right?'

Jimmie nodded his head .

'Can I get you an aspirin? That will help you to sleep.' She suggested.

'No, ta, miss, I'll be alright.'

'Well, everyone else is in the Land of Nod. Are you sure now, that you wouldn't like a tablet?' she asked again.

'I'm sure. Honest I am, I'll be fine.'

'Alright then, but ring the bell if you change your mind. Goodnight, Jimmie.'

'Goodnight miss,' replied the boy.

Nurse Wilson checked that the heavy curtains were well drawn, then quietly left the room.

The fanlight above the door allowed a measure of light into the room. Jimmie lay awake for what seemed hours, listening to the great clock in the hallway downstairs striking the quarter hours. He wondered how he was going to endure being cooped up here for many days, maybe even weeks in isolation? It was beginning to feel like a nightmare. He had only just got his freedom back, and here he was again, incarcerated! The nurses were kind enough, but how was he going to cope with this imprisonment?

He made up his mind that he wasn't going to try, a plan was now forming in his mind, and at an opportune time, he would make his getaway! He wouldn't have to tell his siblings, or they would tell on him, he was sure of that. He listened for a while to aircraft overhead, wondering whether they were Lancaster's or Wellington's, the great bombers that were going to knock hell out of the enemy. He prayed that they would do just that, then return home safely.

His sleep was shallow and disturbed, and when he did sleep he dreamt of Mrs Hughes in Bangor, chasing him up the stairs in Glynne Road, then he awakened with a start to find himself in his present awful situation. This made him more determined than ever to make his escape.

Day two at the hospital, consisted of baths every three hours, followed by the usual smothering of messy ointment all over his body, and a change of pyjamas, all of which were several sizes too big, most likely designed for a giant.

After dinner Eric looked at some back-dated issues of Picture Post, asking Jimmie questions from time to time. Meanwhile his big brother was making plans for a way out, and gazed out through the window, across the fields and over the River Ribble.

He wondered which would be the easiest route to take, though maybe not so much the easiest, but the most suitable so as not to be seen. It seemed to him that Pendle Hill was the wrong way round, to the way that he usually saw it from Nelson, which indicated that he had to get to the other side of the great hill, which would then be the Nelson side. He wondered how long it would take him, though that wasn't too important, he only knew that after nearly two days here, he had had enough. He didn't really care how long it took, he only knew that he had to get away. He would do it tomorrow after breakfast. The staff would be having their break around nine o' clock, so he would go then.

His own clothes had been laundered and returned to his room, though he wasn't allowed to wear them as pyjamas were the order of the day whilst at Waddow Hall, but he would be wearing them tomorrow when he left.

Day three arrived, and with it E-Day or Escape Day! After breakfast, he scrubbed the smelly cream from off his arms and legs, then dressed in his own clothes. Though they weren't up to much, they felt good, for at least they fitted him, so he no longer felt like a freak.

He had saved two thin slices of toast from breakfast, and wrapped them in San Izal toilet paper, as this was the only thing he could find. At least it was clean, and he would need something to eat before the day was over. He shoved the toast into his trouser pocket.

He turned round to see Eric watching him, tears were streaming down his face. 'I know what you're up to. You're running away!' he cried.

'No! I'm only going for a walk around the grounds, so I'll be back before long. Now shut up, what yer crying for?' said Jimmie.

'You're not going for a walk at all our Jimmie, yer going home, so you are!' Eric sobbed louder than ever.

'Ssh! Ssh! Someone will hear you, you silly little sod. Put yer head under the bedclothes if yer want to yell,' Jimmie said. He could see that his plans would never come to fruition, if someone came to see what all the fuss was about. 'No, he wasn't going to be cheated out of his opportunity to escape, he was going no matter what!'

Eric, though would not be pacified, 'I'll yell more and more, and louder and louder, if you don't take me with you,' he screeched. 'I don't like it here either, take me with you or I'll tell.'

'I must be wrong in my loaf of bread, but alright,' Jimmie said relenting. 'Get yourself ready, and be quick about it before the staff come back on duty. Go on, have a wash first, don't bother to put your boots on though, or they'll hear us going downstairs. Do the same as me, tie the laces and hang 'em around your neck, that's a good lad, you can do that can't you? Be quick now or I'll go without you.'

After wiping away the ointment from his arms and legs, the best way he could, Eric dressed and stood behind Jimmie, who by this time had opened the door quietly, and was peering down the corridor surveying to the right, then the left.

Suddenly the old grandfather clock in the hall below, chimed out loudly, startling both boys and causing Jimmie to close the door as silently as he could in a hurry, and in the process falling over Eric and treading on his toes, which caused the boy to cry out.

'Ssh! Shush! How the heck did I know you were so close behind me; you should have whistled or summat. Rub yer foot, it'll be okay.'

'Well you told me to be quick and leave me boots off, so I did. Just look at me big toe, it's all red and it hurts,' Eric moaned. He sat down on the polished floor, rubbing his foot, and glaring angrily at his elder brother, but didn't dare say too much in case Jimmie went off without him.

'Yer'll get over it lad, you've another nine toes, so stop yer moaning. Think yerself lucky that I'm taking you along, I could have been halfway up that road by now, so come on, let's go!'

Once again, Jimmie pressed his ear to the door before opening it carefully, then the two of them tip-toed to the top of the winding staircase. Voices and laughter drifted up from below them, echoing round the hallway.

There was no-one in sight. It was time to go, or so Jimmie thought, until Eric doubled back to the ward to retrieve his stockings.

'Cor! said Jimmie, 'You'd forget your head if it wasn't fastened to yer shoulders, you make me blood boil. Come on now, when I move, you move with me. There's no going back now, not at this stage. They'll clap us in irons if we get caught. They'd lock us up for sure, then that'd be it! Yer'd never get home again!'

He saw the frightened look on his little brother's face and took hold of his hand, then together they crept down the cold stairs, and on reaching the bottom, silently made their way to the large oak doors, easing back the bolt and praying that it had been well oiled.

It was, and young Eric held his breath, looking round to see if they had been spotted.

Jimmie grabbed his arm and pulled him through the half-open door, closing it carefully behind him. 'Come on lad! Leg it! Don't stand there gawping!'

The boys ran as fast as they could, the gravel hard to their bare feet, but they didn't dare pause for breath until they reached the main gates at the end of the driveway.

They sat for a moment to put on their stockings and boots, then trotted up to the road. There was a signpost, but the place names had all been removed because of the war, as a precaution. Should the enemy land in Britain, it would be difficult for them to find their whereabouts.

It was more by luck than management that the boys came across the bridge which spanned the River Ribble. They crossed it and veered left, then clambered over a wooden gate, and made their way along the inside of the hedgerows which bordered the fields. Neither of them spoke, until they judged they were far enough away to stop for a while.

Jimmie told Eric, 'Duck down,' when he heard the clip-clopping of horses' hooves on the other side of the hedge, and the milkman telling his nag to 'gerra move on'.

'Good idea Jimmie, coming this way. Nobody can see us from the road, but we can hear if anything does come,' said Eric as he squelched his way through a muddy ditch.

'Walk up here now; it's safe enough,' Jimmie encouraged, as he helped his young brother onto firmer, drier ground. 'We're far enough away from the road now, and there's a railway track ahead.'

It was much easier walking along the track and out of the long grass, Jimmie only hoped that they were going in the right direction. By now the sun had filtered away the morning mist that had made everything seem damp, and at last it was warm and pleasant to be in the beautiful fresh air and away from captivity.

The disappearance of the mist revealed the huge shape of Pendle Hill, seeming like a whale rising from out of the sea. It was much to Jimmie's relief that his instincts about direction were justified.

They had travelled about two miles when they left the line at the village of Chatburn, and crossed the main road onto a much narrower one, deciding at this point, to move inland across the moors, which Jimmie thought would be safer with less risk of meeting people.

By now, Eric had begun to hobble a little, and when his brother saw him he thought, 'Perhaps it would have been better if he'd stayed behind. We'll rest here for a bit,' Jimmie said, feeling sorry for the lad. 'Reckon we've walked two miles or thereabouts, mind yer lad, we've a heck of a way to go yet, so if your legs are tired now, what are they gonna feel like at the end of the day?'

The sun was higher in the sky and Jimmie was thankful that it was a good day, and also being thankful for the morning mist, for without it they would have been spotted for sure!

He leaned back on his elbows watching his young brother removing his boots, then his socks revealed his blood-stained feet. A look of dismay clouded Jimmie's face when he saw them, 'Hell lad! Just look at yer feet! Have yer got nails sticking into them or what? Why didn't you tell me they were sore?'

'I just wanted to keep going. I didn't want you to leave me behind. I think I cut them on the gravel when we left the big house,' cried Eric.

'Just stay there and don't move. I'll go an' wet me hankie in the stream,' but then, as an afterthought added, 'better come with me, bring yer boots and stockings, then yer can dangle yer plates of meat in the water. It will make them feel a lot better.'

The coolness of the water was refreshing to the boy's sore flesh. Jimmie seriously considered turning back to Waddow Hall, but then the thought of isolation, being detached from the outside world, and of course the scolding they would get, made him think again. On careful examination of Eric's feet, he decided his injuries were not as bad as he had first thought.

'There, I'm sure they'll feel a lot better now,' said Jimmie as he dried the small feet on his hankie. At least they were clean now, and after drinking from the clear, bubbling stream out of cupped hands, they headed towards Downham, a picturesque little village nestling in a valley.

As they passed the village pub, an old man, sitting astride a rustic bench bade them, 'How do?'

'How do what?' Jimmie said to himself, but remained silent, he hadn't heard that expression before.

The boys ambled by without stopping, and cautiously avoided the old man, 'Me mam told me never to talk to strangers,' Jimmie commented to Eric.

Meanwhile the old man stared at them and muttered, 'Look like foreigners to me, don't come frae these parts. Never sin 'em afore, all over they are!' He took a long swig of his ale and replaced his old scorched pipe in his mouth with a tut.

Jimmie hadn't intended to pass through the village but he had no option. Farm workers and Italian prisoners of war, were gathering hay on both sides of the road leading down to the village. However having crossed the bridge spanning the stream, with it's noisy mallards, they scrambled through a hedge at their first opportunity, and up onto the moorland.

He doubled back for Eric once again, and assisted him to a dry stone wall sheepfold, where the two of them flopped onto the grass, grateful for the rest and the security in the shade of the old stone wall.

'We'll rest here for a while lar, rest yer weary bones,' Jimmie said, 'though I don't like the look of him,' he added, pointing to a black-faced ram. 'Still, I don't suppose he'll mind sharing his den with us for a little while.'

Jimmie spread himself out on the dry, rough grass and salvaged his cold, buttered toast from his trouser pocket. 'Doesn't look much, kid, but it'll taste like heaven. Here, get your chops into that. We've a long way to go yet lar, so make the most of it.'

He dislodged some thickly caked mud from the soles of his boots, remarking that he'd be able to walk twice as fast now he'd got rid of it, and hoping that he was inspiring his brother, but Eric was downhearted as he ate the bread, and when he had finished, tried to replace his boots, but struggled to get them on.

'Yer shouldn't have taken them off. What am I gonna do with yer? Can't leave yer here stranded in the middle of no man's land.' Jimmie jumped to his feet and was about to vent his anger, and let loose with his tongue, then thought better of it, as he saw Eric wince, when trying to push his feet, clad in the blood-stained stockings, into his boots once more.

'Leave 'em off lad, and anchor them to your belt, we'll have another ten minutes or so, then we'll be off around the other side of this big hill. Best not to stay too long or we'll stiffen up.'

The sweet sound of a curlew broke the silence of the afternoon, then suddenly, as if from nowhere, a brace of partridge took to flight almost in front of them, noisily flapping their wings, distancing themselves before plummeting back into the purple heather and out of sight.

'Hell! Scared me half to death so they did, blinkin' birds, an' now we have to climb that blinkin' hill,' said Jimmie.

Eric's voice wavered as he said, 'Oh, we don't, do we?' He raised his eyes to the summit. It looked like Mount Everest to the little lad, and he looked as if he was going to cry.

'No course not, not on your auntie Nellie. I was only kiddin', there's an easier way than that. We just get to the big end then get our bearings from there. It won't be as steep as going straight across the top, so don't you worry,' Jimmie said confidently, though not really feeling confident at all. 'It should be plain sailing then, or rather plain walking.'

'Glad we got away from that horrible place, Jimmie. I hated it!' said Eric.

'Me too!' said Jimmie. 'I'll bet the place is in a bloody uproar, they'll be flappin' around, going frantic. Someone's sure to get it in the neck for not keeping tabs on us. I can just imagine the look on our Lily's face when she finds out we've done a runner. Glad we didn't let on to her all the same, or I'd have been like holy Moses, traipsing along in the wilderness with all youse lot. We would never have got home, mind you we aren't home yet, so let's get on our way.'

After having a good rest, Eric clambered onto Jimmie's back, clasping his little hands around his brother's neck, his boots swaying from side to side as Jimmie tramped along, and they headed out across Rimington Moor.

The old black-faced ram munched away at the grass unconcernedly, not even looking up as the lads passed him.

As the afternoon wore on, the rough terrain made it more difficult for Jimmie, forcing him to stumble at times, his legs and lower back aching, like they had never ached before.

He was beginning to wish that he was on his own, by now he would have almost been home, well at least have covered a lot more ground, but he had to bring him along or he would have screamed the place down, and his plan would have been discovered, so he wouldn't have got away at all!

Suddenly the thundering sound of a Spitfire flying low over Pendle made the boys look up. Jimmie loved those little fighter planes, the sound of the Merlin engines excited him, though the noise disturbed the silence and tranquillity of the afternoon, and sent the sheep and the old black-faced ram scattering in all directions.

'That caused a bit of a commotion didn't it? Just think, if we could have a ride in that, we'd be home in a few minutes. Cor! Wishful thinkin', but it must be great to fly one of those, shooting jerries to kingdom come.'

Eric didn't comment, his eyes were on the distraught sheep, he was glad they were further away; he wasn't keen on the creatures being too near him, and had been ready to mount a wall if they got any closer.

After all the excitement, the weary travellers continued on their journey once more. At least the appearance of the Spitfire had given them a boost and their morale was high.

Eric whispered in Jimmie's ear, 'I'm hungry.'

Jimmie told his brother in a sarcastic tone, that if he would just like to get off his back and sit down, Jimmie would run down to the nearest chippie and get cod and chips twice! Or perhaps you would like a nice thick butty with a slice of ham on it instead?'

Jimmie eased the lad from his back, and heaved a sigh of relief. 'There now look! We are almost round the big end now, so it won't be long before we're home, then you can have your fill.'

They had trekked most of the way. The village of Barley was almost deserted, except for a herd of fresians which slowly ambled along into the farmyard. They knew by instinct that it was milking time.

Jimmie chose to get off the road and cross the footbridge over Pendle water, a stream which flowed through to Roughlee, then on to Barrowford, a more populated village.

The two boys found a nice place to rest, then bathed their feet in the cool, crystal clear water, then had a good drink.

'Beggars can't be choosers,' Jimmie told his brother when Eric said he didn't want to drink the same water that they had washed their feet in.

Walking was much easier along the river-bank on the cool, lush grass, which was far less painful for Eric. Though the river-bank twisted and turned, at least it was flat, and Jimmie wished that it could be like this all the way home, but of course, he knew it wouldn't be. He was so proud of himself and what he had accomplished, especially having the responsibility of his young brother, carrying him most of the way, and listening to his complaints which came often.

Eric continued to moan about being hungry, and Jimmie threatened that he would not carry him any more if he didn't shut up.

At this remark Eric promptly closed his mouth, and never said another word until they reached another tiny hamlet, Happy Valley, then he clambered onto Jimmie's back once more as they left the river-bank and headed for the country road ahead of them.

There was a small picnic area opposite the café, which had a card displayed in the window 'CLOSED FOR THE DURATION', though that didn't matter one jot to the boys for they had no money anyway.

Then as they reached the crossroads, they had to decide which was the right way to go? 'If we don't know which way to go, then neither would any enemy spies,' thought Jimmie.

With burning faces because of the sun, burning feet also, and tired eyes and hearts Jimmie decided on an uphill road, calculating that if they reached the top of the hill, they would have a better view perhaps, of the way they should go.

By now Eric was crying, and wanted to be home, he even said, 'I wish that yer had left me behind.'

Jimmie wasn't deterred, he felt that at long last he was getting somewhere, and so with renewed vigour, he set off at an unwavering pace, up the hill aforementioned.

'Aye,' said Jimmie as they plodded along, 'maybe we should both have stayed where we were. Mam will be worried to death wondering where we are, for she will know by now that we've run away.'

He hitched Eric up higher on his back, his hands clasped together over his stomach. His stomach rumbled, and he realised for the first time that he too was hungry, and felt sorry for his young brother and regretted speaking to him the way he had.

By zig-zagging his way up the hill it seemed much easier, and soon they reached the summit where Jimmie turned and looked back. As he turned, he saw Pendle Hill looming up behind them. 'Had they really covered all that distance? He couldn't believe it, but the glorious sight of the rays of the sun, bestowing its brightness across the panorama before him, made him realise that this was a beautiful place in which he had come to live. He was so glad at that moment that he had come to live in this area.

He licked his dry lips and hugged his young brother, as they stood there taking in the beauty of the moment, then they turned and looked ahead over Noggarth Quarry, and in the direction of Nelson.

'We've done it, lad! We've bloody well done it! Just look, I can spot one or two of the mills near our house. Come on, up you get on my back again, we'll just about make it before dusk, and it's downhill all the way. You'll soon be bangin' your choppers on some grub, and by the heck, there'll be a telling off as well no doubt. Do you think it's been worth it coming all this way? Or should I have left you at Waddow Hall? Tell me the truth now, are you sorry?'

'Not at all, I'm glad I came. The only thing is, if it hadn't been for my feet we'd have been home by now. That's the only thing I'm sorry about, holding you up. Anyway, thanks Jimmie, for not leaving me behind.' Eric said tossing his head from side to side, and eventually resting it on Jimmie's neck and falling asleep.

'Poor kid,' thought Jimmie, 'still it's all part of growing up.'

People scarcely gave them a second glance as he strode down past the quarry and onto Carr Hall Lane. Then after passing Jopson's dye works, he entered Victoria Park, coming out on Surrey road, then Scotland road, turning left at last into Dalton street, only to be greeted with a shrill Liverpudlian voice.

'Jimmie Mac, where the hell have you been? They've been out all day looking for you. Yer mam's been worried sick an' yer da' too. He's home!'

The voice belonged to Mrs Adams, a tiny lady, even smaller than Jimmie's mam, and it was her size and shape that Jimmie recognised rather than her face, as by now it was almost dark. She had seven daughters and one son Tommy, whom Jimmie had met shortly after arriving in the town. Mr Adams was a jolly little fellow who always spoke of his ability in the wrestling ring.

'Oh! It's you, Mrs. Adams,' Jimmie croaked, his throat was parched and he ran his tongue over his lips several times before he continued, 'It's nice to see you, well nearly see you, just about made it before the blackout. How's your Tommy? Is he alright? Tell him I'll see him around some time.'

'Yes, I'll tell him, but get off with you lad, yer mother's worried to death. Yer da's home on leave. Oh yer ma had a little girl on the same afternoon that you all left in the ambulance. Everyone's been out looking for you, so go on, get home. Ta-ra!'

Jimmie watched as the plump little figure disappeared into the shadows.

Following a lengthy scolding from Kate, and all the names under the sun she could muster up, she asked Jimmie to explain himself clearly, and tell her what he'd been up to?

'It's three days since you went away, and you decide to go walkabouts across the countryside. The police have been out looking for the both of youse, as well as the nurses and some of the staff at Widow Hall,' shouted Kate angrily.

'Waddow Hall Mam,' Jimmie piped up, 'it's called Waddow Hall!'

'Widow, Waddow, what's the difference, and shut up when I'm talking.' retorted Kate. 'You left in a sneaky way, not telling anyone, and dragging little Eric with you as well. I'm surprised at you, you weren't thinking straight at all. Your head must have been up in the clouds. Stupid, that's all I can say! The pair of yer coulda been abducted, so yer could!'

'What does abducted mean Mam?' asked Jimmie innocently.

'Kidnapped, yer daft little bugger, kidnapped!' exploded Kate, puffing out clouds of smoke from the cigarette she had just lit.

Jimmie watching them drifting up to the ceiling, and thought he had better try changing the subject. 'How's yer little girl, Mam? Mrs Adams told me you'd got a baby girl. I saw her at the top of the street. She told us that you were all looking for us, didn't think we were that important, a lot of panicking for nowt if you ask me.'

'Yer new little sister is in bed, an' that's where you should be. But before you are you're gonna get tubbed, both of you. There's a block of red carbolic soap in the cupboard under the kitchen sink, and clean towels in the tank cupboard upstairs, so get up, both of yer, yer smell as if you've been lodging in a cowshed. I'll go and make something for you to eat, yer'll be ready for it. Are yer hungry?'

'Been ready to eat since eleven o'clock this morning, Mam, but honestly, it was like prison being in that place.

Nowt to do only lay in bed, in fact I nearly came home the first day, and as for bringing Eric, well he said he'd scream the place down if I didn't bring him.'

During this time, Eric had curled up on the sofa and gone to sleep.

Kate put out her half-smoked Woodbine, gave Eric a gentle shake, then started to remove his boots and socks, saying once more how much the pair of them stunk.

'It's only cow and sheep muck, Mam,' said Jimmie.

'Well it's not welcome in my house whatever it is, so get away now, upstairs, and don't wake the baby up. Yer can both peep in and have a look at her if yer like, though she'll probably turn her little nose up at you if she gets a whiff of that aroma. Still yer home now, and safe, so thank God for that.'

Kate might have ten children, but she loved them all despite her seemingly hard exterior, she was soft inside, though she didn't often show it. She didn't like anyone to take it as a sign of weakness.

'Fancy Mam, you getting another little girl. Is that what you wanted?' Jimmie asked, trying to sound enthusiastic. 'That's nice, another little sister.'

Kate glanced at him, sensing a little scheming and soft-soaping, to get on the right side of her.

'Pity you can't have another girl Mam, then you'll be like Mrs Adams with seven girls, they'll be able to play against each other at netball.'

'I'll netball you, if you don't get up them stairs! There won't be any more babies. This is what the cobbler threw at his wife - the last, so get up! Don't take all night, get down before your dad gets in, he's gone to the Derby with Bobbie for a pint.'

Eric followed Jimmie, almost crawling on their hands and knees, up the stairs. They took a quick look in Kate's room at the new arrival, then soon they were plunging into the large cast iron bath, the hot water felt soothing to their aching limbs as they both stretched out top to tail.

Jimmie stared at the ceiling and began to meditate on how he had managed to walk all that distance when they didn't even know their way home. Yet he knew instinctively that he needed to be home, he'd been away from his mam and dad and the rest of the family for too long, He couldn't and wouldn't let it happen again. He reflected on the fact that he could be sent back, but he would run away again, and again, if he had to.

Egg and chips with lashings of baked beans and fresh bread and butter, washed down with a pint of sweet tea, were more than the boys had hoped for, and they were well and truly satisfied. They sat back on their chairs, Eric patting his tummy, Kate, as usual at the kitchen stove, preparing a meal for the return of her husband, Robert and son Bobbie. Suddenly there was a loud hammering on the front door.

Kate told Jimmie, 'Go and see who it is, if it is that silly little warden tell him that there is no-one in.'

Jimmie returned to the living-room, his face white as a sheet, 'It's a policeman, Mam, wants to see yer.'

'Don't look so surprised lad, I've been half expecting Constable Bentley. I've lost count of how many times he's been here today. Got boys of his own, so he knew how worried we were, bless him, he's only doing his job.'

Kate handed a mug of hot tea to the policeman, saying to P.C. Bentley, 'Help yerself to sugar and milk, lad.'

He turned to Jimmie, and Eric, 'Well boys, you've certainly led us a merry dance, you'll have your name in the local rag next week I shouldn't wonder,' he said as he stirred his tea. 'Some reporter fellow got wind of you both absconding, made everybody look right idiots, disappearing the way you did. Anyway you're back home again now and quite safe, thank goodness, so we'll all sleep better tonight knowing that. I'll report back to the station, then ring Waddow

Hall to let them know you've arrived back home okay. Then they'll probably come to collect you again in the morning.'

'Well I'm not going back! Never!' said Jimmie resolutely. 'If you send me back I'll do it again, but this time I won't come back here, I'll go back to Bangor. I mean it Mam, there's nothing wrong with me, I shouldn't have gone away in the first place, even one of the nurses said I shouldn't have been there, so tell them Mam, tell them that I'm not going back!'

Jimmie was exhausted after his announcement, but the look of determination on his face made Kate realise that the boy meant what he said. Wild horses wouldn't drag him there.

'Now don't go upsetting yourself,' Kate said, 'you've had a hard day, so I'll tell you what we'll do, we'll leave it up to your dad when he comes in. Let him decide, he'll know best.'

The policeman who had been watching the scene, and didn't want to interfere said, 'Well I'll be on my way now, Mrs Mac. And you, young Jimmie, no running off now, your mother's been worried enough, so think on lad, just see what your dad says, and be a good lad.'

'I'll see myself out, Mrs Mac. And thanks for the tea.'

'You're welcome constable,' Kate said as she turned the burning embers over in the grate. 'Goodnight and thank you for all you've done, it's been a long day for all of us and I'm very thankful to you.'

As the policeman left, Kate turned to her sons saying, 'You'd both better get up the dancers before yer da gets in. What he'll have to say about all this I don't know, but he'll have cooled off a bit by morning, so up you go.'

'Goodnight Mam, good to be home, come on, kid,' he got hold of Eric's sleeve and dragged him towards the stairs. 'An' don't think I'm gonna carry you either, not now, not ever again.'

They both laughed as they climbed the stairs to bed.

Jimmie lay awake for some time when he heard his mother coming upstairs, she had left the remains of a ham shank from dinner time simmering on the stove, with split peas and dumplings.

'That'll do them for supper,' she said to herself, and she smiled, 'Stick to their ribs it will.' They loved a good feed after downing a few pints, always gave them an appetite. She nestled her new daughter to her breast for feeding, as proud of her, as she was of all the rest of her brood.

Suddenly the wailing of the air raid sirens broke the silence of the night, but it didn't bother her any more, not like it did in Liverpool. She had experienced real air raids there, in fact she'd lost two homes to Hitler's bombs, but now she was in a safe area she felt secure, and was thankful that she had been given a fresh start. The sound of a siren here only indicated that German planes were approaching, but they usually dropped their bombs on places like Manchester, Chorley, Bradford and other major cities where the ammunitions factories were situated. They passed over the Nelson area without any incidents, so Kate continued to feed her baby without fear.

Jimmie meanwhile, was too busy wondering what his dad would say to him tomorrow, how he would react. He heard Bill come in and come straight upstairs, he went into his room and closed the door. The rattling of keys could be heard as Bill unlocked his wardrobe.

No one ever knew what he hoarded in there and Jimmie remembered what Bobbie had said, 'That Bill would get nabbed one of these days and carted off to the clink.' Though knowing Bill, Jimmie thought, 'that he was too cunning to get nabbed as it were, he was one step ahead when distributing his commodities.'

'It's all legit,' he would say, 'no flies on me.' Then he would chuckle slyly as if sharing a secret with himself, which of course was correct. This was why his wardrobe was always kept locked.

Jimmie's thoughts turned to the time he ran away from Bangor, and tried to follow the railway lines, the Aber run, as it was called by the evacuees. 'It's a wonder he wasn't killed by a passing train! What an idiot he was!'

He stretched and yawned, wondering again, just before he finally fell asleep, how things would go with his dad on the morrow?

At eight o'clock the following morning, Jimmie hesitated outside his parents bedroom door. Rob, who was awake, nudged Kate with his elbow. The creases on his forehead, and the stern look on his face turned into a smile and his blue-grey eyes twinkled.

'Hello son,' said Rob, 'how did you know I was ready for a cuppa? See Kate,' he said to his wife, 'we've got room service this morning.'

'It's soft-soaping if you ask me,' replied Kate, re-arranging her pillows, 'you don't half know how to get round people, Jimmie Mac. Anyway, thanks lad.' said Kate. 'Would you just get me those tablets from the dressing-table, please.'

'Sure Mam, are these the ones?' asked Jimmie, handing the bottle of tablets to his mother.

'Yes, thanks, there's a good lad. I'm stopping in bed today, I've got to take things easy. Dr. Third will go mad if he knows I've been downstairs, cooking and doing other chores.'

'Yes,' said Jimmie, eager to please, 'you do that Mam, I'll light the fire and I'll see that Ollie gets her breakfast.'

'You're a good lad, give her a wash as well, then get her dressed and take her over to Evie Foster's, she said she'd look after her today to give me a rest. Oh, and see Eric gets some tea and toast, not forgetting yourself, that'll keep you out of mischief for a while,' she laughed.

'I'll do that with pleasure, and don't you worry yourself about anything, just stay in bed, you look all in doesn't she dad?' he said, drawing his father into the conversation much to Rob and Kate's amusement.

'Yer right lad, I don't know how I've coped over the last few days,' said Kate.

'It's a good job I came home then, isn't it? Summat must have told me I was needed at home, that's why I legged it back. Don't you think so, dad?' Jimmie said.

Rob sipped his tea, not daring to look at his son, for inside he was bursting with laughter, knowing all too well that Jimmie was smoothing his way into his father's favour, and into staying at home, so he wouldn't have to return to Waddow Hall.

Jimmie replaced his mother's tablets on the dressing-table, 'I really can't believe you're home dad,' he said looking into the mirror, then blurted out the inevitable questions of when was his father going back? 'Where had his last trip taken him? Did he see any Jerries?'

Rob grinned, 'We'll have a chat later lad, go on hoppit, let yer ma have her tea in peace, an' see to yer brother and sister.'

'Can I make some breakfast for both of you?' asked Jimmie, wanting to be on his best behaviour.

'No, thanks lad, I'm getting up now. Be careful lighting that fire, and don't burn the shovel with the newspaper when yer blowing it up.'

Jimmie didn't need to be told twice, he ran from the room, jumping down two steps at a time until he reached the bottom.

In no time at all everything was prepared for Eric and Ollie's breakfast, the fire was well alight with no mishaps, and the large kettle whistling merrily on the stove in readiness for whatever use it was intended.

Just as Jimmie was about to take Olive to Evie Foster's to be minded, his father appeared in the living-room. He was stripped to the waist, and though not very tall, he was wiry and muscular. Tattoos decorated his arms to the shoulders. Jimmie looked at them in admiration, that was until his dad told him.

'Get round to Evie's and to be back in double quick time before the reception committee arrive from Waddow Hall.'

The colour drained from Jimmie's face, he panicked thinking that he could be made to go back in a flash. Eric was outside in the yard playing and out of earshot, oblivious to everything that was going on. He was content for now to sit on the doorstep in the sunshine, and was at this moment inspecting his legs for any sign of a spot that would mean he had to go back to that awful place.

By the time Jimmie had got back from Evie's, his father had washed and shaved. He had the privilege of straightening Rob's sailor collar over the rough navy tunic, hoping he had wormed his way into his dad's good books. After Rob had knotted his black ribbon in front of his tunic he noticed Jimmie's scratched and bruised legs.

'How did they get like that?' he asked the boy.

'Aw! It's nowt dad, walking through the bracken I guess, and scrambling over barbed wire fences. They're not too bad, though a bit stiff, but that's through carrying our Eric on me back.'

Jimmie sensed a softening in the tone of Rob's voice as he said, 'Well thank God you're home and safe. They say there's unexploded mortar bombs scattered across Downham Moors. Apparently the Home Guard have used them and then were unable to find them. Hell if you'd stood on one, you could both have been blown to smithereens! It was a daft thing you did lad, letting loose yer moorings without saying a word to anyone. Besides you coulda been picked up by anybody, yer don't know who's kicking around these days.'

'We only saw one ole feller sat outside a pub, the Ashetton Arms at Downham, an' he seemed harmless. Anyway dad, like yer said we're safe now,' said Jimmie, as he picked a stray hair from his father's collar.

Robert smiled as he replaced his comb and brush, along with his razor, into his black leather zip travel bag. 'Touching my collar won't bring you any luck lad,' and he turned facing his son and put both his hands on Jimmie's small shoulders, saying. 'Never let this happen again. I'll let it slide this time lad, fer yer mother's sake. She doesn't want any more upset. She's had a rough patch this time with the baby, so no more of that, the matter is closed, so think on okay?'

Jimmie nodded his head, glad to be let off so lightly and looked at his father who had taken a half-crown from his pocket.

Jimmie thought his luck had changed after all, the collar touching had worked after all. He planned in his mind a night out at the Alhambra or the Majestic with a bag of chips from Whittaker's as he walked home, but Rob had other ideas, and Jimmie's dream faded when Rob said, 'Pies, get some potato pies down at Ashworth's on Scotty Road. There's some marrowfat peas soaking in the pan, we'll cook them and have them with the pies for dinner.'

Jimmie looked at the large silver coin in his hand thinking, 'So near, so far!' He dropped the coin into his trouser pocket.

Rob watched his son's face with amusement, he had an idea what was going through the lad's mind, hadn't he been a lad himself?

'The nurse will be coming to see your mam today, so see that there's hot water ready for her, and clean towels are in the bathroom tank cupboard. Your mam says she's getting up tomorrow, though I think nurse Sutcliffe will have other ideas.'

'Me Mam? She's going to be alright, isn't she?' asked a worried Jimmie.

'Course she is, she just got out of bed too soon didn't she? Don't worry your head about that, you know what your mam is, she can't rest like anyone else, likes to know what's going on. Trouble is she's worn out and needs the rest even though she won't admit it, so a few more days in bed will do her the world of good.'

So with that Jimmie was satisfied and more convinced than ever that he was definitely needed at home and had the perfect excuse for not going back to Waddow Hall.

Just at that moment there was a loud rat-tat-tat at the front door, Jimmie's stomach turned over, but he was determined that he wouldn't change his mind. Nothing on earth would make him go back, he was going to stick to his guns.

Rob strode off down the lobby leading to the front door, returning with two women, dressed in navy blue coats, and with page boy hats perched on the back of their heads.

They stationed themselves one on either side of the dining table, standing stiff as pokers, and looking rather like book-ends Their faces had no expressions, and their flinty faces only emphasised the fact that they had received a telling off from the authorities for having been neglectful of their young patients in allowing them to run away from the hospital premises.

Rob tried to ease the situation by commenting in a light-hearted way. 'These are the two fugitives, well one of them anyway, fetch Eric in lad,' he addressed his son Jimmie, who was making for the back door in an effort to get out before he could be questioned about his little escapade.

Rob grabbed him by the scruff of the neck and made him stand before the two nurses. Eric was by this time coming in to see what the fuss was about, but wishing he'd stayed where he was.

'It's alright lad,' said one of the nurses, sounding nicer than they looked, 'we aren't going to take you back, we just want to examine you to make sure your skin is clear.'

Jimmie was given the once over, and declared to be clear, then Eric, who had been hovering in the background, afraid that there could be a spot or two on him, was persuaded to take off his shirt. That was no problem, but when asked to remove his trousers, he created a commotion until his father threatened that he would go back with the nurses if he didn't behave and do as he was told.

A scarlet-faced Eric fumbled with the clasp on his snake belt and was duly examined.

Again he was told he was clear except for a few patches on his legs, due to him scratching, but Rob was given a box of ointment and told to apply it regularly to the sores, and with daily bathing, using Dettol in the water, these should soon disappear.

Eric jerked up his trousers, pleased at the results, though the next words made him hold his breath.

'It really depends upon you now, Mr MacLean. If you want the young boy to come back to the Hall with us, or if you wish him to stay at home. We realise your wife has just been confined and needs her rest, so what do you think?' asked one of the ladies.

Eric looked petrified, and Rob smiled and looked at him, 'Well, lad, would you like to go with these ladies?'

'Let me stay at home dad. I'll be a good boy and I'll help Jimmie to look after mam, I will, I promise.'

'There you are ladies, you have your answer,' smiled Rob, 'now would you like a cup of tea before you go?'

The nurses thanked Rob, but declined his offer, then enquired about Kate and her new daughter, and had she got someone to care for her whilst she was still in her bed?

'We have a very good friend, Mrs Foster who lives over the road. She looks after our next youngest daughter, Olive, who is a lovely child,' said Rob, proudly. 'She was born in the May blitz in Liverpool, poor little mite, she almost didn't make it as she was hit in the chest with shrapnel. It flew in through the window at the hospital and she had to have it removed. Nearly died she did, but God blessed us when we prayed to let the little child live. That's how she got her name Olive, that's what my wife prayed. O live! It was a miracle!'

'That's a very moving story, Mr McLean, one for the archives I would say. I can see how much you love your children and they are very well looked after; rather unusual in a large family, some parents don't care!'

'Thank you ladies, and now shall we say the boys are going to be fine at home and leave it at that? I'm home for another seven days yet before I join my ship, so I'll see to the treatment for Eric.'

'If his spots get any worse get in touch and we'll take him back in. Don't worry about the girls, they're getting better and are now able to walk around the grounds.' Then she added as an afterthought, 'with an escort of course.'

They all had a good laugh at that remark, then Rob opened his canvas kit bag taking out three bars of chocolate and a bag of fruit gums, and handing them to one of the nurses asking if they would give them to the children to share out?

'These are for you,' he said offering a packet of Capstan cigarettes to each of the women. 'Take them with my compliments and thank you. I'll make sure Eric gets his daily baths, apply the ointment, and uses his own towels until he's completely clear.'

The women thanked Rob, and as they moved towards the door, he opened it for them and wished them a safe and pleasant journey back.

On returning to the kitchen he smiled at seeing the boys washing up the dirty crockery from breakfast. 'That's it lads, all ship-shape and Bristol fashion. Keep the decks clean. Look,' he said, 'I'm off out now.' He placed his sailor hat squarely on his head, the rim just one inch above his eyes, Eric grinned like a Cheshire cat, with relief no doubt, at not having to go back with the nurses.

'Oh! By the way,' Rob said, as he walked back into the kitchen.

Eric's face changed colour, thinking that he wasn't being so lucky after all, and his dad had changed his mind.

'It's alright lad,' laughed Rob, 'I was just going to say, perhaps Jimmie, you can walk down with me to get the pies, otherwise there'll be none left by the time the mill workers come out. Eric, you go upstairs and stay with your mam until Jimmie gets back with the pies.'

'Where are yer going dad?' asked Jimmie as they walked along.

'I'm going to yer Auntie Molly's in Lomeshaye Road.' Rob said, as he swayed from side to side as all the old salts do.

It reminded Jimmie of the time three and a half years ago in Bangor, the last time he had walked out with his da', and that was only to say goodbye, he was as proud as Punch to be seen in his company, and again, as then, Jimmie glanced around as they walked together to see if any of the neighbours were watching, he was so proud of his sailor dad.

'Look after Eric now, and see that yer mam gets her dinner, won't you lad? No marlickin' about either of yer, or you'll be back in Waddow Hall. Think on now?' He patted the boy on the shoulder as men do. 'Ta-ra lad, see you later.' With that Rob departed up Scotland Road.

Jimmie stood watching until he was out of sight, then he went into Ashworth's confectioner's shop and ordered three potato pies from a red-faced woman behind the counter.

'Was that your father I saw you with just now,' she asked in a friendly manner. 'Mrs Mac's son aren't you?'

'Yes that's right,' said Jimmie as he counted his change.

'You must be the lad just back from Wales then? How is yer mam, lad? She got another little girl I believe?'

'Yes, I'm back from Wales, my mam's okay, and she did get a girl.'

He was shuffling the bag of hot pies from one hand to the other, and the lady laughed, 'Give us them back lad, I'll wrap them up in the Nelson Leader. Stop 'em from burning your hands. Ah now what was I saying? Yes, yer mam, what a wonderful woman she is. Take this jam slice for her an' tell her I was askin' about her won't you? She'll know who I am, Ethel's the name. She was really good to our Dolly when she was poorly; she wouldn't have been here now if it hadn't been for your mam, bless her, looked after her for nights on end, rubbing her body with goose grease and garlic and sweated the pneumonia out of her. I would have had to close the shop and would have lost my trade, and maybe Dolly too, but she let me stay at work and looked after Dolly herself, and now she's as fit as a fiddle. Wouldn't think she'd ailed a thing. God bless that mam of yours.'

'That sounds like my Mam,' said Jimmie sticking out his chest. 'Yes he was proud of his mam as well as his dad, and the new neighbours thought very highly of them too. It was good, starting a new life in Nelson. I'd better get along home now Missis, got to see to the dinner for mam and my brother, then see to mam before the nurse comes.'

'Yes do that,' said Ethel, 'before the stampede comes. It's like a flamin' cavalry charge when they all get out of the mill. Oh! What's your name lad?'

'Jimmie Missis, and me brother is Eric, though you won't be seeing him for a bit, or our Lil, she's from Wales too, 'cos they're covered in scabs.'

Ethel retreated into the back bake-house for fear of catching something, and calling out 'Ta-ra.'

Kate was in bed, a tray on her knee, she had almost finished her dinner. She thanked her son saying, 'You're a good lad. What's our Eric up to? Not playing out I hope?'

'No,' replied Jimmie, 'he's stuffing himself in the kitchen.'

'That's alright then, if he doesn't behave, tell him his dad will send him back to the hospital, that'll quieten him down. My! You can't beat Ethel's pies,' she said as she ate the last forkful.

'Ethel was asking about you, she thinks a lot about you, so she does, she told me about when you looked after her sick sister, she's a nice woman, she sent you the jam slice,' said Jimmie looking at the cake on the plate.

Kate smiled and cut the slice in two, giving half to her son, who munched greedily at it.

'Yes, her sister had pneumonia, the treatment was the same as the one your father used on many a seaman, he always has a jar of goose-grease in his kitbag. He should have furthered his studies when he lived in Wavertree, that's before he met me. He'd passed a lot of exams, studying medicine and the like, but hard times forced him to do other things, 'specially when we got married and the children started coming along. He went into the Merchant Service like lots of others in Liverpool, then the drink got to him and it's had its grip to this day.'

'Is that where he'll be now, Mam? In the rubbedy-dub,' (the club).

'You've guessed it in one son. First he'll go to see his sister yer Auntie Molly, then he'll spend the afternoon at the New Inn, treating all and sundry. He'll be back home at three on the dot, sleep it off for a few hours, then back out at seven until closing time.'

Jimmie stared out of the window overlooking the Goit. 'Hasn't been much of a life for you Mam, has it? We could have been livin' on easy street, things could have been better for all of us, in a nice house. I've not seen much of my dad, he's always away at sea.'

'Got to do something lad, mind you he shouldn't be in the Royal Navy now at his age. There's lots of lazy young buggers, dodgers, skiving and living off the fat of the land. Spivs, while lots of family men are out there, spilling their guts, fighting for such as them.

Bernie King for instance, Sally's husband, you won't know them, but they're from Liverpool. She's a good sort, well her Bernie is with the desert rats in North Africa, she hasn't seen him for years, but yer never hear her grumbling. They have a large family like us, and she's always got a smile on her face.'

Jimmie was glad that he had his back to his mam, so she couldn't see him grinning, as he wondered, 'Where else Sally could smile except on her face?'

'Anyway, as I was saying,' Kate continued licking her fingers, 'it was forced medicine for your dad, joining up in the early days. I've missed him a lot over the years. It will be a relief when the war is over and he's home for good. He'll probably be able to get a stoking job in one of the mills.'

Jimmie turned to face his mother, 'Well, I think it's been a sheer waste of time, sweating his guts out in the bowels of a stinkin', rusty merchant ship, riskin' his life, then comin' home with his earnings to piss it up against a wall...!' Jimmie's words were suddenly cut short.

'Don't ever let me hear you say that again! Yer dad would knock yer bleedin' head off yer shoulders. He earned what he spent, he can do whatever he wants with his own money, so there!'

'I'm sorry Mam, but it makes me mad to think what that money could have been spent on? Maybe we could have had a nice house like Mrs Hughes in Bangor.'

'Mrs Hughes didn't have any kids did she?' retorted Kate angrily, 'she could afford to have a nice house!'

'Well then,' added Jimmie, 'maybe if we hadn't had so many kids maybe we could have had decent clothes. Me arse was always on view. The first time I had a pair of shoes they were hand-me-downs from cousin Peter, black patent, fancy that for a lad. I remember they had pointed toes and all the kids at school used to call me, 'Fred Astaire', I didn't even know who Fred Astaire was until I saw a picture of him on a poster, wearing black shiny dancing shoes. I had to wear dancing shoes for school!'

Kate drained the contents of her cup and smiled at Jimmie. She remembered the shoes well. 'Life isn't easy, son, 'specially for folks like us, but there's brighter times ahead now. We have a good house, plenty of space, and even though there's a war on, we have plenty to eat and lots of new friends. I have you and Lily home again and that means a lot to me. You'll understand one day what life is all about, the ups and the downs, and sometimes there's more downs than ups. So be thankful you have a good home, we are better off than lots of people. You don't know what goes on in your dad's head, what he might have been, what he could have done to change things. He probably had his dreams too. He works hard and he plays hard, that's his life, and because I love my Robert I don't care as long as he keeps coming home to us. Anyway lad, off with yer downstairs and get yer pie. It'll be cold by now, that's if our Eric hasn't eaten it.'

Jimmie gathered up the crockery on the tray and made his way down the stairs, muttering at the same time that Eric would get walloped if he had. Jimmie was deep in thought as he ate his cold pie. 'He wasn't enjoying it and wondered why anyone could get enthusiastic about Ashworth's pies?' He fiddled around with his fork, pushing slivers of potato around the plate.

Eric watched his brother's strange behaviour, he didn't usually play around with his food. 'You've got the sulks on haven't you?' Eric asked, as he lowered his stocking to give his leg a good scratch, 'What's been goin' on up there?'

'Nothin', nothin' to do wi' you!' Jimmie replied.

'You've been a long time sayin' nothin',' retorted Eric.

'Just stop yer soddin' questions, and knock it off scratchin' yer leg, or dad'll be sending you back to Waddow Hall, an' those witches'll get you. It's haunted you know, some young girl haunts the place. Headless she is too.'

'Yer 'aving me on,' Eric said pulling up his stocking in fear.

'Well you'll soon find out if they take you back, you'll have to sleep in that big room all on yer own, locked up with a headless woman.'

A nervous look crossed Eric's face, 'Yer won't tell dad I was scratching will you?' he asked.

'Not if you behave yourself okay?'

Eric nodded and ran from the kitchen without saying a word, galloping up the stairs two at a time.

Jimmie, laughing to himself, washed the dishes and did his other chores hoping his little tale would stop Eric from scratching. In fact it did the trick, for Eric no longer had to be reminded about his baths and applying the obnoxious ointment. He didn't scratch to relieve the itching, so was soon clear of spots, due no doubt to the witch of Waddow Hall, rather than to his isolation.

That afternoon seemed endless to Jimmie. He peeped out through the curtains and saw Tommy Adams with two of his sisters, Doris and Lily. They were coming home from school. Then Dorothy Howlett and her friend Gladys passed by. He jumped back from the window, he didn't want to be seen, there would be enough gossip about the Maclean children being off school for such a long time.

When the schoolchildren had all gone, he wondered if he dare venture out to look for his dad, then thought perhaps he had better not. More than likely his dad would be four sheets to the wind, and in full sail when it was closing time. Jimmie thought that very shortly his dad would come rolling down the street, swaying and staggering down past Dyson's mill. Everyone in the cloth warehouse would see him and snigger and smirk at the Liverpool sailor, home on leave and drunk as a lord.

During this time, Eric hardly looked up from the battered Knock-out comic, and wasn't interested in anything that was going on.

Jimmie on the other hand, was tense with expectation, running to the front door several times when he thought he heard a knock. Just by chance he went out into the backyard and opened the gate to see his father stumbling down the street, swaying and tottering from side to side.

A group of youths were sitting on the edge of the kerb, watching, jeering and laughing at his brave sailor father. They were singing, *'What shall we do with a drunken sailor.'*

Jimmie saw red, he couldn't hold back his anger. 'How dare they?'

He raced past his father to do battle with the brazen-faced jesters, as they sat in a row on the ground. With clenched fist, Jimmie lunged it into the face of the first one, then just as a pianist runs his fingers the length of the keyboard, he ran his fist down every face that he passed. The bewildered gang jumped up intending to strike back, but Jimmie was too quick for them as he hightailed it back into his yard, his father rolled along behind him.

'You should have ignored the buggers, they'll have it in for you when you get back to school,' said Rob.

'Not likely dad. Making fun of you, if they gang up on me, I'll make sure the odds are even.' Jimmie said as he lit the gas under the kettle. He remembered being confronted by a much larger and older boy when he was in Bangor, the lad coming off the worst getting a Glasgow kiss from Jimmie.

'There's enough fighting going on in the world lad without scrapping with yer mates.' Rob drew on his cigarette before placing it on the ashtray. 'Try and gerron with 'em, everyone's not your enemy, yer know.'

Rob was struggling to get his tunic off over his shoulders, and Jimmie came to his rescue, pulling from the front and rolling it down his dad's arms, rather like a banana skin, or perhaps more like a sausage skin, it was so tight.

'Why don't they make these a bit looser dad, they'd come off easier?'

'There's a reason for that son, I'll tell you some other time. I'm ready for a pot of tea now, then I'm off for a nap.' As Rob was speaking he was putting his tunic on a hanger and folding his navy collar, then he wrapped his black ribbon around his hand and placed it inside his hat.

Meanwhile Jimmie had made him a strong pot of tea.

Rob disappeared up the stairs, asking Jimmie, 'See how your mam is? I don't want to disturb her, I'll take my rest on one of the lad's beds.' He then turned and said, 'Oh by the way was there any change left over from the pies?'

Jimmie, who was hoping his dad had forgotten, said, 'Yes dad, sure. To tell you the truth I just forgot all about it, there's one and sixpence.' He delved into his trouser pocket, and handed the shilling and sixpenny pieces to his father.

Rob smiled as he took the shilling from Jimmie's hand. 'Keep the sixpence for yourself you've been a good lad. Give me a shout at six o'clock and I'll have a brawn sandwich when I gerrup, thanks lad.' And he continued on his way to bed for the rest of the afternoon.

During this time little angel-faced Eric had been watching what was going on, not missing a trick, and on his father's departure said to Jimmie, 'You don't half know how to get round me dad.'

Whereupon Jimmie told him, 'Shut yer gob Eric.'

Feeling threatened, Eric did just that!

On Friday, Kate was feeling more like her old self, as was displayed in the dusting, polishing and scrubbing the kitchen floor that was her weekly routine. For all that she said she was okay, Jimmie and Eric did their best to help her, while Rob spent the biggest part of his leave at the New Inn.

Sunday was the highlight of the week, for Kate had been churched at St. Mary's, as was the custom, and returned home feeling like a whole woman once again. Needless to say the celebrations got underway early with Liverpool friends, relatives and neighbours in attendance. Bobbie had ordered a couple of crates of pale ale from the Derby Arms. The landlord sent a miniature bottle of rum for Kate, for medicinal purposes of course.

Auntie Molly, Evie Foster, Mrs Adams and Sally King were all cooing over the new baby, who had been christened Cynthia.

The table groaned with sandwiches of all descriptions. Biscuits, tinned fruit and cake; indeed no one would have thought there was any such thing as rationing and coupons, thanks to Mr Feather at the Co-op.

In true traditional Liverpool style everyone did a turn. Kate herself, singing the song of the moment to Rob, *Yours till the stars lose their glory,* sounding as much like Vera Lynne as it was possible to sound. She always sang with a passion and closed her eyes, her right foot tapping out the rhythm.

Then Bobbie, enlivened by the pale ale, suddenly sprang to his feet, to give a thunderous discharge on his mouth organ. The tune was fast and furious and all joined in to his rendering of *Sons of the sea.* He was usually very proficient in the art of sucking and blowing his beloved instrument, but the pale ale had taken it's toll, therefore he had become a little confused as to whether to suck or blow.

After that it was Sally King's turn to give her rendering of *Maggie, Maggie May,* with which she brought the house down.

Evie, who had become a little downcast and sorrowful, thinking of her husband who had been killed whilst coming home on leave, was resurrected by little Mrs Adams, who took her hand and pulled her to her feet to take the floor in a lively jig, accompanied by Sally's voice and Bobbie's mouth organ.

Rob laughed heartily at seeing Evie's garter slip down her leg to below her pink bloomers, and pointed to the offending item, at which Evie blushed madly, then tucked it up her bloomers once again, before continuing her prancing with Mrs Adams.

After several verses of the story of the notorious Lime Street Girl - *Maggie May*, and with the perspiration pouring down their faces, they all collapsed in a heap of laughter. Sally's strawberry blonde hair stuck to her forehead, her blue eyes twinkling with merriment.

Evie meanwhile, had disappeared into the backyard for a breath of fresh air and to adjust her underwear. Though very plain in appearance, she had a heart of gold and her kindness made up for her lack of beauty.

As Jimmie's dad used to say, 'Beauty is in the eye of the beholder.'

She re-appeared into the living-room, wagging a finger in a friendly gesture and saying to Kate, 'Just watch him, you know what sailors are, and all the nice girls love a sailor.'

'Yes,' said Kate laughing, 'but this sailor's spoken for,' and she kissed Rob on the cheek, 'this one's anchored to me, and will be forever.' After saying these words Kate felt very emotional and gave way to tears.

Rob, put his arm around her saying, 'Come on now queen, it'll all be over one day, and all the lads'll be home for good.'

Evie too, gave Kate a kiss, they had become very close, more like sisters, and they were a great comfort to each other, especially since Evie had lost her husband.

Kate didn't have any sisters, only three brothers, Alex the eldest who had spent many years in the Royal Navy. William who had been lost at sea, and Hugh the youngest, who was in the army. Where though? Only God knew.

Evie who had been overcome by the emotion of the day and memories of her husband, not least the glasses of pale ale that she had consumed, broke into a popular Vera Lynne song, *'We'll Meet Again'*.

'Go on Evie gairl. Let it rip,' encouraged Sally, joining in herself. *'But I know we'll meet again some sunny day.'*

Soon tears were flowing from all the women, though it didn't stop them from singing with gusto.

Bobbie commented to his dad, 'I can't understand anyone writing a buddy song like that, which makes everyone buddy cry, and made all the fighting forces buddy homesick.'

He was interrupted from his remarks by a loud knocking on the front door.

'Go and see who that is lad,' said Kate to Bobbie. 'If it's that little A.R.P. chap, ask him to come in and have a drink with us.'

Meanwhile Evie continued the song with her weeping companions.

Bobbie returned from his mission of seeing who was at the door, but this time accompanied by his sister Mary and her friend Betty Dyson. They were auxiliary nurses with the W.A.A.F. and were stationed in Wilmslow, Cheshire, they had managed to wangle a weekend pass, though due to transport problems had arrived later than expected.

Mary kissed everyone in turn, including Jimmie, and he realised that the last time he had seen her was just before she left home to go into service with a Jewish family. That was six months before the war had begun, so it had been about four and a half years. He wouldn't have known her, and could have passed her in the street not even knowing that she was his sister. He took in her description as quick as he would take a photograph. She looked smart in her uniform and the air force blue enhanced the blue of her eyes.

Her golden hair was dressed into a victory roll, the style of the present day, though he suspected that it was long. Though she wore a little lipstick of a pale pink shade and light brown mascara, she really didn't need any make-up, for her skin was soft, and reminded Jimmie of roses. He reckoned she'd be about twenty-one years of age, though she looked much younger.

Then she spoke, in that soft lilting voice that he remembered, 'Nice to see you again lad; it's been a long time hasn't it?' she hugged him, giving him the nicest and most loving greeting he'd ever had.

He felt embarrassed, and hardly dared to look into her eyes. 'Yer,' he mumbled. 'Nice to see you Mary.' Then he realised that she had kissed him, and as young boys do, he rubbed his cheek where the kiss had been planted.

'Me kisses aren't that bad are they kiddo?' she laughed, as she undid the buttons of her tunic. 'I'm just going up to the bathroom to freshen up, then we're going down to the Derby for the last hour.'

Her friend, Betty, who had not yet completed her round of kisses, and had made Jimmie blush to the roots of his red hair, followed Mary upstairs to get ready. Time with family and friends was limited during war-time and they all had to take what they could, when they could.

'Bobbie didn't need to be asked twice, and combed back his Brylcreamed hair, then flung on his checked sports jacket, waiting patiently at the bottom of the stairs for Mary and Betty.

Mary linked her arm through her father's saying, 'Come on let's go.'

Bobbie followed Betty.

Kate wasn't going anywhere, she was happy with her friends, and Bobbie had promised to bring back another crate or two. The night was still young.

Kate shoved a pound note into Bobbie's hand, whispering, 'This will help you out. It's my treat.'

'Thanks Mam,' said Bobbie, 'we'll be back just after ten.'

'Think on that you do.'

Then turning to Evie, said, 'Right, where were we? Ah! Yes *We'll Meet Again*. Carry on, Evie, no more interruptions. Like the wind, our Mary, never know when she's gonna blow in.' She laughed, happy in the thought that all her loved ones were all together for once, along with her dearest friends.

The revelry went on until the early hours. Mary and Betty were the worse for wear from the cherry brandies and the odd gin and tonic. Betty spent the best part of the early morning spewing up over the railings into the goit, vowing never again to partake of the demon drink and cursing Mary for making her dash home with her on a weekend pass.

Needless to say, Bobbie was late for work after the celebrations. Bill hadn't bothered to attend anyway, but went out with his mate Gerald, then stayed the night at his place.

After lots of cups of strong tea, the two girls left the house, being waved off by the men at the mill opposite. Mary strode briskly up Dalton Street, Betty running alongside to keep up with her, and they both wondered if it had all been worth it?

Tuesday morning was a dismal day, it had rained most of the morning. Kate had been busy cleaning and ironing. Hardly anyone spoke, Rob was to return to his ship that afternoon. Kate hated goodbyes, and always tried to put on a brave face, though she was well experienced in departures, for hadn't her Robert been away at sea for longer than she cared to remember? She was certainly an old hand at it, but when you loved your man, there was no easy way to say goodbye.

She said a fond farewell to Rob, then took her baby up to their bedroom to give her a feed, giving way to tears only when she was out of sight of her husband. She didn't want him to be worried, he had a hard job to do, and didn't know when they would see each other again, if ever!

Jimmie offered to walk to the station with his father, but Rob said no, telling him to look after Kate instead, and the younger children.

Rob then called from the foot of the stairs, 'I'm off then now Kate. See yer, love.' And with that he closed the front door, then swayed with his seaman's gait up the street, not knowing when he would return.

In the bedroom Kate shared with her husband, she wept silently, occasionally smiling as she thought about the celebration last Sunday. Everyone had enjoyed it, though there were more than a few thick heads, but at least baby Cynthia's head was well and truly wetted!

CHAPTER THREE
Washing and Reminiscing

Without exception, Monday was washday.

Everyone admired Mrs Mac's washing on the clothes lines. Her sheets and pillowcases were whiter than white, blue-white, for she always used dolly-blue and boiled her wash. The clothes blew vigorously on the line, sparkling in the morning sunshine, and as well as the inevitable shirts from her boys, there were all the dresses and underwear from her girls, and of course the baby's nappies. Kate was proud of her lines of sweet smelling clothes, and was always the first in the street to hang out her washing.

It was Jimmie's job to turn the handle of the heavy mangle, and he swore that it was doing that job that developed his puny muscles into something to be proud of. Though when Kate folded the clothes thicker than usual, and fed them in through the wooden rollers, water squirted in all directions, and she laughed not realising how much it annoyed Jimmie.

'Gosh! Look Mam, it's going all over the kitchen and the table too, just look will ya?'

'Sorry lad, I was miles away back in Liverpool. Hell they were hard times then,' Kate said as she fed the clothes in between the rollers.

'Yer,' said Jimmie, wanting to add his little bit of remembering. 'I remember too, standing outside a red brick building in a long queue, we must have stood for hours. Me feet were freezing an' you lifted me up and wrapped me inside your shawl. You were crying going home, I couldn't have been very old then. Was it the workhouse?'

'Yes it was, lad, Brownlow Hill Workhouse, full of poor people, desperate to find a way out, you were about six-years old at the time. Scrounging and begging, that's what we were doing, a bowl of soup, or something warm to wear for the kids,' only to be told by some toffy-nosed sod that, 'I didn't meet the criteria,' because Bobbie was earning a few shillings a week, and your dad's allotment from the Merchant Navy. 'All the same it didn't amount to much, hardly kept body and soul together. They always said the same thing, they would give it their serious attention, but there were thousands in the same situation or even worse than the Macleans.'

The snooty old feller would say, 'How many of you are there?'

'He knew damn well how many we were, just trying it on, the sly devil.'

'See what I can come up with, you have a few children, how many?'

I felt so humiliated but beggars can't be choosers, so I said, 'Six and meself, and another on the way.'

'So that'll be eight,' the balding bespectacled man said as he scribbled the details into a large black book.

'The man's a bloody genius,' remarked Kate sarcastically for all in the queue to hear.

'Never again lad, do I want to venture near that God-forsaken place. I'd rather starve to death than belittle myself in that way.'

Jimmie agreed, 'Aye they must have been bad days for you then, Mam. Don't want to be like that ever again.' He lowered his head as he turned the handle of the heavy mangle, then smiled as he visualised the contents of his mam's larder and cupboards stockpiled with foodstuffs, that they never imagined they would ever be able to have in their past circumstances. As he reflected on the changes in their lives, he wondered if his mam would change her mind about him going to work in the cotton mill when he left school? 'Flippin' hope so,' he reflected.

He strained and groaned as the last of the washing squirted from the rollers. 'Thank goodness for that,' Jimmie said, puffing.

Kate laughed, 'Put muscles on yer. Here dry the floor,' she threw a floor cloth to him. 'I'll just peg out the last, and hope it keeps fine. Then we'll have a cuppa and something nice to go with it, before the rest of the gang get home.'

Having downed egg and beans on toast, Jimmie, his mouth clogged with rich brown parkin, mumbled something about mill work. 'It wasn't as bad as going down the pit or mines, and that he would probably just have to make the best of it. Just one of those things that can't be helped.'

Kate smiled to herself and didn't respond, as she went about preparing a meal for the rest of the family, she knew the lad didn't want to work in the mill, but all the young ones did it, so it wouldn't harm him. The wages were decent enough. Any wheedling from Jimmie about not wanting to take this sort of job, was met with a wave of Kate's hand, dismissing the subject, as never to be brought up again unless he wanted the full fury of Kate's Irish temper upon him.

Jimmie got the message. For that day at least, work in the mill was forgotten, a tanner for the Majestic, and a choc-ice was more than he had hoped for helping with the washing. Nevertheless he would win her over, he was sure of that. It was just a case of choosing the right time, that was all he wanted. He had enjoyed the film, but as he left the Majestic he wondered about getting home in the blackout. He had always had company before, he felt fairly confident, but soon lost his way, so what normally would be a ten minute stroll back home, turned out to take over an hour, wandering in the opposite direction. More by luck than management he finally got his bearings and arrived at 58 Dalton Street.

Kate looked up from her task of sewing on buttons, she always had something to do. She waited for the excuse as to why he was home so late.

'Sorry Mam, lost me way in the blackout; hope you weren't worried about me. I wouldn't like you to worry again like before when we ran away from Waddow Hall. I'm really sorry.'

'Worried? Worried?' shouted Kate, 'I've been worried sick out of my mind wondering what had happened to you on your own? You'd better gerrup them dancers (stairs), and there'll be no late night pictures for you me lad, just look at the time!'

Jimmie blinked hard several times before saying, 'Sorry Mam, it won't happen again.'

'Yer damn right it won't happen again, because you won't be going. Saturday matinee that's when you'll go, if you go at all, with the rest of the kids. Now get upstairs, don't think you're getting a drink at this time!'

'Alright Mam,' said Jimmie meekly, as he turned slowly and slipped out of the room, turning slightly to look at his mam as he left the room, 'g'night then.'

Kate didn't reply, but when he had gone she chuckled to herself, as she imagined Jimmie groping about in the darkness, and wandering aimlessly around the strange town. 'That'll teach him,' she thought.

Then her heart softened, 'Be ready for a hot drink I expect, better take one up for him. I'm ready for one myself anyroad.'

CHAPTER FOUR
School, New Clothes, Jobs and Sports

Swallowing his pride, Jimmie eventually put in an appearance at Bradley School, after a lot of coaxing and the occasional threat from Kate.

He soon made friends with the other boys in class from the different localities, but he wasn't very pleased to find himself having to share a desk with one of the opposite sex, and distanced himself as far as he could from her, without actually falling off the edge of his seat. Though one cheek of his little bum did hang over at times. His last school in Bangor had been a boys only school, so this one took some getting used to.

It was a very trying time for him, as though he tried to avoid looking at the girl in question, if he did ever glance briefly her way, she would be looking at him and glaring. So obviously it seemed she had the same problem as he did.

The weeks passed very slowly for Jimmie, and he was always glad when school closed for the weekends. Eventually Lily returned to school, and he was delighted to say the least, as she took over many of the household jobs that he had been burdened with. Especially those jobs that were more suited to girls, like ironing and bathing the younger members of the family.

Jimmie's mind was wandering in class, about what he would do with all the extra free time he would have, when suddenly his day-dreaming ended, when Smithy, a pal of his, was dragged out in front of the class, and Mr Jackson, a normally placid man, threatened to stop Smithy's morning milk, wondering if it was that which was giving him the urge.

Mr Jackson was nearing the end of his tether, as he noticed on several occasions Smithy and a few other boys, manipulating themselves beneath their desks. He immediately ordered the dirty mongrels to go to the headmaster's office, announcing as they went, that they should save their energy for their marriage bed, a few years ahead. That's if they managed to live that long. He advised them to have a cold bath whenever they felt this strange feeling occurring below their belts.

Eventually the class became segregated, making things a little better, but the habit persisted, so with little fuss, and without losing his sanity, Joe Jackson ejected them from the classroom and into the schoolyard regardless of the weather.

Come hail, snow, blizzards or thunderstorms, in fact whatever God rained down upon them, they were ousted without hesitation, and without any mercy, so that they could cool down their ardour.

Well this was Mr Jackson's plan at least. At the same time he shouted at them, 'That one day some of them would end up in a mental institution, or go blind!'

1943

The cold winter months blossomed into spring, and by now Jimmie was fourteen-years old. There were no real school-leaving exams as such, much as he would have liked to have proved his ability, in order to obtain a better job.

For children like Jimmie, jobs in factories were plentiful. The mill manager at Wm. Fell's in Pendle street welcomed Jimmie with open arms. Once having been given a job in the cotton mills, it was compulsory to remain in that situation for the duration of the war, or until his National Service, whichever was the earliest.

The same rules and regulations didn't apply though, if a person's workmanship was not up to standard, then they would be dismissed on the spot.

'So you've come here from our Joe's class have you? Well I tell you young Jimmie MacLean, Fell's is a good mill, you'll get on like a house on fire, I said a house on fire, you'll soon be at home in no time at all. Lots of other young 'uns' have settled in with no problems. You'll be fine,' he said.

Jimmie stood pushing his hands into his pockets, doing his utmost to shove his short trousers over his knees without success. He shuffled nervously, as Billy Jackson, the mill manager interviewed him. He was small and wiry in his build, a swarthy little fellow with a glass eye, not much taller than Jimmie himself. It seemed more than a coincidence for Jimmie to end up at this mill, with the manager being his ex-teacher's father.

It took five minutes, maybe less, for Billy to evaluate Jimmie's potential. During which time Billy must have covered a full square yard on the stone floor with black tobacco juice. A number of questions were asked, which left Jimmie not sure whether to say yes or no, as he was too busy trying to fathom out which of Billy's eyes he should look into, and at the same time trying to dodge the loathsome discharges from the tobacco chewing manager.

Then his brief encounter ended, ZDAJ 140/3 was added to his document of employment, and the sum of nineteen shillings and 5d, agreed to be his wage for the working week of forty-nine and a half hours.

Monday to Friday 7a.m. till 5.30p.m, and Saturday morning 7 to 11.30a.m., with his breakfast and dinner breaks amounted to one hour and a half each day, (Saturdays excepted).

After the Easter holidays, Jimmie donned his bib and brace overalls, handed down from his brother Bill, and left the house to mingle with the crowds of flat-capped mill workers, and girls wearing head-scarves, black stockings and the inevitable clogs. The latter clip-clopping along the pavements sounding like an army tramping along the stone cobbles.

That sound he could get used to, but as for wearing them, he vowed he could never do that. As he entered the cart shed, an area adjoining the weft cellar, he joined the mixed groups of work-people waiting to start their various jobs. Jimmie almost choked as the air was thick with tobacco and pipe smoke, as all the smokers were having their last drag before entering the weaving shed.

The noise from the huge engine, which groaned loudly, was started by the steam boilers. In turn the massive fly wheel started to turn, gathering up speed and rotating the overhead shafts from which leather straps were suspended, and were attached to almost a thousand looms. The noise was deafening, and as the workers moved along behind one another, Jimmie heard remarks like no rest for the wicked, or back to the grindstone.

His heart sank as he visualised spending the rest of his working life amid this conglomeration. Weavers, warpers, loomers, tapers and dressers, men skilled at their work, made their way to their assigned places. It was all a fearsome sight to the young lad, and the noise was horrendous. His eardrums felt as if they would burst, and he heaved a sigh of relief as he was escorted from the thunderous sound of the clattering looms into a heavy lift, soon to be known to Jimmie as a hoist.

The hoist ascended, taking Jimmie and ten other employees to the top floor of the building, where the preparation department was located, and where he was to learn how to arrange coloured patterns in the warps, in readiness for the looms. Jimmie knew from the outset that this wasn't the work he was cut out for, but of course he had been against mill work from the start, but what could he do?

He was introduced to a small chap with snow-white hair, though he usually wore a cap, so he didn't always display it. He seemed to be a pleasant little fellow, always smiling, so at least that was something, as this was the man who would train him, and whom he would work alongside, for how long though, Jimmie didn't know. The man's name was Harold Duerden.

Jimmie took in the surroundings of the large room where he would spend a third of his life. The walls were white-washed, though badly in need of re-doing, and tall windows dominated the room, though situated too high up in the wall for folks to be able to see out of. Large beams finished, awaited ready to be dispatched to the weaving shed, and empty beams were waiting to be started and filled by the beamer who prepared them for the loomer.

Part of Jimmie's job was to sweep up every night all the waste cotton lying on the floor, mingled with black spittle discharged from the tobacco chewing mouths of loomers. He really hated this job, and wondered how long he could stick it before rebelling?

The reaching-in, which was Jimmie's actual job was interesting, he had to hook threads onto the loomer's hooks along the length of the beam, until the pattern was completed, though sometimes the hooks caught his fingers and pulled at his flesh, making them sore.

Sometimes, when doing a plain warp, he could let his mind wander a bit, and he would think of Bangor and what kind of a job he would have been doing if he had lived there permanently? 'It wouldn't be in a mill, that's for sure,' he thought.

He thought of hot summer days when he and Lily and young Eddie would climb the mountain or swim in the Straits. It all seemed so far away now, as if it had never really happened.

His mam had painted a rosy picture of mill work, that mills were light and airy and clean, but he should have known, his mam had *never ever* been in a mill. So how could she know?

He wondered about the little black slaves in the Southern states of America, before the civil war, and thought that in fact the children of the 1940's were exploited in the same way, working for a pittance, long hours and in dreadful conditions.

Nevertheless Jimmie had assured his mother that he would do his best at the work to which he had been assigned, but he couldn't help thinking about the rich textile manufacturers, living off the fat of the land, so to speak, or rather from the misery and discomfort of these humble workers.

He would imagine them drinking their brandy from crystal glasses and smoking fat cigars. Sometimes when they walked around the mill on a rare visit, he would see them fingering the gold medallions hanging on the end of their watch-chains.

Very soon the sparkle left Jimmie's blue eyes, and dark rings appeared beneath the pale lashes. His rosy complexion disappeared, and as Kate looked at him, she wondered if she had done the wrong thing in insisting that her son went into the mill, but to her at that time, money meant a lot. In fact it was the most important thing; she had seen poverty, a lot of it, she knew what it was like to degrade herself for handouts at the workhouse, so she was determined that it would never happen again to any of her family.

When it was pay-day she always wore a clean white apron and held it out for Jimmie to place his wage packet in it. It was rather like a game. The Government took tax from the small wage leaving 17/6d, but Kate gave Jimmie 2/6d, keeping the 15/- for herself. Always, as she placed the half crown in his palm, he would laugh.

On one occasion she asked him, 'Why do you always laugh when I give you your half-crown?'

'Well it's like this Mam. It feels as if I'm taking holy communion, you with your sparkling white pinny, like a priest, and me waiting for the hand out, expecting you to drop the half crown on my tongue,' he laughed.

Kate took a friendly swipe at Jimmie, 'Don't you make a mockery of the church, or you'll get no pocket money. It's a good thing your tea is on the table, or you'd get no tea either.'

They both had a good laugh, and Kate saw the funny side, saying, 'Next week I'll stick a wafer in your mouth and give you a glass of water. Yer a real one Jimmie Mac, don't know how I put up with yer at times.' Then she poured him another ladle of scouse onto his dish.

Jimmie had made many friends in Nelson, and when he joined the Youth Club in Ann Street he made many more. The Rev. Hugh Fielder took everyone under his wing. He was a tall man, with a rosy face and pale blue eyes, and was kind and gentle to all. He was an athletic type, and he encouraged the boys in his care to become involved in football, cricket and swimming, and arranged to compete with neighbouring towns.

All this came as a complete delight to Jimmie, as sports of any kind were eagerly taken up by him. He soon began winning various events, and became very popular with the club.

Football was another sport that Jimmie enjoyed very much, at least he would have done if he had any football boots, but he couldn't see that happening in the near future, as he never had any spare cash.

Nevertheless Hugh, who was always aware of the young people's needs, came to his rescue, and willingly lent Jimmie his very own, even though they were a couple of sizes too big for him.

That didn't matter, Jimmie just wore two pairs of socks then it was not so bad. Eventually as the months wore on, so did the football boots, much to Jimmie's embarrassment.

Yet the Rev. said 'not to worry, that it was better to give than receive,' and prayed that at some future date Jimmie would have saved enough money for some new ones.

Jimmie then said, 'If I had my own boots, maybe I would soon start scoring some goals, seeing that the team has lost their matches every week.'

Hugh commented, 'It's much better to take part, than not to play at all.'

August 1944

'You'll be turning into a fish our Jimmie, out so soon after tea, your swimming trunks still wet from the night before. You'll catch your death or summat,' warned Kate.

'Don't worry about me Mam,' Jimmie replied, 'I look forward to it after being cooped up in that horrible mill day after day. Outside of mill hours is me own time, I'll be glad when I'm eighteen, and get called up into the forces. You won't see my backside for dust, then some other poor young bugger can have my job.'

'You'll never have another job like that our Jimmie, yer always moaning about yer job, you should have got used to it by now.'

'I don't want another job like it, or anything that resembles it either, and as soon as I can get out of it I'm off,' and with that Jimmie flung his wet trunks over his shoulder and ran out of the back door, only to bump headlong into his dad. Jimmie stood for a moment too stunned to speak, then when he got over the shock of seeing his father he hummed and hawed not knowing what to say.

'What's up son? Cat got yer tongue?' Rob barked.

'Er no dad, just surprised to see you, especially as you're not in uniform. Why are you not in uniform?'

'They'll take you away Jimmie Mac, talking to yourself,' shouted Kate as she emerged from the kitchen. When she caught sight of Rob the blood drained from her face, and her whole body trembled, 'Yer home Robert, home for good? But the war's not over yet, what's happened?'

Jimmie stood motionless as his mam and dad embraced, then slipped away unnoticed.

'Well Rob, thank goodness it's all over for you. What is it that made you come out, and where the hell did you get that awful suit from? It looks as if it's fallen from a hand-cart.'

'Yer asking too many questions Kate,' Rob said as he dropped his battered suitcase. 'Bronchitis, or something or other, you know how it is when they spout off these medical terms. Doesn't really matter, they've discharged me an' that's that. As for the suit, I scrounged it off our Eddie (his brother) in Liverpool. That's where I got me marching orders at H.M.S. Mersey. It's a shore base,' continued Rob, as his limped into the kitchen.

'A shore base? For what, lad? And why are you limping. Come on out with it. You can't fool me,' Kate said with anxiety in her voice.

'Who's limping? Oh forget about it Kate, just a bit of a scald that's all. There was this explosion on the minesweeper. Don't know what it was, didn't care, but all hell broke loose down below. Thank God we all got off safely, that's the main thing.'

'I can never get a proper tale off you Robert,' Kate said as she poured him a pint pot of tea. 'Never heard a dickie bird from you for ages. Didn't know your whereabouts or even if you were dead or alive?' Kate's eyes reddened, and the tears flowed down her cheeks. She quickly wiped the tears away. 'What a homecoming,' she thought, before saying out loud, 'Anyway you're home now and that's all that matters, you've done your whack, more than enough if you ask me. It's been awful Robert, I was worried sick about you. I tried to hide it from the kids, no good having them worried as well. I had visions of being a war widow, with ten kids an' all.' With that she threw her apron over her face and gave way to sobbing.

'Come on Kate, that's enough girl. It's over now.' Rob stroked his wife's black hair, noticing a few strands of grey among the black. 'Come on now Queen, you can turn the tap off now. I'm home to look after you all.'

Rob then lit two cigarettes, lifted Kate's head and handed her one. Then gave her one of his clean folded hankies, which he always carried.

'You seem like a stranger to me Robert,' Kate sniffled. 'It's hard for me to believe that you're home at last and for good.' Tears welled up again and threatened to spill over, and she inhaled on her cigarette deeply, blowing out a narrow shaft of blue smoke. That seemed to settle her, and she took her husband's hand, intertwining her fingers into his, and inwardly grieved to think that someone as old as her Robert, should have to fight in the war. Her inner emotions almost got the better of her, until Lily appeared and ran to greet her dad, then the other girls followed, Maisie, Cathie and little Olive, each waiting eagerly in turn to kiss and hug their father.

'You've done me proud Kate,' Robert said as he stroked the silky hair of each of his young daughters.

Then to the girls he added, 'What fine young beauties yer all are. See now, look into me case there's some coloured ribbons and stuff fer yer, and some chocolate bars, go on now help yerselves.'

Kate held onto Robert's hand, she felt like she did when they were courting. They both smiled, as they watched their little daughters delve into the brown case, eyes sparkling as each of them chose their favourite colours of ribbon to tone with their hair. It was funny how each of them had a different hair colour, black, strawberry blonde, and auburn, yet they all had that red streak.

For once Rob felt at a loss for words, as each of his daughters spoke excitedly with their Liverpool accents, while

Kate having detached herself from her husband, went into the kitchen to prepare a meal. Of course Mary was away in Wilmslow, but the boys would soon be home, then the rest of the family would for the first time in ages, surround the table amid a noisy, happy, family tea, Kate's family and Robert's.

The weeks passed, and Robert had eventually parted company with his naval allowance. At least the hangers on at the New Inn saw to that. Every afternoon and evening, the scroungers waited like a pack of hyenas ready to scavenge whatever they could from their easy victim. Kate knew he was an easy target, and told him so in no uncertain terms.

'It's time you started saving your brass now, them scroungers up at the pub can get it somewhere else from now on. I can't understand why you keep going all the way to the pub up in Nelson, when at least you can pop to the Derby Arms at the bottom of the street. It's time for a change Robert, so get yourself sorted out. One other thing you can do as well,' Kate added, as she took a five pound note from her purse, and handing it to him said, 'You can go and get yourself a decent jacket and new trousers. I'm sure that suit you got from your Eddie will drop off your back before long. It looks so shabby, and I want you to look nice, so I can be proud of you. So go on, get down to Wraw's on Leeds Road and get yourself kitted out. You want to look decent when you go looking for a job don't you? There's a few vacancies for fire-beaters in the Leader. You could do a job like that easily, having been a first class leading stoker.'

Robert seemed ready for anything, and Kate's words had the desired effect. It stirred Rob to action and he was eager to show what a real fire-beater could do armed with all his experiences in the merchant marines.

Kate wanted Robert to be proud of himself too, just as she was. She handed him an extra pound note, telling him to get a proper boiler suit for when he got his job, and of course she gave him the necessary clothing coupons to accompany the money needed.

'Hell! Kate!' exclaimed Rob, 'you've been saving up?'

'I have,' replied Kate, 'for such a day as this. So now get along with you, and make sure that you get everything I told you. No skimping, and don't go spending it on your cronies in the New Inn or there'll be trouble and no mistake.'

With that Kate gave her Robert a kiss, and Rob assured his loving wife, 'I'll batten down the hatches, and settle into a job, as soon as I get one.'

'I'll expect you back in an hour then, don't get side-tracked if you see any of those lob-lolls. The lazy scroungers.'

'Come with me if you like, if you don't trust me,' said Rob. 'Besides the fresh air will do you good.'

'There's no way I'd walk out with you in broad daylight with that suit on.' Kate laughed. 'It smells of mothballs as well. Off you go, I'll see you soon.'

As Rob scuttled along the goit-side, then onto Leeds Road, he felt ashamed of what Kate had said regarding his suit, and he imagined that all eyes were upon him. He momentarily glanced at his reflection in a shop window, almost colliding with a smartly dressed, rather stout gentleman. He apologised to the man, who nodded his acceptance, and Rob could now see why Kate had said what she had. The suit was absolutely dreadful to say the least.

Rob had never even looked at the display in Wraw's window, but he couldn't wait to get inside and get this awful suit off his back. He very quickly discarded his jacket.

He said to the young bespectacled assistant, 'This was just a put me on.'

The only thing the spotty assistant was interested in was the bonus he would earn from this sale. He was sure he would make a sale as he looked at the way the man was dressed.

'There now! You look a different man altogether now,' he said as he brushed his experienced hands across the shoulders of the pale blue tweed jacket that he had helped Rob into. He also angled the cheval mirror, so that his customer could see all sides of himself.

'Feels a bit tight under the arms,' Rob said as he pulled at the sleeves. 'Maybe it'd help if I rolled down my sleeves?'

'Well yes,' said the assistant smiling, as he helped Rob out of, then back into the jacket, after the sleeve adjustments had been made.

'There, a perfect fit. Not pulling at all now is it?'

Rob nodded in agreement.

'I can match the jacket with a fine quality trouser. I take it you do want some strides?'

'Strides? What's strides, lad? I'm at a loss as to what you mean. I'm not from these parts.'

'I guessed you weren't from these parts by your accent Sir, forgive me; trousers is what I should have said to you. You'll be needing some I suppose. No good spoiling the ship for a ha'porth o'tar is it?'

Rob laughed at the last expression, he being a seaman, or ex-seaman. He tried on the strides that the assistant handed to him. After trying on several pairs of trousers, he chose a nice pair in grey flannel and said he would keep them on.

The assistant cut off all the labels, and put the old suit into a carrier bag at Rob's request. Rob then asked about a boiler suit? The assistant, ever helpful, rummaged through piles of overalls in various sizes. As luck would have it there was a pair of the blue, Rob's first choice being a navy man, in the correct size, and these were parcelled up and put into the carrier bag.

The young lad was grinning like a Cheshire cat as he mentally reckoned up how much commission he would have on pay-day. 'Call again, sir, thank you for your custom,' he said politely.

Rob left the shop smiling, and feeling like a millionaire.

He had barely left the shop before the assistant, young Derek Rowbotham, was rubbing his hands as he calculated the increase in his pay packet for the commission on the jacket and trousers. What he hadn't accounted for was Rob's boiler suit, as he had quite forgotten to charge for it in his excitement. 'Ah well, nobody would know about that if he kept his mouth shut and acted innocent like. He wasn't going to pay for that out of his well-earned bonus!'

As Rob re-traced his steps along the goit-side on his way home, he had been tempted to call at the New Inn, but his conscience got the better of him. He felt good in his new togs, and for the first time in weeks he began to feel better, and to believe in himself once more. He chuckled to himself as he thought of the suit his brother had given him. 'Eddie never gave anything away of value, but at least he could wear the trousers under his boiler suit and the jacket for work, that's all it was good for anyway.'

On reaching home he entered the kitchen to find Kate mashing a pan of boiled potatoes, with a good knob of butter and the cream off the top of the milk, she paused as she looked him over, inspecting his changed appearance 'My you do look smart, you're a real handsome laddie now. I didn't expect you back so soon, you've been quick. I'll just prick the sausages before they burst, cor! Should have done them before I started to cook them, but my mind's been on other things, and is all at sixes and sevens. There now that's that,' she said as she stabbed and chased the bangers around the huge frying pan. 'Two more minutes then they'll be done, there.

Let's have a better look at you. Yes indeed, very smart and more like my young man. Take your jacket off, and hang it on the back of the chair, then park yer bum. I'll bet yer ready for a meal?'

Rob did as he was told dutifully, saying at the same time, 'There's a couple of clothing coupons left, and here's yer change £1/3/6d.' He placed it on the table adding, 'So what about a night out at the Derby Kate?'

'Are you asking me for a date Rob MacLean? Where on earth did you get that money now? Yer didn't get that boiler suit for work did you?'

Two large dollops of mash flopped onto his plate, and four beef sausages crackling and sputtering as they fell.

'Everything's been done just as you said, Kate. Me jacket and me strides, as that feller at the shop called them, and me boiler suit is here in the bag along with Eddie's old suit, so there! I've paid what the feller asked for, nothing more, nothing less. Happy now are yer?'

Rob tucked into his sausage and mash and lovely apple turnover with custard, 'She sure knew how to make a good meal did his Kate,' he thought well satisfied.

Kate, along with Cynthia in her pram, accompanied Rob to the Labour Exchange in Seldon street.

'Don't suppose we'll ever go back to Liverpool now Kate,' Rob said. 'Still we could be living in India street yet if it hadn't been for old Adolf. He sure did us a favour don't you think? We've got the kids in school, the countryside not far away in any direction, and a great house plenty big enough for all of us, I reckon we're okay in Nelson. Maybe one day we'll have a house with a garden for the kids, who knows?'

Kate squeezed her husband's hand, 'That would be nice Rob,' she remarked. She was still very much in love with him and they had their dreams like anyone else.

'In you go now,' said Kate as they reached the building, 'and good luck. You've got everything you need haven't you? Your discharge papers, ship's books, just check before you go in.'

'I'm only going for a job Kate, don't fuss so much. I won't be long. Have a walk around the block, go on. I should be out by then, and keep yer fingers crossed.'

'Good luck anyway.' Kate had the last word, as her husband disappeared through a glass-panelled door, and into a large hall, where he gave his name to a scruffy-looking bloke over a counter, and was directed into a side office to be interviewed for a fire-beater's job.

'Can't seem to get good men these days to fire Lancashire boilers. They're few and far between, but with your experience, and the length of service you've put in, along with your fine references, I'm sending you down to Jopson, Bardsley and Jopson dye works, near Victoria Park. I'll phone them to say you're on your way, you should walk it in 15 to 20 minutes. You're almost certain to be taken on. Here's a card of introduction. They'll discuss pay and hours and so on, and show you around, saying what your duties will be, and on seeing your record, I should think they'll snap you up immediately. Best of luck Mr MacLean,' said the man, shaking hands cordially with Rob.

When Rob exited the building he found Kate waiting for him.

'My you haven't been long. No jobs then? Never mind we'll have another look at the paper to see if there's anything else going.'

Rob smiled impishly at Kate for a moment remarking, 'You've guessed wrongly. I have to go down straight away to see my prospective employer.'

Kate was so excited, and thought that Rob was teasing her, but soon changed her mind when her husband showed her the letter of introduction.

'I'll go down now straight away,' said Rob, 'you'll be alright going home won't you? No good dragging you all the way with me.' He bent and kissed her to Kate's surprise.

'S'truth!' she said happily, 'you'll have people talking, snogging in the street. Away with you now,' Kate looked rather flushed as Rob walked away.

He limped slightly, then turned at the bottom of the street to wave to her.

By the time Rob had returned home, Kate, as always had the tea prepared and ready to serve, and by the look on his face she was convinced that her man had been successful in securing the job.

Bill and Bobbie had had their usual encounter at the kitchen sink, ending in their not being on speaking terms.

'Glad someone's got a smile,' Kate said, 'these two buggers haven't a smile for the cat.' She brushed past Bobbie, knocking his arm on purpose, just as he was about to stab a piece of steak from the pie she had made.

'Come and sit here,' she said to Rob, as she pulled a chair out from the table, 's'pose you're too excited to talk eh?'

'Not at all,' Rob replied, 'There wasn't much said from either the boss or the engineer. I had a walk around the plant, looked at various gauges and pumps and explained what levels they should be at, the important thing being the water level in the boilers being correct. A demonstration of my stoking made a big impression, and that was it. I start on Monday at 4a.m.'

'So you'll be up before the cock crows? Hell what a time to start.'

'It's a necessary time for getting the boilers going, and beggars can't be choosers can they? At least it's a steady job, the pay's good, and I'll be glad to get back into the swing of things.' Rob was enthusiastic as he spoke.

'Well it will stop you always whinging about being the first up to take the milk round.' This remark was aimed at Bill by his elder brother, and if looks could have killed, Bobbie would have choked on his steak pie!

'We'll have less of the arguing youse two, it will do you both good to do a spell in the forces like yer dad. Have you no respect, I'll bet yer never even noticed his new jacket and kecks, and now he has a job to go to on Monday. You should be proud of him, and here you are carrying on in front of him. The army'll teach you a bit of respect when you get your calling up papers, that's if they'll have you.' Kate raised her voice to the lads.

'No such thing Mam,' replied Bill in a cocky manner, 'I'm doing no square bashing, or being ordered about, no fear! It's the coal mines for me when I get called up. I'm not joining any blinkin' army or navy. Er no offence dad, if that's what a feller likes to do, then good luck to him I say, but it's not my cup of tea, no sir. I'll get a decent wage in my pocket and still have my freedom. Besides the war might be over soon, then they won't need us at all.'

Rob ate his dinner quietly, not showing his true feelings, but was deep in thought as he ate. There was an air of disquiet about him. 'Had he come home to listen to his sons bickering with one another? This wasn't what he imagined home life to be when he was away in foreign waters, serving in the navy. He wanted a bit of peace and quiet now and family harmony.'

Kate sensed the situation as she stood behind Rob, motioning by putting her finger to her lips, and silently telling them to pipe down. She then blurted out, 'If you've finished, just skedaddle youse two, and let your dad finish his meal in peace.'

Bill and Bobbie left the table still bickering at each other under their breath, only to continue more aggressively in the parlour.

Kate sat at the table with Rob, 'It was very unkind the way they behaved, don't know what gets into them at times. Then there's our Jimmie, pestering the life out of me to let him come out of the mill. I wish sometimes I'd have had all girls, a lot less trouble they are. Would you like some pudding to finish off with?' she added as she removed his dinner plate.

'No thanks Queen,' said Rob, 'that was just fine, you know how to get to a man's heart Kate, and as for the lads, take no heed it's all part of growing up. It's a case of who wants to be number one, or cock of the midden. They see it at work, then think they can try it on at home with one another. They'll finish up knocking the hell out of each other, but they'll learn the hard way. It's a pity I haven't been able to be around much, but they're almost grown men now.'

'Well I wish they'd sodding well behave like men instead of a couple of half-witted school kids. Our Jimmie never gets involved.'

'Leave it Kate,' counselled Rob, 'they'll sort it out between themselves eventually. They'd be the first to help if anything happened to one of them. So forget it, just leave them to it.'

Kate knew when to close the subject, saying, 'Okay then, you just go into the parlour and read your newspapers, while I wash up. Tell the girls to come in for their meal. We'll go down to the Derby tonight to celebrate your getting a job. How about that?'

'Sounds good to me Kate,' said Rob stretching his arms, 'sounds good to me. It's great to be home, and to sit in front of my own fireside regardless of the arguing, that's what makes it a family.'

CHAPTER FIVE
A Bevin Boy and New friends

Bill was as good as his word about not going into the forces and volunteered to be a Bevin Boy. After his training, and much to his annoyance he was sent to Blyth in Northumberland. He sent heartbreaking letters home about his situation, being miles from the town, and having to walk what seemed like miles underground to reach his place of work, and being constantly wet through to the skin. 'No, things hadn't turned out as he had expected, and he wished he was back home, even the forces couldn't have been as bad as this. I thought that at least, I'd have been working at Bank Hall colliery at Burnley, knowing my way around, and being able to go home, but here, well I'm sick of it already.'

On one occasion, Kate handed one of Bill's letters to Bobbie for him to read, but he had heard Kate telling everyone about his brother's misfortunes.

He said sarcastically, 'Bet he wishes he was back on his buddy milk round Mam. Serves the bugger right. I had reasons why I couldn't go into the forces, if they had passed me fit I would have willingly gone. It was that stupid accident in the park when I was a kid, that plank swing nearly knocked me head off. But I lived to tell the tale after my eye operation, though I could have lost my eyes altogether.'

'Don't remind me our Bobbie,' said Kate, 'pity it didn't hit you in the gob, we might have had a bit of peace and quiet all these years. He'll wangle his way out before long if I know our Bill, just mark my words, then he'll have to go into the forces whether he likes it or not.'

'Aye,' replied Bobbie, 'and if I know him he'll land himself a cushy little job somewhere.'

'Just less of it,' shouted Kate angrily, 'if you haven't got a decent word in your head about your brother, don't say anything, keep your gob shut. The lad can't help it, just had a bit o' bad luck, you should feel sorry for him having it rough like that. I'll bake him a nice fruit cake, that's what I'll do. He'll like that, it will make him think of home.'

'And how much d'you think it'll cost to send it to Northumberland? Knowing what you put into your baking it'll cost the earth, and as for thinking of home, it'll just make him more homesick. Food parcels from home! Ha! Ha!' Bobbie almost split his sides when he visualised Bill getting the cake.

Kate stood and watched Bobbie, bent double, tears of laughter streaming down his face, then said coldly, 'You're beginning to get on my nerves, so you are, just button it, or I'll button it for you. Go on, get out! Out!' She pointed to the door.

Bobbie got the message, and was out of the kitchen double quick.

Rob looked up from his paper, 'Just behave yourself. I've been listening to you there in the kitchen, just stop tormenting your mother.' Then Rob started coughing.

Bobbie noticed that there were specks of blood on Rob's white handkerchief.

'I'll just have a lie down on the sofa, I'm alright now,' Rob said when he saw Bobbie's concern. 'I'll just have ten minutes, then we'll pop down to the Derby for a pint and a game o' dominoes.'

'I think it's time you paid a visit to Dr Third, Dad. How long have you been like that? Buddy hell, you put the wind up me, you could hardly get your breath. And the blood, Dad, you've got to see someone about that.'

'Look,' said Rob, 'forget it, I'm okay, don't make a fuss, and keep it to yourself, don't want to worry your mam, do we?' Rob took a swig of his cold tea, 'there now, that's better, a few minutes and I'll be my old self again. Go an' get changed then we'll go down and shuffle the dominoes, see what we can win eh?'

'Be better if you stayed in tonight Dad, I'm not too bothered about going out, It'll do you good to have an early night, you have to be up early in the morning for work.' Bobbie did his utmost to persuade his dad to stay home, but Rob was just as determined not to miss his Friday night out, especially now that he had decent friends, friends that he could trust.

'Boozin' wit der bugs,' (solitary drinking at home) 'No! I'm off to the boozer, so get yer best duds on there's a good lad.'

Rob would always have his strong Liverpudlian accent, and his new friends at the Derby had deep respect for him and the service he had put in for King and country most of his life. He told them many a tale of his travels and experiences.

Old Judd from Manchester commented that, 'The salt air had blown up from Liverpool the day that Mr Mac. had set foot in Nelson,' and they thoroughly enjoyed hearing of Mac's exploits over a pint.

Jack Wilkinson, or 'Wilkie' as he was known, often partnered Rob at dominoes, and quite a few tanners would come their way when they were on a winning streak, which paid for their ale for the night.

'Ee Rob,' Jack would say to his friend, 'the nearest I've been to the sea is at Blackpool, with me strides rolled up, paddling in the briny. I used to get sick just watching the tide come in, and yet here you are having spent twenty-eight years on the ocean. They should 'ave given you a bloody ship of your own after so long!'

So with friends of this kind, a new job and home with his family, Robert felt quite happy and settled at last.

Kate on the other hand wondered whether or not she had done the right thing in telling Rob to have a change of venue and make new friends. 'He never seemed to want to come home once he got down to the Derby. Still as long as her Robert was happy, she didn't care. At least he was home with her once more, so there was no more worrying and wondering when she heard of ships being torpedoed, and fretting about what may happen? No life was much better, and the war seemed to be drawing to its close at last.'

Mary had got her release from the nursing in the W.A.A.F. and moved into Bill's old room, he having done his utmost to wangle his way out of the coal mines on medical grounds, was immediately conscripted into the army, and had now finished his square-bashing at Carlisle, and had been sent to Warminster on Salisbury plain, a very remote part of the country, serving with the R.E.M.E.

Mary and Kate laughed hilariously as they sat together on Bill's single bed when they heard the news! 'Poor Willy!' (Sorry, Bill), 'out of the frying pan and into the bloody fire,' was the way that Kate described Bill's misfortune.

Bobbie, who walked into the room at the time joined in the laughter, then he rattled the several padlocks on Bill's large wardrobe saying, 'Got the bleeding Crown Jewels in there I shouldn't wonder, if the buddy house burnt down, we'd never know what he had hoarded in there.'

Kate waited anxiously that evening for Jimmie to come home from work as he never arrived at the usual time, and that wasn't like him at all. 'Not like him to miss his tea and his swimming,' Kate said to her husband. 'Can't imagine where he's got to, the mill's been closed for hours, not unless of course he's doing a bit of overtime. Silly little bugger, should have let me know at dinner time, I don't know, kids these days, they've got a lot off so they have.'

Rob responded by assuring Kate that the lad would be okay, and could look after himself well enough. 'You worry too much Kate,' he said. 'Most likely gone to his mates after work then straight to the swimming baths, so don't start getting upset.'

'Upset! Upset Rob, I've reason to be upset, he was seen along with some other lads from work, swimming in the canal last week. Never know what the lad gets up to these days, he's attracted to water, thinks he's Johnny Weissmuller! When I think of what people throw into the canal, it makes me feel sick, I don't want him picking up a serious illness. Just look at the time, he'll catch it when he does get in, I'll give him what for.'

Rob smiled and his eyes twinkled at Kate's outburst. 'All these children and she protected them like a mother hen protects her chicks.'

'Don't know what you have to smile about,' she snorted, 'you can just have a few words with him when you see him. Oh! And don't forget my bottle of stout when you get home, and don't stay down at the Derby all night!'

'You sound like our petty officer Kate,' laughed Rob as he knotted his white silk scarf around his neck, 'giving your orders, I'm glad you weren't aboard our ship.'

He kissed Kate full on the lips, 'I'll not be late,' he promised. 'See ya later.'

'Jimmie's the one ship's officer, who can always take care of himself.' He closed the back door behind him.

Kate felt more at ease as she ironed her way through a mountain of shirts, sheets and pillowcases, though the niggling worry was still there.

Kate kept her eye on the clock, and once or twice the hot iron touched her hand leaving ugly red burns. She abandoned her ironing, something she never did as a rule, and went into the kitchen to run the cold water from the tap over the small burns to help ease them, still worrying about her young son. Then like a bad penny, who should pop his head around the kitchen door but the lad himself.

'Hello Mam!' he said cheerfully, 'see yer've been busy ironing?'

Shoving aside the mound of ironing, Kate shot over to the door and gave her son a clip on the side of his head.

Jimmie drew back against the door.

'D'you know what time it is you young bugger? Me an' yer dad, we were worried to death about you. Where were you? Just start explaining yerself, that's if you've got something to explain, no feeling sorry for yourself, just let's have it! Spit it out!'

'Oh who cares?' Jimmie answered his mother scornfully, rubbing the side of his head where Kate had landed him one. 'Who cares what time it is, it's not all that late anyway.'

'I was sick,' shouted Kate. 'I was sick, wondering where the heck you had got to? Still if you don't want to explain to me, you'll still have some explaining to do to your father when he comes in, he'll be here before long, so you might as well say where you've been till this time, and what you've been up to and who with?'

Jimmie looked sullenly at his mother, knowing that she meant business, then he told Kate briefly that he and Jimmie McCarthy, a friend, had been to Liverpool. They had planned weeks ago to have a day off, and to go to join the merchant navy.

'So there now! That's the story! I'm going to bed now!' Jimmie said. 'I'm sorry if you were worried Mam, honest I am.'

'Hey! Steady on me lad! Not so fast, you'll stay till your father comes in and see what he has to say about it.'

Kate pushed him back into the chair, saying at the same time, 'I've made some brawn sandwiches, you can have some with your dad for supper when he comes in, and give him the full story. It'll be a wonder if he doesn't skin you alive, and don't think I'm going soft by giving you some supper.'

An hour later, after having his fill of sandwiches, Rob standing with his back to the fire listened carefully to Jimmie's day of events, and his apologies.

'Who did you see at Cannon Place?' Rob asked, burying his face in his handkerchief in order to hide his amusement?

'It was some big feller in a navy blue uniform. He asked me and Jimmie Mac's names, and where we lived and all that, and the jobs we were doing at the moment? Then he told us to reconsider joining, and to wait until we were called up officially. He said something about the battle of the Atlantic being over, then giggled, and said that there were hundreds of men now waiting for ships. Experienced men! So that was it! A blinkin' waste of money if you ask me. Mind you, we did have a scout around Liverpool, well what's left of it. It got a real battering didn't it? We went to see Auntie Maggie in China Street, got the tram from Lime Street. We were stuck at Preston for two hours, that's why we were late home, and that's the truth. I would never have gone if my job wasn't so monotonous. I hate it, over two years now I've had to put up with it, day in, day out; it's like a prison sentence. If you don't get me out of that mill Mam, I'll run away, and I won't come back, I mean it!' Jimmie was really distressed by this time as well as being extremely tired.

'We'll have less talk about running away, and especially to Liverpool. Your home's here now, and here you'll stay. There'll be no pocket money next week either, for losing a day's pay. You'd better get up the dancers now, and we'll hear no more about it,' Kate said, now feeling a bit of remorse.

All this time Rob could hardly hold back his laughter, his son was so much like he himself was at the same age. He told Kate, 'I'll have a word with the mill manager about Jimmie getting a change of job. Maybe he will settle down a bit better then. After all,' Rob added, 'another two years and Jimmie will be called up for his National Service, the war has unsettled so many people, so let's give the lad a bit of leeway. He's a good lad really.'

'I s'pose yer right, Robert,' said Kate, stubbing out her Woodbine, 'then that'll be another goodbye.'

Jimmie thought about Liverpool as he dropped off to sleep, mulling it over in his mind, thinking that it had been worth a day out to see the old place again. 'His mam wasn't so bad after all, her bark's always far worse than her bite. All the same, he wondered, I do hope I get my pocket money next week!'

CHAPTER SIX
National Service

Much to his delight Jimmie was transferred to another job in maintenance. There was more painting for him to do than anything else, but he was pleased about that, as it gave him the opportunity to work without supervision, though it kept him on his toes, because he was afraid that if he didn't come up to the boss's expectations he would be thrown back to the lions, back to his old depressing job. He made every effort to work hard and to do everything in his power to gain approval.

It seemed as if that had been accomplished when he was given the job of painting the mill owner's house, a big detached in Reedyford Road opposite the hospital. He even had an increase in his pay packet, though not amounting to much, 2/3d per week extra, but he was delighted. His appetite returned and he gained a bit of weight, he revelled at working outside in the fresh air, having a chat now and again to people passing by.

Swimming, weight-lifting and boxing were the hobbies he enjoyed, and his fitness for a seventeen-year old was well above the average. If only he could gain more height? That is what he would like, he could become a policeman then. That would be great! But he never did grow above 5 feet six and a half inches!

He got himself involved with competition swimming, against local teams and brought many trophies home for his mother. As these were usually in the form of Pyrex dishes, flower vases and fruit bowls, it was still an achievement, and

Kate was delighted, not only with the gifts, but much more importantly to see her son feeling more positive and happy in his work.

Jimmie and his friends had seen a notice about dancing classes at Bradley School, and thought it would be a bit of a lark to go along, and maybe see some of the girls who went to school at the same time as themselves. So off they went to take advantage of this facility.

Jimmie learned how to do the quickstep in a fashion, and also the foxtrot, though the older dances were more to his liking, like the barn dance, especially the progressive one where everyone changed partners as they danced around the floor. This was very interesting, especially so if he managed to progress to a pretty girl, though Jimmie, being a bit backward at coming forward, never progressed any further than the dance floor.

The Royal Empress tango was a dance that he liked, but 'Porky' Maguire, an acquaintance who tagged along with the lads, relished the performance more than any other person there.

Porky was the image of a young Charles Laughton, with a thick lower lip and chubby cheeks. His walk was the same, and he even managed to put on Charles's posh accent. Along with his crinkly black hair which was highly Brylcreamed, he went down well with the girls. His manner was so gentlemanly and refined, that is until he took to the floor for the Royal Empress tango! Then he seemed to lose himself in the dance, bending his partner over backward at certain steps, and the girl slapped his face and rushed from the dance floor with blushes covering her cheeks.

George and Mary Bell, the teachers, were horrified to learn that Porky had suddenly come on heat, his excuse being that it was a pen-knife in his trouser pocket that had been the cause of the offence. Nevertheless, word must have got around among the female students, and he seemed to have no shortage of partners when it was a ladies' choice!

All too soon the time arrived when Jimmie was called up to do his National Service. In one way he was rather excited at the prospect, but disappointed that not many applicants had been able to choose the navy, he being among them. He would have liked to have carried on the tradition of his father and uncles, but at least there was an escape from the usual humdrum life he had experienced up till now, though things had been much better at his place of work after being taken on in his new department.

No. 19165385 Private Jimmie Mac. was more than ready to spend the next two years or so in the King's service. Weathering six weeks attached to the East Lancs. Regiment, square-bashing and bull-shitting at Fulwood, Preston, he was then sent to Woolwich Arsenal for another two weeks of polishing and drilling, like he'd never heard before, and ended his primary training as a gunner and was drafted into the Royal Horse Artillery.

He met other young lads like himself from all over Britain, as if all had been flung into a large cooking pot and stirred and mixed altogether, with the end result being a smart fighting force, that he hoped would make the King proud of them all, just as he knew his mam would be.

Some lads cried wanting to go home, the same ones were bullied by others, and put upon for their weakness, but Jimmie, even though not a tall lad, could well look after himself, and he soon had the opportunity to do that.

Scots and Scousers didn't always mix well, and one such gunner from Clydeside tried it on with Jimmie, pestering and badgering him for days, only to come off the worse for wear after Jimmie showed him his mettle.

He served only two of his seven days C.B. then everyone was sent home on fourteen days embarkation leave, after which they ended up in Itzaho, Germany, instead of the initial destination they had been prepared for of Singapore.

Many of the lads couldn't contain their excitement, to think they would be able to see first-hand the destruction and devastation that up to now they had only heard about on the news. Germany had taken a real beating from the R.A.F. and the invading allied ground forces. Jimmie saw children begging and crying out for food, as they ran alongside the troop train, though orders were given that the troops were not to throw anything down to them, for fear of the children falling under the train, or for them fighting among themselves.

It was a most pitiful sight and dreadful to look upon, and Jimmie looked down upon the little kids who resembled scarecrows, for want of a better word, their clothes hanging from their backs in rags from their scrawny little bodies.

He couldn't ignore the fact, as he briefly recalled his own childhood days in Liverpool, when he had to go to bed many nights without a meal in his belly, and the bottom hanging out of his trousers more often than not, and having no shoes to his feet.

Though he was not starving in the true sense of the word, he had experienced a measure of what these children were now going through, so he felt a deep compassion for these poor souls.

He drew away from the train window and tried concentrating on a few letters from home, preferring not to see the plight of the civilians – the enemy.

The long journey from Beilefeld Transit Camp to Hamburg came to an end at last, and he was relieved to abandon the straight backed latticed seats. Everyone was aching and sore, and made comments about being glad to leave the 'Hermann Goring Express'.

The last leg of the journey was by road in three ton Leyland lorries to Itzaho; they were crammed in like sardines.

They eventually reached the 32nd Regiment R.H.A. B.A.O.R. and paraded on the barrack square, where they were told by B.S.M. Squires that they looked like an army that Napoleon had dragged back from Moscow.

B.S.M. Squires was a slim man with wiry, short grey hair, or what could be seen of it under his firmly fixed beret. Everything about him was immaculate. His two rows of campaign ribbons and oak leaves proved his worth, and he would without a doubt rearrange this shambles into a fighting force second to none, for he had a look and a snarl that would cut through anyone.

'Your mothers won't recognise you by the time you've finished here,' he shouted, 'you won't even recognise yourselves when you look in the mirror, but you measly lot will recognise me anywhere and everywhere you go, and remember me in your old age, if you live that long, you'll most certainly always know that Battery Sergeant Major Squires was here! I'll be watching your every move. You'll have bloody nightmares and wake up in cold sweats before I'm finished with you rabble!'

Then came the inevitable phrase, 'You broke your mother's heart, but you won't break mine! You're now in the senior regiment of the British army. We are the elite; though looking at you lot from where I'm standing,' he rasped, slapping his leg with his polished stick with its brass ornate handle, tucking it smartly under his left arm, 'you look like a pile of shit dumped on my parade ground. Take over Sergeant Dean!' B.S.M. Squires turned smartly and marched away.

Sergeant Dean walked up and down the rows of men, his bright blue eyes glaring menacingly at each and every one; no-one escaped his scrutiny. Beads of sweat ran down the sides of his freckled face, and after another dressing down in the foulest language ever heard, the toothless ginger sergeant screamed out, 'The last man to leave the parade ground will be put on a charge.'

Jimmie dashed into their quarters like a bat out of hell, there was no way he was going to be last man!

The three storey concrete-faced building had central heating, shower rooms and private toilets, the latter having thick wooden seats, designed so that the user had no option but to sit with his back straight and rigid as a ram-rod, whenever performing ablution No. 2.

Everyone was amazed at the comparative luxury their quarters provided; each spacious room housed six men, and there was ample locker space.

Along the corridors were bold images stencilled of the once famous German military might in the form of S.S. Gestapo and various regiments of the Fatherland.

Meals were served mainly by women, and far surpassed the food in the army camps in Britain. The lads enjoyed a real tuck in, the best they had tasted for many weeks.

It was a long hot summer with scarcely any rain, and the sun's rays bore down relentlessly on tired gunners. Everything they did had to be carried out virtually on the double, gunnery training, square-bashing, small arms drill and P.E. all took their toll on some of the weaker men.

On very rare occasions, in the evenings, it was good to splash about in one of the several swimming pools designated to various ranks, and it was on one of these evenings that Jimmie had been spotted by the sergeant.

'You Maclean, you and Lambert! You are now in the regiment's swimming team. Get some practice in! Spotted you a couple of nights ago, and have had my eye on you both. We shall be using the N.C.O.s pool in the future for training.' The sergeant smirked showing an empty space in his face. 'Individual events and relay, let you know later when you will be competing, better have a small valise prepared as you'll be stopping overnight. Carry on!' he said, leaving the pool area.

When some of their mates heard the news, they were greeted with 'Jammy sods!' and 'bloody crawlers!'

Jimmie and his pal Eric Lambert laughed, and Eric remarked in his broad Sheffield dialect, 'Can't help it if we're popular and gifted can we?'

'Yer tae bloody fat!' grunted Ray Thompson, a Scot from Clydebank, 'yer gorra shape like a haggis!'

'Jealousy will get you nowhere, so shut it Jock!' snapped Eric, squaring himself up to Thompson, the latter having second thoughts about mouthing off at Sergeant Dean's protégées, and promptly withdrew, murmuring under his breath for fear of recoil from Sergeant Dean, if he got wind of his team being jibed, or in military jargon taking the piss out of them.

It felt good to get out of camp and into new surroundings and garrison camps, to mix with men in other regiments. Competition was keen to say the least, but it was results that counted, and it was always the same old story, that their best wasn't ever good enough! More effort was required, much more, until starting time was cut and seconds taken from the whole team in speed and finishing.

'Hell! Who cares whether we win or lose?' commented Eric.

'Yer right,' replied Jimmie, 'an' we're not even getting any prizes for it!'

Still as Reverend Hugh Fielding used to say, it was the taking part that really counted, rather than not taking part at all.

Gunnery training was almost complete, and it became more intense. Abel, Baker and Charlie troops all in fierce combat wanted to win at all costs. In the end it didn't matter one iota, all were complimented, and training was completed with manoeuvres at Eckinforde in Northern Germany. That's when they became real gunners and used live ammunition.

At the passing out parade, again the battery was praised for their hard work, endurance and fine performances. One thing for certain was, they never knew whether or not they came up to B.S.M. Squire's expectations, although someone did remark, 'Even a trained seal was rewarded with a kipper for its performance!'

It wasn't a fond farewell to Itzaho, but more a thank God it was all over!

Jimmie was convinced when the intake were subjected to a lot of verbal abuse, that this was a typical ritual he was experiencing at his new camp in Verdun.

B.S.M. Ianto Jones was a pot-bellied disciplinarian from some Welsh valley. He was as hard as granite and showed no mercy. He had an inbred instinct, and could filter out the vulnerable squaddie in the blink of an eye. His red-veined face and wicked grey eyes, were complemented by his thin, grey-waxed pencil moustache that twitched from side to side when he bellowed out his orders. Everyone knew that he was going to be a thorn in their sides, albeit he was a truly dedicated professional soldier.

Nevertheless his soft-soaping, and brown-nosing, had perchance, rewarded him with his rank for having the tendency to please, smile and eulogise his senior officers. To put it bluntly, he was a crawler!

'Yes Battery Sergeant Major! No Battery Sergeant Major! Yes! We are nig-nogs, and yes we are a rabble and we will jump when told to jump, and will be a credit to the King's Senior Regiment!'

'Now move you shower of shit and get off my parade ground! Last man dawdling will be put on a charge! Move! Move! Out of my sight!' Ianto squealed in his high-pitched Welsh accent.

This now was much to the amusement of the troops as they scrambled into their new billets, and mimicked their new B.S.M.

Having settled into a routine of more training, this time on M.T. each man could choose the type of vehicle he would like to learn to drive, a 3 ton Leyland, 15cwt. Jeep or half track. It was the jeep that Jimmie chose. He was glad that he did so, as many who chose the heavier vehicles, took longer to pass their test. Jimmie, as soon as he was used to driving on the wrong side of the road, and had become accustomed to the area, passed his test quite quickly, and was given the job as driver and batman to Captain Hatch, being housed in batman's quarters and dodging guard duty, fire picket and other assignments. Sometimes though, he had to work well into the night to accomplish his new duties of cleaning, pressing and polishing. The vehicle was maintained and serviced by the R.E.M.E mechanics.

Jimmie thought of his brother Bill also in the R.E.M.E and still stationed on Salisbury plain, and wondered if he would ever meet up with him? He knew from experience though that Bill would be huffy about Jimmie's advancement.

As well as his duties, Jimmie volunteered for the boxing team, and notched up four out of his five bouts; in the last one though, he got a hammering from a particular Sergeant Logan.

It was a typically one-sided contest, and as genuine as an Irish five bob note. Jimmie gave almost two stone away, and almost had his neck broken with rabbit punches, yet he managed a straight left, and two good punches full into his opponent's face, adding a left and a right to his bread-basket.

Jimmie thought he had him in the second, when he stumbled against the ropes, yet instead of going in for the kill as he should have done, Jimmie's troop roared and egged him on, screaming for him to go after his quarry and to flatten the Sergeant. Nevertheless Jimmie's rival was a tough nut, a trained pugilist, his scarred face and cauliflower ears gave evidence of his professionalism.

Jimmie didn't know whether he had genuinely hurt this tough brute, and maybe, just maybe he could swing everything at him and go in for the kill, as he was swaying from side to side on the ropes. Jimmie prodded straight lefts to the head, but dared not let his guard down, and so it was that this bruiser feigned fatigue, then came back at Jimmie with his arms swinging like sledgehammers, only to drop Jimmie three times to the canvas, though he survived each time, not taking the full count. There was a grand ovation from all ranks, and jeers from the lowly gunners.

The following days Jimmie ached and hurt and could hardly hold up his head, on account of the rigorous and heavy punching he had received.

Sergeant Logan became known as bull-nose, and was the talk of the regiment, but no doubt he was rather needled because he hadn't been able to K.O. Jimmie, though his previous challengers had all been floored relentlessly.

Many of the lads suspected Ianto Jones had set up the match, and silently threatened that they would knock the head off the Welsh dragon some dark night, with a pickaxe handle.

All this didn't bother Jimmie, he felt he had shown his mettle and was proud of his achievement, even though he hadn't been the winner.

Jimmie concentrated on his new appointment with Captain Hatch, and learnt quite a lot about the man he was serving. He had been taken prisoner in the latter months of the war, and had been beaten, dragged and kicked along the railway platform in Hamburg, and left with both of his legs broken in various places. He now hobbled on two sticks as he awaited his release from the army, swearing what he would do if ever he came across the S. S. Officer responsible for crippling him.

The winter of 1948 in Germany was very cold and bleak, they also heard that in England the weather was just as bad. Everything was frozen, even the anti-freeze in the radiators. At times the jeep skidded off the road, and Jimmie was thankful that Captain Hatch wasn't in the vehicle when this happened.

There was no more boxing for Jimmie, instead he played football for the regiment, and joined the concert party, being invited to play a harmonica solo, then joining in with six other instrumentalists. This allowed Jimmie a break from his normal duties, which helped him to relax a little. This was all arranged by Captain Hatch, and by Christmas a well-organised variety concert was performed for the regiment, and repeated at other garrison towns.

The festive season had started with coffee, laced with vodka, served in bed by the officers. At dinnertime, the gunners were honoured by having their meal served by those in command, though there were some killjoys - Ianto Jones being one of them, who would cheerfully have broken with tradition. Instead it was the gunner's day, so they ate, drank and were merrily joining in together, much to the amusement of Captain Hatch, with their song about the unpopular B.S.M.

'You'll never go to heaven, with Yanto Jones,
'Cos Yanto Jones is a lazy bones,
With a big brown nose and lazy bones
Who'd want to go to heaven with Yanto Jones?'

The following day no one in their right mind would have turned a dog outside; it was bitterly cold and windy, with hail lashing across the parade ground and biting into red faces. It was malicious to say the least, that Ianto Jones would have the battery standing to attention longer than usual, and if looks could have killed, the B.S.M. would have been dead and buried on the spot a hundred times.

Without inspection, Major Plant quickly dismissed the parade, though by that time every man was soaked to the skin as they wore only fatigue dress.

The day after that though, there was no respite from Ianto's villainous schemes, in that he had various troops stripped for P. E. in vests, shorts and boots and running across the German countryside before breakfast, and for once the N.C.O's aided the gunners, as it became quite clear that Ianto was a thorn in everyone's side. Fortunately no one came off with anything worse than a common cold.

Kate's letters to Jimmie were infrequent and informal, and on one occasion she wrote to say that Evie Foster had been taken to hospital having had a baby, and that a certain gentleman had taken the infant into his care. Kate prattled on saying, 'It was a sin and disgrace that a fine upstanding young woman had been take advantage of, and that she had succumbed to the weakness of the flesh. Now poor Evie was suffering and having to pay for the error of her ways.'

P.T.O. (Jimmie turned the page) 'I'm sorry to say lad that Evie has just died, poor gairl, she didn't deserve that. Must have broken her heart. I'll miss her so I will, and so will everyone else. She liked to come over and have her morning breaky with me. I was unaware that she was expecting, you could have knocked me down with a feather. Mind you she was a big lass all round. Still she was a good friend, and no doubt she's now with her husband somewhere in God's heaven, bless her!

There's another thing I'm sorry to have to write to you about lad, and that's Joan King, Sally's eldest girl. She passed away, it was her heart, poor little thing. A leaking valve they said it was. It's terrible isn't it? These tragedies, always inflicted on the poor and innocent. Still what will be, will be!

Everyone else at this end is okay. Our Willie writes quite often; he's never moved from Salisbury plain, not like you getting to see a little bit of the world.'

Kate's writing was getting smaller and smaller, clearly she was running out of space, though she managed to get it in at the end with:

'Little Tommy Adams had been for his medical, and his mam had said to me that he'd like to go into the infantry 'cos he likes horses. I don't know how I managed to stop cracking me sides laughing.

Ta-ra son. God bless X X Mam.'

CHAPTER SEVEN
Home on leave

Service in Germany came to an end in late March 1948. Captain Hatch remained behind, and Jimmie had no option but to team up once again with Baker troop, travelling independently to Hanover transit camp, then under his own steam to the Hook of Holland and sailing to Harwich. From there he went by rail to London, and finally took the long tedious journey to Manchester, then on to Nelson, walking once more down the cobbled slope from the station.

'Ee lad, I'd never have known yer. Yer look so different!' Kate said kissing him on the cheek.

Instantly Jimmie recalled B.S.M. Squire's remarks, 'That their own mothers wouldn't recognise them by the time he had finished with them.'

Jimmie dropped his kit-bag from his shoulders and replied, 'Yes I suppose I have changed a bit after almost thirteen months in the army.'

'A bit!' exclaimed Kate, 'you've changed a lot my lad, and fer the better too! You've broadened out and got a good colour. Wait till yer dad sees yer, poor soul, he hasn't been too well lately, his chest you know. Now get that gear off and put that rifle somewhere safe up in our Willie's room. I mean Bill. He's home on leave. Gone out with Bobbie for a drink.'

'Steady on Mam,' laughed Jimmie. 'Come up for air. I'll catch up on all the news later.' He therefore proceeded to discard his canvas packs and webbing, and finally his tunic and beret.

He later shared the remains of a pan of scouse with his father, who had arrived home late from work. They talked around the table, Kate butting in at times with tales of woe about people Jimmie didn't even know. No doubt some of the new friends she had made since moving to Nelson. 'Though of course,' she added, 'there was little Tommy Adams, you know him don't you?'

'Only too well,' said Jimmie, winking at his dad.

'Well,' continued Kate feeling she was telling Jimmie an important tale, 'he never got into the army you know. His mam talked about bantam corps, or something like that he could have enlisted in, but he never made it. Just as well I suppose, he could have been picked on because of his size. Rough lads taking advantage, rotters!'

'Aye, you might be right Mam,' Jimmie said as he handed a small packet to his dad, then one to Kate saying, 'You always wanted a real gold necklace didn't you, well now you've got one.'

'You shouldn't have lad, this must have cost a small fortune.' She drew the chain across her hand, gazing fondly at it, and a signet ring for your dad, how generous of yer.' Kate had tears in her eyes.

'If you're gonna cry I'll take 'em back,' laughed Jimmie, 'We could get anything in Germany for cigarettes, so I saved mine up to get these for you both.'

Rob in the meantime, was having a fit of coughing, then said, 'Never had a gold ring before, and my initials engraved on it too. I'll just wear it on special occasions and treasure it forever.' His father was very moved by the generous gift.

'Glad you like it Dad. I got the size right too didn't I?'

Rob held out his hand to display the ring from different angles in order to catch a glint of the gold in the light.

After a few bottles of Massey's pale ale, Rob started to talk about his convoy trips, sympathising with his son that he didn't make it into the navy. 'You'd have liked it son,' he said, 'it would have broadened your outlook on life, seeing the world.'

'Just as well he didn't!' snapped Kate, butting in, 'he's better off having his feet on *terra firma*, that's what I say. I can remember watching the *Titanic* sail from Queenstown, when I was a girl. S'truth, a giant of a ship and unsinkable, so they said, but look what happened. Keep away from the sea our Jimmie. It's alright for the fish to swim in, and to paddle in at New Brighton and that's all! There were all those poor souls who lost their lives in the battle of the Atlantic as well.

I've had many sleepless nights when thinking of your dad away at sea and in danger. Never knew where he was or what was happening to him? I have had first-hand experience too of losing a brother at sea, as you well know. William, so dear to me, and to die like that in the cruel sea– lost!' Kate was getting quite emotional. 'It's no wonder I'm turning grey, just look,' she said holding out a tress of her dark hair.

'Tis beautiful, Kate,' Rob said with a glint in his eyes. 'You'll always be my girl.' Then he started to sing:
'I'll take you home again Kathleen
Across the ocean wild and wide,
To where your heart has ever been
Since first you were my bonnie bride.'

Then Kate started to sing along with her Robert, closing her eyes as she always did when singing, and doing her best to harmonise, though making a bit of a hash of it.

During his ten days leave, Jimmie went along to the youth club in Carr Road to have a friendly spar with some of the lads, though most evenings he went out with Bill, who by this time was an avid drinker, almost a veteran. It was pointless trying to keep up with his brother who downed pint after pint of Massey's bitter. After a couple of the same ale, Jimmie made a hasty retreat to the nearest lavvy, or gutter, only to bring back all that he had drunk.

'You'll be alright now, kid,' Bill always said as he pressed and kneaded Jimmie's bloated stomach. 'It must have been summat me ma gave us for tea. Yes that's it, it's definitely summat you've eaten. Get it up lar.'

Usually after the stomach pressing, there'd be a gushing cascade of sour ale, followed by groans that sounded something like RALPH or HUGHIE.

'Take him home and get him to bed,' some smart ass shouted from a distance. 'If he can't hold his booze he shouldn't be drinking it. Give him milk instead!'

Jimmie took offence at these remarks, and was ready to take on the world and it's mate, so word got around to keep away from the Macs, and that Jimmie was a real trouble-maker, and best left alone and not to mix with him. Jimmie eventually saw the light, and also the stupidity of blowing good money up against the lavatory wall.

When Kate heard what had been going on, she was like a raging bull, or should I say raging mad cow? He was glad to see the back of Bill for he was a bad influence on Jimmie.

'Must have got his bad habits from down the pit, never know what the bugger's up to,' she said, smiling at the same time as waving off her son at the railway station with Jimmie standing meekly by her side.

'You Snooks,' Kate admonished pointing her finger, 'we'll have less of this brawling in future, yer can have a drink, but don't go mad, don't wallow in it. So just behave yerself, we have a good reputation here in Nelson.' She lit up a Woodbine, blew out the smoke, then said, 'A little wine for the sake of the stomach, that's what the good book says, not to drown yerself in it.'

As they left the station platform, and started to walk down the cobbled slope to the exit, she said to Jimmie, 'Remember coming down this slope when you came back from Wales?'

'Yes I can Mam. Gosh it must be five years ago!'

'So? What's funny, what are yer smirking at? Something tickling yer?'

No Mam, just thinking of you making a beeline for the Co-op to use Percy Feather's toilet. Yer were busting to go. By the way, I bet you never paid him for that bacon!'

Mother and son laughed companionably together.

Jimmie said wickedly, 'You don't want to go now do you?' Then gave her arm a squeeze.

'Gerraway with yer,' Kate laughed, giving him a friendly shove, 'and yes I did pay for that bacon, so there!'

With Jimmie's leave almost over he had a friendly night out with some of his old pals, Alan and Terry, with whom he'd worked at Fell's Mill. After a couple of drinks at the Derby Arms, they decided to drift across the road to the Romany ballroom, to try out their dancing skills, but didn't feel very confident.

'Glad Porky MaGuire isn't with us,' Terry said impishly, as he straightened his R.A.F. tunic before entering the ballroom.

'Wonder if he's still got his penknife in his pants?' Alan Waterworth piped up, his shoulders shaking with laughter, 'he was a right bugger with the girls. Trouble is they liked him,' he added, raising himself up to his full height of five feet and one inch.

They ordered drinks at the bar, 'And how old are you?' asked the barman before pulling the three pints of beer.

'Old enough to be drinking!' Alan snapped, as he produced his identity card.

'Fair enough,' laughed the barman looking down at Alan, 'that'll be 2/9d.'

Jimmie and Terry smirked at each other, not daring to let on to Alan that the barman was taking the mickey out of him.

After a couple of pints Alan was getting high-spirited, and acting stupid. He was heading for the dance floor, when he stumbled against one of the supporting pillars, on which a large red fire extinguisher was fixed by a bracket. The bracket snapped, the fire extinguisher fell to the floor with a crash, and started to do its job of squirting out water, scattering its contents far and wide. The ladies, in their colourful fancy dresses became soaked, they scattered as quickly as they could, leaving the dance floor deserted, but still the band played on!

Terry, Jimmie and Alan were apprehended, and escorted to the exit at the top of the stairs. Alan sang along with the band as the trio were removed.

So tired was the song. Someone gave Jimmie a push in the back, causing him to miss the top two steps. He saw red, and grabbed the fat man who had shoved him. Getting a firm grip on the fellow's shirt neck, he swung him round, and threw him down the remaining stairs.

Jimmie scurried down to his victim, only to be confronted by a burly police sergeant. After an explanation and notes being taken by the sergeant, he was allowed to leave. Home wasn't far away, and he headed there as fast as he could muster, going straight to bed, not even bothering to have any supper.

'What's all this I've been hearing about you setting a fire extinguisher off in the Romany ballroom? Can't hide anything from me lad, you deserved to be thrown out, as well as those who were with you. Here's yer breakfast, though I'm not sure if you deserve it!' scolded Kate when Jimmie came downstairs the following day around 12.00 noon.

'Wasn't me Mam,' Jimmie said, as he dipped his bread in the egg, 'I just got roped in after Alan Waterworth squirted the damn contraption all over the ballroom. It was when I was leaving that the fat-arsed M.C. pushed me. I just managed to grab the stair banister, otherwise I'd have gone sailing from top to bottom. I had a right to retaliate, so I dragged him down the stairs instead!'

'By his dicky bow I believe?' interrupted Kate.

'Yes mam, that's right. It was in my hand, but I gave it back to him after I was collared by this police sergeant, he recognised me right away. It was that copper who came here when I ran away from Waddow Hall.'

'A sergeant now is he?' asked Kate. 'Mm, I remember him, Bentley was his name. It's a blinkin' good job he knew you or you'd have ended up in the cells for the night. I get rid of one mischief and I'm left with another, you Jimmie Mac.'

'Well I did apologise to the man and paid up for a new bow tie, so he shook my hand. He said he was sorry for the mistake and apologised for any insults, especially to one wearing the King's uniform. So that's that Mam, the whole story. Don't know what happened to Alan and Terry, but I reckon they'll have a tidy sum to pay out between them.'

Kate laughed, 'What about Welbury's wig?'

'Soaked to his crust of bread (head) and his wife Mona, was drenched right through to her brassiere. S'truth! What a night!'

Kate laughed heartily, and Jimmie joined in, when Kate said, 'That Alan Waterworth has the right name to be setting off fire extinguishers!'

*Please note: Welbury and Mona Petty, were professional dance teachers, and the elite of the Romany Ballroom at that time.

CHAPTER EIGHT
Rochester, Otterburn, and Civilian Life

The posting to Rochester in Northumberland was the only move which peeved Jimmie. His previous camps had been an adventure, but this one, after the comforts of Verdun in Germany, was harrowing and bleak to say the least.

There was no running hot water in the wash sheds. Only on a Sunday morning were they allowed a warm shower, that's if they were lucky. At other times they had to brave the stinging cold jets of water, even in the middle of February. The cookhouse was over a third of a mile away from their huts, and so was the N.A.A.F.I., and even there they had no music or games, and hard wooden chairs and tables were the only means of seating.

As Stanley Holloway put it in one of his famous monologues, 'In fact – nothing to laugh at, at all.'

In their hut there was a cast iron stove in the middle of the room, which could only be lit at 18.00 hours, as there were coal shortages all over the country. On top of that, the food wasn't plentiful either. It consisted of cold salted porridge for breakfast, two sausages, normally frozen to the plate in fat, two slices of bead, and a dollop of jam or marmalade with tea. The tea was laced with bromide regularly, not to enhance the flavour, but for other purposes, which the lads were very well aware of.

Every Sunday, they each had the special favour of having an egg, along with the above usual breakfast, but if they were just one minute late on arrival, the door was slammed shut by the duty sergeant or officer.

Jimmie allotted his mother fourteen shillings from his pay each week, the remainder being spent on polish, Brasso, blanco and toiletries. If he had anything left over, he bought a cup of tea now and again, with the added luxury of a rock bun from the N.A.A.F.I.

No one dared to complain that there wasn't enough food. At mealtimes every single morsel was devoured, and there were never any scrapings left over for the swill bin. Yes things were bad! Very bad! So much so, that one dark night the N.A.A.F.I. was raided. Entry was gained through the loft space, which resulted in someone falling through the ceiling, and landing in the kitchen. The aroma of frying bacon lingered around the rows of huts, though no one was ever charged for the offence, but from then on the premises became out of bounds.

Three months was more than enough at Rochester, and to everyone's relief, and without warning, the battery moved to Otterburn to team up with the rest of the 45th Field Regiment. It was a much better camp, with more up-to-date latrines, and wash sheds that had the luxury of hot water. There were no complaints, except again for the food, or the lack of it. If anyone took the attitude of Oliver Twist, and wanted more, they were given extra duties like spud-bashing and mopping and cleaning the dining hall. It became known as rubbing it in.

Those with sleight of hand, lined their tunics with vegetables, so they could make a soup of some kind in their billy cans, or roast potatoes on the stove at night.

Life at Otterburn became a routine. 6.30a.m. reveille, showers, washing, shaving, hut cleaning, which meant that everyone did it in teams of four, buffing the floors until they sparkled. Laying out their kit, tidying lockers, ablutions thoroughly cleaned and hosed down. Hut inspection came after breakfast, and at 8.45a.m. drill parade for the regiment. One of the things that Jimmie and the rest of 70 battery hated most about that, was that they came into contact with their old enemy, Ianto Jones, whom everyone thought had been left behind in Germany. He had suddenly turned up again like a very bad penny.

Their new Captain, Jerome, was a replacement for Capt. Hatch. He was an amiable man, fair-haired, very good looking, and a competent athlete. He had a pretty young Irish wife, and a two-year old son Sean, who had joined him there, and were billeted on the edge of the camp in a four bedroom detached house.

Much to Jimmie's astonishment, he was promoted to Lance Bombadier, and taken on as batman to the captain, and ordered to live in with the family, though taking his meals at the mess.

Often Jimmie went with the battery to firing ranges for weeks on end, assisting the T.A's, though many of these left, not being able to cope with the strenuous training and rough sleeping under canvas, and objected to bursting their guts for the few shillings they got for weekend camp.

Eventually manoeuvres came to an end, and Jimmie was glad to be able to slide between the white sheets in his bedroom at the captain's house. What a wonderful difference this was to lying on ground-sheets in the wet grass for weeks.

Mrs Jerome gave birth to a little girl, and whilst she was confined, it was Jimmie's job to look after her small son, and to take his meals with the child, and to generally care for him, until the captain returned in the evenings. Jimmie didn't mind the cleaning and polishing as well as his duties to the captain, and he was well rewarded for his efforts, earning himself a few extra shillings which were very useful.

Alas all good things come to an end, as they say, and in August 1948 the Regiment moved to Branspeth in Co. Durham. Jimmie was recommended for the officers' mess, and to be batman to Colonel Carl Dane, and took up his duties in the dining hall and drinks bar, staying there until his two years National Service came to an end.

Ianto Jones and other senior N.C.O.s did their utmost to coax and encourage Jimmie to sign on for five or seven years, and to take up soldiering at Woolich Arsenal in the R.H.A.

He would rise in the ranks straight away, and get pay increases, and they of course they would have a feather in their cap if Jimmie had been that way inclined.

Jimmie though had not taken much time to make his decision, and was demobbed at Aldershot, the camp infamous for its glass house, and detention centre, which dealt with deserters, and others not measuring up to military standards.

So it was that 19165385 Lance Bombadier MacLean left his two years with the British army behind him. At least he thought, he felt that he had learned something, discipline and carrying out his duties in a fine manner. He had entertained in a concert party, given all his energies to boxing, football and swimming. The reward being that he was now physically fit and ready for anything.

At one point he had second thoughts about signing on again, until he saw a couple of redcaps screaming abuse at a group of prisoners, and making them double until they almost dropped, and that convinced him that enough was enough. He collected his two week's pay, and made a beeline for the barrack gates. He was once more outside, but this time as a civilian. It wasn't that long afterwards before he found himself walking down the familiar cobbled slope of Nelson railway station.

Sit yerself down lad, it's been a long day for you. I'll bring you a tray of summat to eat. Fancy having to wait all that time at Manchester for your connection. Still you're home now, you're at your mam's! Thank God now all my children are home again, and no more goodbyes.'

444

Jimmie held onto the door frame watching his mam cut the usual thick slices off a new loaf.

'Another ten minutes and you'd have been knocking us up,' Kate said, as she spread the creamy butter onto the soft bread, and added lots of corned beef and pickle. 'That okay for you now?'

'It's fine mam, I'm ready for it,' said Jimmie gratefully, 'but you usually stay up till after midnight.'

'Not now,' she replied, 'got to get me shut eye, I'm working shifts now. Six till two and two until ten. I'm on earlies this week, so I'm up at 5.30 for a quick cup of tea and a Woody, then I'm off to Hill Brown's just along by the goit.'

'You're not working Mam? In the mill? Surely not!'

'Yes. I'm afraid so Jimmie. I'm spinning. It's good money too, and guess who my boss is? He's the manager there.'

'I don't feel like guessing games Mam, just tell me,' he said as he chomped his jaws into the thick sandwich.

'It's Percy. Percy Feather. He's ever so good, and doesn't mind if I'm a bit late and creep past him. You remember Percy don't you? You know, he used to be at the Co-op?'

'Course I do Mam, but shouldn't you be at home looking after the kids? Can't honestly see why you have to go out to work at your time of life. Don't you think you've done enough? You should be having it easier now, you're nearly fifty, and had ten kids. Hell there's enough of us working now. Well I will be when I get a job for God's sake.'

'Don't take the Lord's name in vain,' said Kate, 'mentioning hell and God in the same tone of voice. Work is nothing to me, I take it all in my stride, and besides, I enjoy it too. There's a lot of Scousers work at Hill Brown's. You want to go along there to get a job, I'm sure they'd set you on. They have very good rates of pay. It's a Jewish firm, three brothers Gustav, Hermann and Joseph Braunsberg. Two of them were prisoners in a concentration camp, and escaped to Britain where they were given asylum. They started the factory up between them. They are very good to work for.

Anyway, finish your supper now, and get up the dancers. Goodnight son.' And as an afterthought she added, 'It's nice to have you home again. Thank God, there are no more goodbyes.'

EPILOGUE

JANUARY 1950

Jimmie gripped his mam's hand as Robert, his father was laid to rest. He had died peacefully in his sleep, aged just 54 years.

'I never had the chance to say goodbye to him, but I'm sure he's waiting for me somewhere,' Kate sobbed.

'Sure he is Mam,' Jimmie said, comforting her, 'then you'll be having a right knees up, and no more goodbyes! No not ever!'

THE END

NELSON LEADER - Times Series

"A beautifully evocative and deeply personal account of a young boy's childhood in Everton, Liverpool, just before the outbreak of WW II.

The poverty which serves as a background to this novel is humorous and always evident, one never loses his sense of hope which pervades throughout."

CRAVEN HERALD

"A refreshing unpretentious book…"

"A marvellous portrayal of a child's antics and emotions observed and remembered through older, wiser eyes…"

Sinclair convincingly describes the appalling conditions, hardship and poverty endured by Jimmie and his friends."

LANCASHIRE EVENING TELEGRAPH

"An evocative look at life through the eyes of a ten-year old in Pre-war Everton…"

"You can almost taste the 'connie-onnie' butties as the young Jimmie MacLean gets into his juvenile scrapes…"

"A right good read!"